P9-DEO-174

DESERT ISLAND DECAMERON

Once in a while a book appears that will lend itself to a desert island like a beautiful girl to a dream, or sheep to Elliot's Wool Pullery. What people mean by a book to take to a desert island is one they like to take to bed, to the office, to the locker room on the nineteenth hole, but, lacking a beautiful girl and not being faced with the immediate prospect of being marooned on a desert island, they like the book more than fine and say, "Joe, did you read the story about the —— laugh, I thought I'd die."

There isn't room enough here to reprint the table of contents, and anyway it's just a couple of pages on, right close where you can look it over. This remarkable anthology of humor contains an impressive list of famous humorists and some that you didn't expect to find here. In most cases the stories reprinted are not found in the usual run of humor anthologies, and for that reason they make the book all the more entertaining. And where else could you have the running commentaries of H. Allen Smith preceding each story and explaining each choice? We say to you, "*Nowhere else!*"

BOOKS BY

H. ALLEN SMITH

Lost in the Horse Latitudes

Life in a Putty Knife Factory

Low Man on a Totem Pole

DESERT ISLAND DECAMERON

SELECTED BY

H. ALLEN SMITH

DOUBLEDAY, DORAN & CO., INC.

GARDEN CITY

NEW YORK

1945

LINECUT DRAWINGS BY LEO HERSHFIELD

PRINTED IN THE UNITED STATES
AT
THE COUNTRY LIFE PRESS, GARDEN CITY, N. Y.

FIRST EDITION

ACKNOWLEDGMENTS

THANKS ARE due the following authors, agents, and publishers for permission to reprint the selections indicated:

F.P.A.—for "A Pair of Sexes," from *The Column Book of F.P.A.*, copyright 1928, by Doubleday, Doran & Company, Inc.

Fred Allen—for "Mountain Justice."

D. Appleton-Century Company, Inc.—for "Daughters of Joy," from *Short Turns,* by Barry Benefield.

Albert & Charles Boni, Inc.—for selections from *The Devil's Dictionary,* by Ambrose Bierce.

Mrs. Mary Rose Bradford—for "Steamboat Days," from *Ol' Man Adam an' His Chillun,* by Roark Bradford.

George T. Bye and Company—for "Six-Day Race" and "Myriad-Minded Us," from *The Dissenting Opinions of Westbrook Pegler,* and "Colloquy at Second," from Mr. Pegler's column of September 28, 1942, in the New York *World-Telegram.*

Dodd, Mead & Company, Inc.—for "A Man May Be Down," from *Bed of Neuroses,* by Wolcott Gibbs; "A Model Dialogue," from *Literary Lapses,* by Stephen Leacock; "The Retroactive Existence of Mr. Juggins," from *Laugh with Leacock,* by Stephen Leacock; and "God Rest You Merry," from *Soap Behind the Ears,* copyright 1941, by Cornelia Otis Skinner.

Doubleday, Doran & Company, Inc.—for "A Harlem Tragedy," from *The Trimmed Lamp,* by O. Henry.

Duell, Sloan & Pearce, Inc.—for "The Crack," from *Journeyman,* by Erskine Caldwell; and "Professor Sea Gull," from *McSorley's Wonderful Saloon,* by Joseph Mitchell.

Harcourt, Brace and Company, Inc.—for "Mr. Kaplan's Dark Logic," from *The Education of Hyman Kaplan,* by

Leonard Q. Ross, copyright 1937, by Harcourt, Brace and Company, Inc.; and "The Secret Life of Walter Mitty," from *My World—and Welcome to It,* by James Thurber, copyright 1942, by James Thurber.

Harper & Brothers—for "The Mystery of Bridge Building," from *Benchley Beside Himself,* by Robert Benchley; "The Tooth, the Whole Tooth, and Nothing but the Tooth," from *Inside Benchley,* by Robert Benchley; and selections from *The Innocents Abroad* and from *A Tramp Abroad,* by Mark Twain.

Alfred A. Knopf, Inc.—for "The Sawing Off of Manhattan Island," from *All Around the Town,* by Herbert Asbury, copyright 1929, 1930, 1931, 1932, 1933, 1934, by Alfred A. Knopf, Inc.; and "Clarion Call to Poets" and "Chiropractic" from *Prejudices Sixth Series,* by H. L. Mencken.

J. B. Lippincott Company—for "Blood Pressure," from *Guys and Dolls,* by Damon Runyon, copyright 1931, by Damon Runyon.

Little, Brown & Company—for "Love Makes the Filly Go," from *A Pearl in Every Oyster,* by Frank Sullivan.

O. K. Liveright—for "There Ought to Be a Law," from *There Ought to Be a Law,* by Nunnally Johnson, with special permission from the author.

Harold Matson—for "Birthday Present," by Thorne Smith; "Gavin O'Leary," by John Collier; "The Bedchamber Mystery," by C. S. Forester; and "The Golden Key," by James Street.

Harold Ober—for "I Drink American," by Donald Hough, from *The Bedside Esquire;* copyright 1940, by Esquire, Inc., with special permission of the author and *Esquire.*

Charles Scribner's Sons—for "Mr. Frisbie," from *Roundup,* and "Dogs," from *First and Last,* by Ring Lardner.

The Viking Press, Inc.—for "The Missing Idol," from *A Book of Miracles,* copyright 1939, by Ben Hecht; "You Were Perfectly Fine," from *The Portable Library Dorothy Parker,* copyright 1930, 1944, by Dorothy Parker; and "Entrance Fee," and "Our Mrs. Parker," from *While Rome Burns,* copyright 1934, by Alexander Woollcott.

CONTENTS

ANTHOLOGY,
N. THE STUDY OF ANTS

I. ANTHOLOGY, n. The study of ants

THIS BOOK had its origin in a night club at noon. Four men were having lunch—a publisher, an agent, a novelist, and myself. Under similar circumstances many of the books published nowadays have their origin.

We were talking shop, and you should hear a group of book people talk shop. Our shoptalk is duller than the shoptalk of cigar makers. A seminar of slab-happy undertakers would be livelier.

Someone mentioned an anthology of humor that had recently been published and someone else asked me if I had read it. I said I had and that I was disappointed in it.

"It ain't funny," I said, employing the cultured accents I reserve for literary discussion.

"Why don't you do one of your own?" suggested the publisher. Then he appended a remark which I hesitate to repeat. Sort of a trade secret. He said: "I think we could make some money on it."

There you are! The frying pan's out of the fire! You never suspected it, but that's the very reason people write books and edit books and publish books. It's going to come out someday anyway so I might as well be the first to tell you. The general public has not been aware of this hidden motive behind the publishing of books. I know from personal observation that the public doesn't know books are brought out with the intention of swinging a profit. Not long ago I was in a New York bookstore, lurking near a table where a couple of my own bawdy pamphlets were on display. I watched a citizen pick up a copy of my work. He examined it fore and aft, sniffed, explored briefly into the interior, and finally turned to a clerk. "You mean to say," he said, "they actually charge money for this?" You see? The man quite obviously didn't know about the profit motive in the book business. If I could have put my hands on a boxed copy of Fabre's *Book of Insects* at that moment I'd have knocked him unconscious.

Returning to the night club and the challenge flung so abruptly at me by the publisher—I responded with mental vigor. I said that lately I had been ruminating over the possibility that I might be cast away on a desert island. It is a thing that might happen to anybody and at any moment.

I realize that it is not customary nowadays to be cast away on a desert island without a companion, usually Dorothy Lamour or some other dish out of Hollywood. I also realize that a man can't be choosy about his desert-island companion. He has to take what Destiny gives him, be it Dorothy Lamour or Dame May Whitty.[1]

Given a desert island and Miss Lamour, it doesn't seem reasonable that a man would start hollering for membership in the Book-of-the-Month Club. Yet there are two schools of thought on this proposition. Personally, I am getting along toward forty.

Of course there are many people who have little interest in reading and who would eschew both the Encyclopaedia Britannica and Dorothy Lamour in favor of some other commodity: a sharp knife for whittling, a puzzle made out of two bent nails, a ton and a half of chewing tobacco, a Ouija board, a calculating machine for adding and subtracting pebbles, or a big red barn.

Given my choice between Dorothy Lamour and a book, I believe I'd take Miss Lamour. She could cook. Yet, as I've suggested, when the fateful day comes that I'm cast away, I doubt very much that she'll be with me.

[1]When I was in Hollywood I heard about the dilemma of an assistant director when shooting started on a picture in which Dame May Whitty was appearing. He didn't know how to address her. He didn't think it would be proper to call her "Miss Whitty" or "Mme. Whitty" or "Lady Whitty." Nobody else seemed to know the answer, so he took a chance. His first words to her were: "Stand right over here, Dame."

This desert-island idea has been tossed around a lot in recent years. For example, when the late G. K. Chesterton was asked which book he would want to have with him on an island, he specified Thomas' *Guide to Practical Shipbuilding*. Then there was the case of Madeleine Carroll. A group of college boys once voted Miss Carroll to be the girl they would most enjoy having as a companion on a desert island. They didn't say why. Shortly after that Miss Carroll came to New York and was greeted at Grand Central by the usual press gang. One of the reporters, Cecil Carnes, asked her what person *she* would like to have as companion on a desert island. Miss Carroll answered without hesitation: "The best obstetrician in the world." She didn't think the crack would get into the papers, but it made the *World-Telegram*.

As for a book or books, here again a man can't be choosy. He can't very well decide in advance which book he wants to have with him when he's cast away. He doesn't have much time to pack. If he does reach shore with a book clutched to his bosom, the chances are it'll be something of little practical value to him. He might land with a copy of Emily Post and spend the rest of his life with nothing to be polite to except bananas. He might find himself alone with *Just Yells—The Science of Cheer Leading*. He might struggle ashore with *The Ashley Book of Knots* and no rope.

In my own case I would hope to have a book that would make me laugh. A person can laugh only so long at sand, then it ceases to be funny. What he needs is people. And if he has no people, the next best thing would be a book with a lot of amusing people in it. I think this book meets that specification. It'll be just my luck, however, to get myself cast away on a desert island without it, to find myself dripping on a sand bar with a pair of gloves that don't fit me, a left-handed putter, eight bottles of Lydia Pinkham's Compound, and a copy of *What Shall We Name the Baby?* by Winthrop Ames.

Inasmuch as this book is supposed to be mainly humorous, I should now be getting into an analysis of humor. That would appear to be the custom. I don't intend, however, to get off on any involved attempt to define the stuff. Max Eastman wrote a whole book trying to do it and I still don't understand what he was trying to say. Mr. Eastman went so far as to draw diagrams of jokes—such things as zigzag lines with little flowers growing out of them and Victoria Crosses stuck on at the end. I suppose he knew what he was doing.

All I know about humor is that certain brands of it will cause one man to laugh until he comes down with the gut rumbles while his neighbor, after taking the same dosage, will groan in anguish and cry out for the perpetrator's execution. Take me, for an example. I have never been able to read comic strips. I know quite well that millions of men, women, and children fairly devour them. I have watched these people on the subways, opening their newspapers straightway to the comics, ignoring all else. I have been told by people who ought to know that in nine cases out of ten the newspaper in any given city with the largest circulation is the newspaper which carries the best, i.e., the most popular, comic strips. Now and then I make an effort to read them but I get nothing out of them. I suffer socially as a consequence. My ignorance of the doings of Dick Tracy and Barnaby and all the rest proves embarrassing remarkably often when the conversation, at social gatherings, turns to the exploits of this one or that. I don't know what the hell they are talking about. And when I openly profess my ignorance and admit that I never read the strips, the others look at me in awe and begin edging away from the punchbowl (my customary station at social gatherings).

Yet I have got my biggest laughs, I believe, out of a picture. It is a photograph of a Negro man with two billiard balls and a golf ball in his mouth. The guy's cheeks are distended far out beyond the spread of his ears, the billiard balls being on the outside and the golf ball in the middle. I don't know where his teeth are. Probably has none.

I first saw that picture several years ago when I was a rewrite man on the New York *World-Telegram*. It appeared in *Life* magazine as a sort of photographic curiosity, having been sent in by a man named McCord in Corinth, Mississippi.

After it appeared in the magazine I sat and looked at it for a long time, and all the time I was looking at it I was laughing. It simply made me feel good. I put the magazine away in my desk and several times thereafter, when I was feeling low, I got it out and turned to the picture again, and in no time at all I was feeling better and giggling over it. Finally the thought struck me that I had discovered a sovereign remedy for the blues. I clipped the picture out and glued it to a piece of cardboard as a means of preserving it against wear and tear.

Before long everybody in that newspaper office knew about my picture. One by one the members of the staff discovered that I could cure their minor mental ailments. It became a common procedure for people with hangovers to visit my desk immediately on arrival at the office. They'd simply walk up and say:

"Let's see 'im."

I'd get out the picture and hand it over. They'd stand and look at it and in a few moments they'd be smiling, and then they'd be laughing and, if their hangover were sufficiently severe, they'd end up howling with tears streaming out of their eyes.

Guys who had been fighting with their wives recaptured their emotional equilibrium through looking at that picture. Reporters whose by-lines had been misspelled through typographical error (a most horribly depressing thing to have happen) sat and looked at the picture for three or four minutes and then decided against telling the boss what he could do with the job. Copyreaders under assault from the Morris Plan found temporary surcease at my desk. Even B. O. McAnney, the paper's city editor, grown morose over the invincible stupidity of certain members of his staff, overcame the urge to run amuck several times through the simple act of staring at the portrait.

In time my crudely mounted copy grew soiled and shabby. I sat down and wrote a letter to *Life*. I explained how the picture had been serving humanity, how my copy was worn out, and begged the magazine to reprint it. Within a couple of weeks a one-column reprint appeared. Soon after that I heard from Mr. McCord, the Mississippi photographer. He sent me a good print of the picture though he never did identify the subject. Nor did he furnish any of the circumstances under which the picture had been taken. I didn't care. I didn't need any details. The picture itself was enough.

It served me in another way besides medicinal. I found that by showing it to a person I could determine whether or not that person possessed a sense of humor. That is, I could determine whether or not he had a sense of humor by my own standards.

I used my photograph as a gauge of humor by simply showing it to the subject. If he laughed I figured he had a sense of humor. If he merely stared at it as if it were the Mona Lisa (a railroad line in eastern Quebec) I put him down as a humorless person. Among those lacking a sense of humor (in my own evaluation, of course) were some who reacted to the picture not with laughter but with simply ripping comments.

One such might look at it blankly for a moment, then say: "What's the idea?"

Another reaction, quite common, was: "Who is it?"

And I remember one fathead, a political writer, who took one look and then said: "My God, he'll stretch his fool mouth out of shape!"

I feel genuinely sorry for such people. They are the Anticlimax Demanders of the world. Tell one of them a simple little story and see what happens. Tell him, for example, this one:

Two famous scientists are at work in the Mount Wilson Observatory. One of them is studying the heavens through the huge telescope.

Suddenly he turns away and remarks: "It's going to rain."

"How can you tell?" asks his colleague.

"My corns hurt."

Tell him that one and your Anticlimax Demander will stare at you a moment and then say: "Well, did it?"

"Did it what?"

"Rain."

People of that caliber find nothing amusing in my favorite photographic work of art. I had planned to include it in the front of this book because it is among the things I want to have with me on that desert island. I don't think I'd ever get bored with it. The editors said, however, that it wouldn't look good in a book that carries freehand drawing illustrations. That's what they said, but I don't think that was their real reason.

At the beginning I thought it would be an easy matter to assemble the material for this book. I figured on a month of leisurely reading and rereading. It took much longer than that. In order to print another person's stuff you've got to ask for permission and make a deal with him about money. Almost all of this detail was handled by Mrs. C. A. Pollard of the Doubleday, Doran & Company staff. Mrs. Pollard had first to run the various authors to earth and, having trapped them, it was her job to haggle about price. She did the thing most efficiently, for she's an old hand at the "permissions" business. She consulted with me only when she came up against an author who was holding out for a fee which seemed to her extortionate. We had trouble, for example, with Westbrook Pegler, as who hasn't? And before that we ran up against a Mr. Hyperion G. Lank in a transaction involving a story by Cornelia Otis Skinner. I made up that name of Hyperion G. Lank and I bring up the matter of Mr. Lank to illustrate my own lack of appreciation of blunt commercial dealing. It demonstrates how stupidly unreasonable a member of the human race (of whom I am one of which) can be.

Mrs. Pollard made a routine request for permission to use Miss Skinner's essay and this Mr. Lank, acting for the author, fired back a demand for a sum that was considerably more than any other author or publisher had asked. Mark Twain, for instance. I've loved that guy for a long time but now I fairly worship him. We got three assorted items from his works and the whole shebang came to a mere five dollars.

I told Mrs. Pollard that I wouldn't pay the asking price for the Skinner piece, all circumstances considered, so she went to work on Mr. Lank and finally reported that she had him argued down a trifle. That still made Miss Skinner the most expensive author on our list and while I confess that it was a piddling sum, she ain't *that* good. Mr. Lank sent word that I could take his price or leave it. So what did I do? I got sore. I started thinking evil, calumnious thoughts about this Mr. Lank. I pictured him as a snuff-dipping old skinflint patterned after Ebenezer Scrooge, thumping heartlessly around his dirty old publishing house, abusing his ragged and hungry employees, cackling fiendishly over the manner in which he was going to rob that upstart of a Smith. Those are the thoughts I had about Mr. Lank—a man I never met. After a while, however, my better nature asserted itself and I came to the realization that I was wrong. I have no doubt that Mr. Lank is a young, alert, personable businessman who scrubs his teeth twice daily, is adored by his employees and loved by his authors. The big heel.

The form letter which Mrs. Pollard sent out to authors and publishers was a heart-rending piece of prose. It told of the plan for this book and then it went into the matter of money. Our budget, it said, was almost nothing. From the tone of it one would suspect that I was in rags, eating out of garbage cans, while the firm of Doubleday, Doran was so deep in financial misery that even the bankruptcy courts would have nothing to do with it. One of these letters was sent to Fred Allen as a matter of routine, since an Allen script was to be included. Fred wrote back, offering condolences, and enclosing a dollar bill for Doubleday, Doran.

Most of the book-publishing houses have a person employed whose job is to handle "permissions," both incoming and outgoing. Usually this person is a female, and over the years the various "permissions girls" have got acquainted with one another. A year or so ago one of their number suggested that all the "permissions girls" ought to band themselves together in a little club. They knew each other through correspondence and telephone conversations, but the idea of the club was to bring them together socially. There was one other purpose in forming the club. It was suggested that prices for permissions were too low; that if the girls got better acquainted they could work toward establishing higher price levels for authors. It was a fine idea but it didn't work. I'm told that the Permissions Club had just the opposite effect. Formerly a girl at one house could call the girl at another, ask for permission to use a certain author's work, offer, say, fifty dollars, and close the deal at that figure. With the formation of the club, however, the girls got to know each other better. Now their business transactions would go something like this:

"Hello, Esther? Oh, say, Esther, I need a selection from Increase N. Tarbox.[2] How much you want for it?"

"Well, dear," says Esther, "we usually get fifty dollars for Tarbox selections, but long as it's you, honey—well, you can have it for fifteen. Did you hear about Prudence gonna have a baby? And, oh yes, Betty's going to . . ."

In organization there is debility.

Preparation of a book such as this ordinarily would require, on the part of the selector, a solid working knowledge of literature and an acute critical sense. I possess neither of these qualifications. Outside of the junk they forced on me in grammar school I went through my first eighteen years without reading a single book that I can remember. On my nineteenth birthday a girl gave me the complete short stories of O. Henry and I was so pleased about it that I married her. I read one other book before I reached the age of twenty. It was a novel by Rex Beach and the reason I read it was that Rex Beach lived in our town in Florida during the winters and I was on speaking terms with him. I thought his book was good.

When, however, I got into my twenties I began reading like mad to make up for wasted time. I'm still at it, yet I never seem to have developed that acute critical sense. Usually if I like a book or a movie or a play or a radio pro-

[2]I didn't make that name up. There actually was an American author named Increase N. Tarbox. He wrote a biography of Israel Putnam in 1876.

gram I like it backwards and forwards and sideways and advocate the gas chamber for critics who search for and find little flaws in it. Let us suppose that an author turns out a historical novel—a book that appeals to me as readable and engrossing against a background of good substantial history. Along comes a critic. He concludes: "The book is all right, except that the author has a woman of 1904 hanging out clothes and using the spring-clamp type of clothespin, whereas such clothespins, as everyone knows, were not invented until the late autumn of 1905." Whenever I encounter carping of this kind I feel the urge to go out and find the critic and raise a knurl on his noggin with an armadillo basket.

Recently my teen-age daughter came to me and, fixing me with a severe look, said she'd like to have a heart-to-heart talk with me. She took me into the living room, planted me in a chair, and settled herself opposite me. She was treating me just as though I were a grownup. I wondered what I had done now. It looked bad.

"Daddy," she said, "it's getting so I'm ashamed to bring my friends around the house any more. It's getting so I just tell them to ring the bell in the lobby and I'll come down and meet them."

"What've I done now?"

"Well," she said, "it's this way. All of my friends have read your books and they think you are a wild and happy man. They come up here and every time they walk into the room, there you sit. You just sit there in the same old chair and read books. They think you ought to be up running around the room and jumping up in the air and clicking your heels together and yelling jokes and wisecracks at everybody and things like that. But what do you do? Just sit there and read books. Honestly, it's going to get around the neighborhood that you are dumb."

I don't know what to do about this thing. I don't intend to spend my days running around the room and jumping up in the air and clicking my heels together. That'd kill me. Be dead in a week. I merely bring up the incident to show you that I do a lot of reading.

I don't go in much for the heavy stuff. This guy Shakespeare must have something, but whatever it is escapes me. People speak well of his stuff but, given my choice on a rainy night between *King Lear* and a Nero Wolfe mystery, I'd take Rex Stout. It's much the same with the book often called the greatest novel ever written—*War and Peace.* A dozen times I've gone into training, got myself in good physical trim, gritted my teeth, and settled down to the job. I've never got beyond the first hundred pages.

I don't know why it is that some of the world's great classics fail to stir me. Sometimes I feel downright depressed about it. I would be a public disgrace if I were ever invited to be a guest on "Information Please" (which I won't). Nonetheless, I think I know what I'd do if it ever happened. The moment Fadiman finished a question I'd have my hand in the air. If he asked me for the answer I'd shut my eyes and say, "*Hamlet.*" If he asked which was the most populous state, Illinois or Pennsylvania, I'd say, "*Hamlet.*" If he asked who wrote the *Bab Ballads,* I'd say, "*Hamlet.*" I'd surely make an ass of myself but at the same time I believe I'd come out in the end with a good over-all score.

I could go into the question of my literary taste at great length but it's not necessary, since the contents of this book tells the story fairly well. When *Time* magazine reviewed my book *Life in a Putty Knife Factory* the anonymous critic said I was "complacently boorish." I looked it up. It means that I am rustic, rude, awkward, clumsy, ungainly, lubberly, surly, sullen, crabbed, possessed of a gross lack of breeding, and that I am content to be that way—almost proud of it.

Soon after that review appeared I met a fellow I know who is a writer on *Time* and in some respects human. He refused to tell me the name of the man who did the review, explaining that such matters are virtually military secrets at *Time.* I ventured to suggest that from the general tone of the review the guy had never been a newspaperman.

"Well," said my friend, "I don't think he ever was, but I'll tell you one thing. He's a poet—a professional poet."

I have no objection to the man's saying I'm complacently boorish, though I deny the charge. I'm boorish, but I'm not altogether happy about it and if I could read Shakespeare without sweating I'd do it. Most matters pertaining to the higher intellect leave me as cold as Birdseye snap beans. I've confessed before that I lack the genteel touch and I confess it again. I never saw a herring until I was twenty-one years old and I never ate one until I was twenty-eight, simply because I was afraid to. The first time I ever ordered broiled lobster, my wife had to snatch the claws out of my teeth when she saw me trying to wolf them down. I can't complain when they call me boorish, but I do object when an editor puts one of my books into the hands of a snotnose poet. A poet has no more qualification to review one of my books than does Mrs. Frances Hackett, the Irish scholar. I wouldn't trust a poet within ten feet of my henhouse if I had a henhouse; within twenty feet of my bond box; or within eighty feet of my wife.

Thus my high qualifications for the job at hand. I trust they are sufficient.

Under the original scheme this was to be a book of humorous writings.

I set up a large table in my workroom. I got out all the humor books from my own shelves and piled them on this table, making a list of the titles so I could check them off as I finished going through them, and then I started reading. At once I began thinking of humorists whose works I didn't own. I went to the bookstores and began ordering dozens and dozens of additional volumes, piling them in the corner alongside the crowded table. Then I thought of Fred Allen's library. He has a fine collection of humorous books so I went to see him and he gave me free run of his shelves. I toted away a lot of his books and added them to my pile. Then I returned to the job of reading.

Within a week I was wishing I were back picking chickens at two and a half cents per chicken in Ditzler's poultry house. I got out of that room, mixed myself a double cherry phosphate, and tried to think. I went back and stared at the enormous pile of humor books—books by Mark Twain, Robert Benchley, James Thurber, Ring Lardner, Joe Mitchell, Joe Liebling, E. B. White, S. J. Perelman, Will Cuppy, Wolcott Gibbs, H. I. Phillips, John O'Hara, Damon Runyon, Corey Ford, Donald Ogden Stewart, Frank Sullivan, Dorothy Parker, Max Shulman, Ludwig Bemelmans, John Collier, Thorne Smith, Don Marquis, Irvin S. Cobb, Stephen Leacock, Oliver Herford, Bill Nye, Ellis Parker Butler, Arthur Kober, Finley Peter Dunne, Eugene Field, Milt Gross, Cornelia Otis Skinner, Franklin P. Adams, Nunnally Johnson, Artemus Ward, Clarence Day, Ruth McKenny, and a couple of million others.

There stood a small mountain of happy laughter, an Alp of joy, and it depressed me as nothing else in this life has depressed me. I just looked at it a long while and then I concluded that life is too brief; that the human mechanism can stand up under just so much punishment and then it collapses; that maybe Doc Weber would give me a job pestling pills in his drugstore.

Right then and there I changed trains. I forgot the pile of books, sat down and started making a list of short pieces I had read in the past–articles and essays and stories that had stuck in my memory, pieces or passages that I had read and gone back to read again. As it turned out almost all of these pieces could be classified as humorous, though humor was not an essential factor in the selection.

There is one other element that the selections in this book have in common: I wish I had written every one of them.

As I've indicated, I have paid no attention to literary values, though it's probable that some literature has crept into this book. I have no objection to it. All of the selections are, to me, entertaining, and sheer entertainment is the sole aim of this book. Sheer entertainment and making money.

WOMEN

II. WOMEN

THERE ARE TIMES when I catch myself believing that Abner Peabody of Pine Ridge, Arkansas, has the proper attitude toward women. I recall the time Abner's partner Lum Edwards asked him what he got his wife for Christmas last year.

"Let me see now," said Abner. "Last Christmas I got 'er a new choppin' ax. No, that was the year before. Last year I got 'er some new horness fer th' mule."

Then again there are times when I get downright sentimental about women and admire them all over the place. I believe, therefore, that my position in regard to women is a normal one, and that I am as well qualified as the next man to select a series of recitations about women.

While I was prowling around searching for stuff to put into this section I remembered a short bit written long ago by a set of initials. I have reference to F.P.A., the Connecticut politician and pool shooter. This little item first appeared about twenty years ago. Some things never change.

A PAIR OF SEXES

By F.P.A.

I. *A Man Telephones*
"Ed? . . . Lunch at one. Whyte's. Right."
II. *A Woman Telephones*
"Hello, Operator. Operator? I want Caledonia 5867, please.

Oh, this *is* Caledonia 5867? Oh, I beg your pardon, I'm terribly sorry. I thought it was the operator. I've had so much trouble with the telephone lately. May I speak to Miss Lucille Webster, please? Oh, speaking? Oh, I'm terribly sorry. Is this Miss Webster? Is this you, Lucille? I didn't recognize your voice at first. Got a cold or something? Oh, you sound as though you had. There's so much of it around this wretched weather. I never saw anything like it in my whole life. Well, I'm glad you haven't got a cold, though at first you certainly sounded like it. . . . I was just talking to Ethel for a second, and she had such a cold she could hardly talk. That's the reason I asked you. There's an awful lot of it around this wretched weather. . . . Oh, nothing particular. . . . Oh yes, there is too. How silly of me! I was so interested in what you were saying, I almost forgot. Lucille, what are you doing tomorrow? . . . No, about lunch time. Or a little earlier. Or a little later. It doesn't matter. Because I expect to be in your part of town about that time, around lunch time, oh, maybe one or one-thirty or so, I have an appointment at twelve-thirty, and it oughtn't to take me more than half an hour, or at the most three quarters, surely not over an hour, I'm almost certain, and probably I'll be through in half an hour, but anyway, I ought to be all through by one-thirty, and I could meet you anywhere you say. . . . Oh, I know, but Maillard's is pretty crowded about that time and isn't there someplace nearer? My appointment is on Forty-seventh Street near Madison—no, it's near Fifth, I guess. But that doesn't matter. I'll take a cab. If I can get one. Did you ever see anything like how hard it is to get a cab nowadays? My dear, last night I was twenty-five minutes trying to get one, and it got me late for dinner, and I *know* they didn't believe me. But if I can't get one I'll walk. It's only a block. And I guess a little exercise wouldn't do me any harm. . . . Maillard's. . . . How about the Ritz? No, there's such a jam there. And it's hard to meet. Well, any place *you* say. . . . Oh, Lucille, that's a dreadful place. The food's so—oh, I don't know. You know. So—bad, if you know what I mean. Well, let's take a chance on Maillard's. Only it's so crowded. . . .

Oh no, I never heard that. . . . No, I haven't. I haven't read a thing in months, absolutely months. Where the time goes to I don't know. I simply do not know where the time goes to. Lucille, you're sure you've got tomorrow at lunch free? Because if you haven't, or there's something you'd rather do, just say so and we'll try again. Well, suppose we say at Maillard's at—oh, do you know that little teashop on Forty-seventh? I think it's between Park and Madison on the—let's see—on the downtown, that's the south side of the street. I'll be there by one, or anyway one-thirty, and if I'm there first I'll get a table, and you do the same if you are. But I ought to be there by one. My appointment is for half past twelve, and it may take me only a few minutes. I might be there before one. But surely by quarter past, and certainly by one-thirty. . . . All right, then. Suppose we say about one, at Maillard's. . . . Oh no, what am I thinking of? We decided that would be too crowded, didn't we? Unless you'd rather go there. That little teashop is very nice. . . . Well, yes, I'd just as soon go to Maillard's. It doesn't matter much. It's seeing you I care about. There's a lot I want to talk to you about. These little snatches at the telephone are so—well, so sort of unsatisfactory, if you know what I mean. . . . All right, suppose we say Maillard's, then. And then if we don't like the look of things we can go somewhere else. . . . All right, then, at . . . oh, let's go to the tearoom. It's quieter. . . . All right, then. I'm longing to see you, Lucille. . . . Tomorrow, then. At the teashop, that's on Forty-seventh between Park and Madison, on the downtown, that's the south side of the street. Tomorrow, then, about one. That's Wednesday. . . . What? Is it Tuesday? Well, I'm *all* turned around. I thought it was Wednesday. I'm terribly sorry, Lucille. I can't *possibly* meet you tomorrow if it's Tuesday. I've got a luncheon appointment I've had for ages, simply for weeks, and I've postponed it so often I don't dare do it again. . . . You can't Wednesday? I'm terribly sorry. . . . Well, I'll try again. Ring me up. I'll be in all afternoon until five twenty-five, and then I have to go uptown. . . . Yes. . . . Well, I'm glad we had a nice little talk, anyway. . . . And

I'll see you soon. . . . What? No, *soon*—S for Sam. . . . Yes, soon. . . . Good-by, Lucille. . . . Good-by. Good-by. Good-by."

I DON'T KNOW whether this next story is based on truth or whether it's pure fiction. It doesn't matter. In my book it ranks as a little classic. I read it the first time before it was published anywhere. It is the kind of a story that you read and then go around talking about, retelling it in your own words. Whenever I told it to bookish people they'd say, "That's wonderful, but you got the author wrong. C. S. Forester doesn't write that kind of stuff." The hell C. S. Forester doesn't. He is best known, to be sure, for his sea stories and particularly for the exploits of Captain Horatio Hornblower. Yet he has turned out several sparkling little things of this nature.

THE BEDCHAMBER MYSTERY

By C. S. Forester

NOW THAT A HUNDRED YEARS have passed one of the scandals in my family can be told. It is very doubtful if in 1843 Miss Forester (she was Eulalie, but being the eldest daughter unmarried, she of course was Miss Forester) and Miss Emily Forester and Miss Eunice Forester ever foresaw the world of 1943 to which their story would be told; in fact it is inconceivable that they could have believed that there ever would be a world in which their story could be told blatantly in public print. At that time it was the sort of thing that could only be hinted at in whispers during confidential moments in feminine drawing rooms; but it was whispered about enough to reach in the end the ears of my grandfather, who was their nephew, and my grandfather told it to me.

In 1843 Miss Forester and Miss Emily and Miss Eunice Forester were already maiden ladies of a certain age. The old-fashioned Georgian house in which they lived kept itself modestly retired, just like its inhabitants, from what there was of bustle and excitement in the High Street of the market town. The ladies indeed led a retired life; they went to church a little, they visited those of the sick whom it was decent and proper for maiden ladies to visit, they read the more colorless of the novels in the circulating library, and sometimes they entertained other ladies at tea.

And once a week they entertained a man. It might almost be said that they went from week to week looking forward to those evenings. Dr. Acheson was (not one of the old ladies would have been heartless enough to say "fortunately," but each of them felt it) a widower, and several years older even than my great-great-aunt Eulalie. Moreover, he was a keen whist player and a brilliant one, but in no way keener or more brilliant than were Eulalie, Emily, and Eunice. For years now the three nice old ladies had looked forward to their weekly evening of whist—all the ritual of setting out the green table, the two hours of silent cut-and-thrust play, and the final twenty minutes of conversation with Dr. Acheson as he drank a glass of old Madeira before bidding them good night.

The late Mrs. Acheson had passed to her Maker somewhere about 1830, so that it was for thirteen years they had played their weekly game of whist before the terrible thing happened. To this day we do not know whether it happened to Eulalie or Emily or Eunice, but it happened to one of them. The three of them had retired for the night, each to her separate room, and had progressed far toward the final stage of getting into bed. They were not dried-up old spinsters; on the contrary, they were women of weight and substance, with the buxom contours even married women might have been proud of. It was her weight which was the undoing of one of them, Eulalie, Emily, or Eunice.

Through the quiet house that bedtime there sounded the crash of china and a cry of pain, and two of the sisters—which two we do not know—hurried in their dressing gowns to the bedroom of the third—her identity is uncertain—to find her bleeding profusely from severe cuts in the lower part of the back. The jagged china fragments had inflicted severe wounds, and, most unfortunately, just in those parts where the injured sister could not attend to them herself. Under the urgings of the other two she fought down her modesty sufficiently to let them attempt to deal with them, but the bleeding was profuse, and the blood of the Foresters streamed from the prone figure face downward on the bed in terrifying quantity.

"We shall have to send for the doctor," said one of the ministering sisters; it was a shocking thing to contemplate.

"Oh, but we cannot!" said the other ministering sister.

"We must," said the first.

"How terrible!" said the second.

And with that the injured sister twisted her neck and joined in the conversation. "I will not have the doctor," she said. "I would die of shame."

"Think of the disgrace of it!" said the second sister. "We might even have to explain to him how it happened!"

"But she's bleeding to death," protested the first sister.

"I'd rather die!" said the injured one, and then, as a fresh appalling thought struck her, she twisted her neck even further. "I could never face him again. And what would happen to our whist?"

That was an aspect of the case which until then had occurred to neither of the other sisters, and it was enough to make them blench. But they were of stern stuff. Just as we do not know which was the injured one, we do not know which one thought of a way out of the difficulty, and we shall never know. We know that it was Miss Eulalie, as befitted her rank as eldest sister, who called to Deborah, the maid, to go and fetch Dr. Acheson at once, but that does not mean to say that it was not Miss Eulalie who was the injured sister—injured or not, Miss Eulalie was quite capable of calling to Deborah and telling her what to do.

As she was bid, Deborah went and fetched Dr. Acheson and conducted him to Miss Eunice's bedroom, but of course the fact that it was Miss Eunice's bedroom is really no indication that it was Miss Eunice who was in there. Dr. Acheson had no means of knowing; all he saw was a recumbent form covered by a sheet. In the center of the sheet a round hole a foot in diameter had been cut, and through the hole the seat of the injury was visible.

Dr. Acheson needed no explanations. He took his needles and his thread from his little black bag and he set to work and sewed up the worst of the cuts and attended to the minor ones. Finally he straightened up and eased his aching back.

"I shall have to take those stitches out," he explained to the still and silent figure which had borne the stitching stoically without a murmur. "I shall come next Wednesday and do that."

Until next Wednesday the three Misses Forester kept to their rooms. Not one of them was seen in the streets of the market town, and when on Wednesday Dr. Acheson knocked at the door Deborah conducted him once more to Miss Eunice's bedroom. There was the recumbent form, and there was the sheet with the hole in it. Dr. Acheson took out the stitches.

"It has healed very nicely," said Dr. Acheson. "I don't think any further attention from me will be necessary."

The figure under the sheet said nothing, nor did Dr. Acheson expect it. He gave some concluding advice and went his way. He was glad later to receive a note penned in Miss Forester's Italian hand:

DEAR DR. ACHESON,

We will all be delighted if you will come to whist this week as usual.

When Dr. Acheson arrived he found that the "as usual" applied only to his coming, for there was a slight but subtle change in the furnishings of the drawing room. The stiff, high-backed chairs on which the three Misses Forester sat bore, each of them, a thick and comfortable cushion upon the seat. There was no knowing which of the sisters needed it.

☆ ☆ ☆

IN MY OWN considered opinion Alexander Woollcott was an ass with a Percheron tinge. Once when he was appearing as an actor on Broadway and I was a dirty-knuckled newspaperman, I undertook to do an interview with him. The thing had to be arranged through a mutual acquaintance and Woollcott finally agreed to it in a letter to his friend in which he stipulated that he was not to be quoted directly. He insisted, moreover, that if I wrote anything about him I was to follow the pattern employed in the *New Yorker* profiles. If I agreed to this, he said, he would consent to receive me briefly. I got a good deal of satisfaction out of the fact that, some weeks later, the *New Yorker* itself let go with a three-part profile of Smart Alec, written by the masterful Wolcott Gibbs—a biographical examination that made its subject bellow like a young goat trapped in a snare-drum factory.

The interview with Woollcott took place in his hotel suite and was satisfactory from one point of view: it convinced me that Alexander the Great was an awful heel and, as Douglas Gilbert later described him—"a jar of vaseline, hospital size."

So what? So he remained, to me, a wonderful writer. I still read his essays over and over even though I thought the guy should have been chained to a stake on a desert island where he would have nobody to insult but coconuts. I see no reason why his personal nastiness should detract from the merits of his work. I've always liked this one.

ENTRANCE FEE

By Alexander Woollcott

Wherein a young cadet from the Saint-Cyr of yesteryear has a bit of luck and learns how greathearted a French cocotte can be.

This, then, is the story of Cosette and the Saint-Cyrien, much as they tell it (and these many years have been telling it) in the smoky *popotes* of the French Army.

In the nineties, when one heard less ugly babel of alien tongues in the sidewalk cafés, the talk at the apéritif hour was sure to turn sooner or later on Cosette—Mlle. Cosette of the Variétés, who was regarded by common consent as the most desirable woman in France. She was no hedged-in royal courtesan, as her possessive fellow citizens would point out with satisfaction, but a distributed Du Barry, the *chère amie* of a republic.

Her origins were misty. Some said she had been born of fisherfolk at Plonbazlanec on the Brittany coast. Others preferred the tale that she was the love child of a famous actress by a very well-known king. In any case she was now a national legend, and in her pre-eminence the still bruised French people found in some curious way a balm for their wounded self-esteem. Her photographs, which usually showed her sitting piquantly on a café table, were cut from *L'Illustration* and pinned up in every barracks. Every French lad dreamed of her, and every right-minded French girl quite understood that her sweetheart was saying in effect, "Since I cannot hope to have Cosette, will you come to the river's edge at sundown?" Quite understood, and did not blame him. Everyone had seen the pictures of Cosette's tiny, vine-hung villa at Saint-Cloud, with its high garden wall and its twittering aviary. And even those for whom that wall was hopelessly high took morbid pride in a persistent detail of the legend which said that no man was ever a guest there for the night who could not bring five thousand francs with him. This was in the nineties, mind you, when francs were francs, and men—by a coincidence then more dependable—were men.

The pleasant blend of charm and thrift in Cosette filled the cadets at Saint-Cyr with a gentle melancholy. In their twilight hours of relaxation they talked it over, and all thought it a sorrowful thing that, so wretched is the soldier's pittance, not one of those who must someday direct the great *Revanche* would ever carry into battle a memory of the fairest woman in France. For what cadet could hope to raise five thousand francs? It was very sad. But, cried one of their number, his voice shaking, his eyes alight, there were a thousand students at Saint-Cyr, and not one among them so lacking in resource that he could not, if given time, manage to raise at least five francs.

That was how the Cosette Sweepstakes were started. There followed then all the anxious distraction of ways and means, with such Spartan exploits in self-denial, such Damon-and-Pythias borrowings, such flagrant letters of perjured appeal to unsuspecting aunts and godmothers, as Saint-Cyr had never known. But by the appointed time the last man had his, or somebody's, five francs.

The drawing of numbers was well under way when a perplexed instructor stumbled on the proceedings and reported his discovery to the commandant. When the old general heard the story he was so profoundly moved that it was some time before he spoke.

"The lad who wins the lottery," he said at last, "will be the envy of his generation. But the lad who conceived the idea—ah, he, my friend, will someday be a marshal of France!"

Then he fell to laughing at the thought of the starry-eyed youngster arriving at the stage door of the Variétés with nothing but his youth and his entrance fee. The innocent budget had made no provision for the trip to Paris, none for a carriage, a bouquet, perhaps a supper party. The commandant said that he would wish to meet this margin of contingency from his own fatherly pocket.

"There will be extras," he said. "Let the young rascal who wins be sent to me before he leaves for Paris."

It was a cadet from the Vendée who reported to the commandant next afternoon—very trim in his red breeches and blue tunic, his white gloves spotless, his white cockade jaunty, his heart in his mouth. The commandant said no word to him, but put a little purse of gold louis in his hand, kissed him on both cheeks in benediction, and stood at his window, moist-eyed and chuckling, to watch until the white cockade disappeared down the avenue of trees.

The sunlight, latticed by the jalousies, was making a gay pattern on Cosette's carpet the next morning when she sat up and meditated on the day which stretched ahead of her.

Her little cadet was cradled in a sweet, dreamless sleep, and it touched her rather to see how preposterously young he was. Indeed, it quite set her thinking of her early days, and how she had come up in the world. Then she began speculating on *his* early days, realized with a pang that he was still in the midst of them, and suddenly grew puzzled. Being a woman of action, she prodded him.

"Listen, my old one," she said, "how did a cadet at Saint-Cyr ever get hold of five thousand francs?"

Thus abruptly questioned, he lost his head and blurted out the tale of the sweepstakes. Perhaps he felt it could do no harm now, and anyway she listened so avidly, with such flattering little gasps of surprise and such sunny ripples of laughter, that he quite warmed to his story. When he came to the part about the commandant she rose and strode up and down, the lace of her peignoir fluttering behind her, tears in her violet eyes.

"Saint-Cyr has paid me the prettiest compliment I have ever known," she said, "and I am the proudest woman in France this day. But surely I must do my part. You shall go back and tell them all that Cosette is a woman of sentiment. When you are an old, old man in the Vendée you shall tell your grandchildren that once in your youth you knew the dearest favors in France, and they cost you not a sou. Not a sou."

At that she hauled open the little drawer where he had seen her lock up the lottery receipts the night before.

"Here," she said with a lovely gesture. "I give you back your money."

And she handed him his five francs.

BARRY BENEFIELD's first successful novel, I believe, was *The Chicken-Wagon Family* and I've heard that Alexander Woollcott's enthusiasm for it contributed toward making it a best seller. I read it before I ever got to New York and I also read his volume of short stories, *Short Turns*. By the time I arrived in Manhattan I was a greater Benefield fan than Woollcott.

One day early in 1931 James Monahan, of the old Century Company, asked me to lunch and as we were leaving his office we encountered a very small, thin man, about as distinguished-looking as a fireplug and not much bigger. Monahan introduced us but I paid no attention to the name and the little guy came along with us. I figured him for a bookkeeper or perhaps a proofreader and did a nice job of ignoring him. Later on I nearly fell in my soup when I found out he was Barry Benefield. I did some high-caliber hero-worshiping after that and Mr. Benefield demonstrated that he didn't resent my earlier attitude of indifference by taking me back to the office and autographing all his books for me.

The Benefield story that follows is one I read before I ever met the man. It stuck in my mind for a long time. Reading it again in 1945, I got the feeling that it had lost something, but I don't know what that something is. I still think it's a fine story.

DAUGHTERS OF JOY

By Barry Benefield

In the morning of one of those early spring days when the wind has dragged up from the bay and pressed down over the smothering city innumerable blankets of oozy gray fog, a wagon that bore the name of the American Express Company in gilt letters on its dark blue sides drew up in front of an old-style, four-story, brownstone-front house in West Twenty-eighth Street, between Sixth and Seventh avenues. Four men lifted out a black coffin, with mockingly bright imitation silver mountings all over it, and carried it up the high front stoop in the strangely mixed manner of slow and gentle pallbearers and quick and destructive express handlers. The door was opened; the coffin went in.

The four men set their burden on two undertaker's stools

that had already been placed in the long front parlor on the first floor, and Madam Margaretta was signing her real, her unprofessional, name in the expressman's book—Margaret Schwartz. The six young women stood reading the bright plate on top of the coffin, which said that the remains of Lucy Painter lay therein. They scrutinized the inscription as if it were stubbornly withholding from them some information that they ought to possess.

The four men went out as the agile little Italian undertaker, with the bristly mustache, from around in Seventh Avenue, rushed in. Unscrewing the board that protected the glass over the corpse's face, he lifted it off with a delicate flourish and stood back, silent, intense, immensely satisfied with his gesture.

The madam came in and lighted all four of the gas jets in the chandelier. The houses in that sinister neighborhood in the early years of this gaudy twentieth century kept their front window shades always pulled down, for the sake of the police. And the seven women crowded around the coffin to look at the white thin face, still and calm, with its final sweet expression of perfect neutrality that gave no shadowed hint of what experiences had passed over the dead woman in her thirty-two years on earth. The rich blue-black hair emphasized the stillness of the face.

There is a similarity about the low-voiced comments of women at such times; we will not listen to the boss and her six girls. After a while the madam said: "We'll go up to her old room. We've got a job ahead of us this week, I'll tell you. You don't know all about it yet."

The ponderous woman labored puffingly up one flight of stairs and entered the rear room on the second floor, followed by the six young women in single file. She seated herself in a rocking chair in front of the white marble mantelpiece—which hinted at nobler days in the history of this house—and the six satellites disposed themselves on the bed and the lounge and the floor.

"Yes, we *have* got a job ahead of us," the boss went on, drawing an envelope from some unseen pocket of the baby-blue kimono enwrapped about her soft, fat-padded person.

"Luce wrote this a month ago from the sanitarium up there in the Adirondacks. You've heard part of it; now hear all. Let's see now. Um, 'Dear Mag,' she says here—don't none of you ever try to call me Mag; she was in this house ten years, that's the reason she could do it."

"We should be glad if you would read the letter, madam," interrupted Sadie, the black-haired Belgian Jewess, who sat on the foot of the bed.

"Yes, go on," said Lil, the thin, hectic girl whom they sometimes called Texas Lil.

"Well, now let's see," continued the boss, running one pudgy hand over her sallow face and back over her sparse light-colored hair. " 'I saw at first that there was no hope for me,' Luce says here.

"I saw it in the open face of the day head nurse, an Irishwoman. I guess I waited too long, Mag, to get out of the city. Lungs must be attended to right off if you are going to save them, and I have waited two years; but I did not know it at first.

"Anyway, I am taking all the milk and eggs I can swallow, though that is not much here lately. All day I sit on a long gallery, bundled up in heavy clothes, like forty others in the row, and look down into the black valley where there is not a single glad thing that I can see yet, and wondering, Mag, what about when I die. Like a fool, I told them when I came up here the name and address of my mother down in Louisiana; and when they asked me who was my nearest friend, Mag, I told them you was.

"I am afraid they will send the body—I call it body, though God knows, Mag, there is not much left of the plump body of ten years ago—down to my mother, who will have it buried out in Oakwood Cemetery, in a space I have seen, between my little sister and my father. I ought not to be there, Mag.

"And still my mother would never rest unless there was a regular funeral and she was at it. So I am going to tell them here to ship the body to you when the cat is dead. I will send you all the money I have, which is six hundred dollars, and you wire her three hundred dollars and tell her to come to the funeral; and say that I so loved the city that had treated me so well that I could not bear to be buried anywhere else in the world."

"Good God!" breathed little Olga, whom they called the anarchist, because she came from Russia and because she gave the impression, somehow, of a black bomb that might explode at any moment. She threw herself back against the wall behind the sofa on which she sat, bumping her head with a thud. The boss looked at her severely, continuing with Luce's letter:

"Lay the body in Greenwood Cemetery—that is nearly like Oakwood anyway—only have a regular funeral; but fix the undertaker, fix the preacher, fix everybody. Do not let her suspect what I was. Get a Methodist preacher if you can. It will be awful tough on you and the girls, this acting business, but it will be over in three or four days. You will do it, won't you, Mag?

"Let me give you a tip. I always pretended when I was at home in the summers that my good clothes and things I had made as a stenographer; you know people away from New York believe anything about the money that can be made there. She thought I got fifty dollars a week. I did leave home to go to a business college, but I was making seven dollars a week then—never mind that now though. You are running a boardinghouse, see? And Sadie, Lil, My Lady, Olga, and the others are working girls. They will help me out, I know."

"I'm going to be a bookkeeper," broke in she whom they called My Lady, a title springing from the truly magnificent diamonds that glittered ever in her ears.

"Are you through?" asked the madam, looking fiercely at the pale, sedate, old-faced girl who sat on the lounge by Rose.

"Quite, thank you." My Lady strove constantly to live up to the diamonds and the title. She studied Ouida for fine manners.

"Then I'll go on."

"Do you remember, Mag [Luce says here], when you were a little girl and swung in the parks or in the woods how, when they would stop pushing the swing it would get slower and slower until finally it came to a dead stop by itself? We called that letting the cat die. Well, Mag, the cat is dying now. I will wire you when the cat is almost dead, and I will tell the sanitarium people here to wire you when it is all dead. Then do some acting, Mag—do some tall acting.

"Maybe I shall not feel strong enough to write again. Read this to the girls when the body arrives. And now let me thank——"

The big woman's hands fell into her lap, her eyes gazing out through the rear window at the oozy gray fog that lay over the little boxed back yards. The moisture congealing on the tin roof drop-dropped down the tin gutter by the window, its pulsing monotone joined by others, grading downward in faintness, from other tin roofs at the back of other old-style, four-story, brownstone-front houses. The hoarse moaning whistles of the fog-bound vessels in the harbor came to the ears of the seven women as they sat there still.

"Pore Luce!" whispered the boss, brushing at her whitish-gray eyes with her left hand, and then, clearing her voice, as if she were ministering to a sore throat merely, went on louder and more distinctly:

"Me a boarding house landlady and you working girls! 'Have a regular funeral,' she says. 'Don't let her suspect what I was.' Whew!"

"I'll be a stenographer, just like Luce was," announced the irresponsible snub-nosed Kittie, who lolled on the floor.

"I'm a librarian, who gives out books to read," ventured the timid, diffident, blond Alice, who sat upright at the head of the bed.

"Be what you please," broke in the boss briskly. "I must be stirring. But tell me tonight what you have decided that you are; we mustn't get mixed up. This is Monday. I have wired the old lady; she'll be here early Wednesday morning, according to her answer."

The six girls went down to the front parlor to watch the little undertaker ostentatiously piddling through his ornate futilities. The madam strode into the front room on the second floor.

After a while she came out, wearing all her furs, though the weather was stifling; wearing all her jewelry, though the fog would hide it. She walked around to the Tenderloin police station in West Thirtieth Street, had a talk with the captain in his private office, and when she returned home after a very busy trip around the city she found a uniformed policeman pacing back and forth in front of her stoop. From various curtain-shaded front windows in the street furtive eyes had noted, with the malice of satisfied envy, the appearance of the policeman, and voices over the telephone said exultantly, "Well, Mag is in bad in Thirtieth Street at last." One or two remarked, "I can't make it out at all; a coffin went in there this morning." But Mag stopped and spoke genially and at length to the policeman as she went in.

That night the six girls were again gathered in Luce's room. "If anybody makes a break while the old lady is here," went on the boss, smoothing out the blue kimono over her right knee, "they'll get their blocks knocked off by me. Sadie, don't *you* get lit. My Lady, cut out the dope until the old lady goes home; if you got to have it, take it at night. Wear them diamonds if you must, but I'd take the things off this week if I were you, for this week anyhow. Hide them dirty novels of yours, Alice; and, Olga, for God's sake, try to hold your temper. Be sweet, Kittie; you know how. And you behave too, Lil.

"That cop you see out there is to keep anybody out of here. A cop'll be there until the old lady leaves. Now I got to go down and give that nigger cook a lesson or two. The undertaker will be easy, because nobody will understand what him and his ginneys are saying. But the preacher scares me. To get him I went 'way up to the Bronx, as far away from here as possible; but we all got to watch him like a stool pigeon. Get him away quick when it's over, see? Don't let him have five words with Luce's mother, and listen to all he does say; if he sees anything and begins to talk dangerous, butt in and switch him. Gee, but there's going to be some acting around here this week."

So the preparations went ahead. There were many pictures and other decorations that had to be hidden; the boss went through the house three or four times to see if anything visible and damning still lurked in any of the rooms.

Early Wednesday morning the doorbell rang. The madam, fully dressed, went down and opened it herself. A small woman in black stepped quickly inside—except for her gray hair, an aged and faded and wholesomely wrinkled image of Luce; tense, electric, her darting gray eyes summarizing her.

"We can't fool *her*," groaned the boss in her heart.

"Where is she?" Mrs. Painter asked in one of those instantaneous voices; and, seeing the coffin through the door, she ran to it, laid her head on it, and moaned over and over again: "Oh, my baby! Oh, my baby!" patting at the black wood with her hands.

The big woman walked out of the door and down toward the back of the hall so as to leave Luce and her mother alone for a few minutes. Hearing a fluttering, she looked up in time to see the six coming down the stairs. She waved them back, making frightful faces at them; they retreated in silent panic to the boss's room on the second floor. "This *is* a job," breathed the madam, wringing her heavy hands.

"And so this is Mrs. Schwartz!" she presently heard a thrilling voice say behind her, and turned upon the tearful but businesslike little woman. "I know I shall never be able to thank you enough," went on Mrs. Painter. "Lucy wrote me how kind you were to her while she was here; and that was a very long time, as I remember."

But in her eyes were latent questions that filled the boss with dread.

"Not at all, Mis' Painter," she answered, feeling that she was talking exactly as she felt—like a fool. "Though you haven't told me, I know you are Luce's—Miss Painter's—mother. You see, she was with me so long that I got to using that familiar name; she preferred it, she often told me. Would you like to meet the other girls in the boarding-house that your daughter knew? None of them will go to work until after the funeral is over."

"That is very good of them," commented Luce's mother. "I should like very much to meet them."

"This was her room," remarked the madam as they entered Luce's old room on the second floor, the big woman suddenly conscious of a feeling that it was horrible to conduct the mother in there; but it was too late to draw back; that should have been thought of the day before.

"Most of her things are packed in that trunk," she ventured. Mrs. Painter went slowly about the room, touching tenderly the white marble mantelpiece, two artificial roses in a glass vase that sat in the middle of it, a comb and brush—anything that Lucy herself might have looked at often and touched and loved. She sat down on the bed, folding her hands with an air of strong resignation.

"I'll bring in the girls," said the madam quickly, her mind dimly and painfully conscious of other uses of that statement. The supporting cast came in and were duly introduced to Luce's mother in their selected roles of stenographer, librarian, and so on; after which they disposed themselves nervously about the room, waiting. The boss insisted vainly that Mrs. Painter leave the bed and sit in the rocking chair, sinking into it herself after a while. Luce's mother cleared her throat, and the big woman quaked.

"I wish, Mrs. Schwartz, that I had been notified about Lucy while she was alive. Couldn't that have been done? Do you know what it is to a mother to be away from the bedside of a dying child? But it is ungrateful of me to seem to censure; most likely a message was sent to me and was not delivered. Wasn't that the way?"

Luce's mother was not melting in tears; only her voice, in spite of her startling control of it, sounded, in tremendous overtones, the sorrow that was in her.

The madam rocked her chair back and forth three or four times while she considered whether to charge anything against the telegraph company. "No," she said, slowly patting the arms of the chair, "that was not the way of it. No message was sent. You see, the end was very sudden. Luce always said not to worry you uselessly, because she had felt a good many times that all was over when it wasn't. And then, of a sudden, the end came. I wasn't notified until it was all over with her, though I was only a hundred or so miles away from the sanitarium. That was when I first wired you."

The doorbell rang, and the boss, now having an excuse, fled down the stairs, though she knew that the Negro cook was on her way to answer it, and that it was only the undertaker's assistant anyway. She hoped the girls would act their parts, for a little resting space, without her guiding presence, but she was very nervous about them. "My Lady puts on so," she said to herself, "and Olga might explode some of her cranky notions. Kittie talks a whole lot and don't think none at all. Thank heaven, Sadie ain't been near a gin-mill back parlor. Well, the funeral will be over by noon tomorrow. Here's hoping the old lady don't tarry long."

In the afternoon, for the sake of two or three hours of certain safety, the boss called a cab and insisted that Mrs. Painter go out with her.

"You got to get some air," she explained. "Then you'll want to see the city that Luce—Miss Lucy, I mean—loved so well. Lordy, how she did love it; that was the reason, you know, as I told you, that she couldn't bear to be buried anywhere else in the world."

And so the day got through to a satisfactory close; nothing untoward had happened, so far as the madam knew. At dinner, she thought, the family had conducted themselves with credit. The six working girls retired to the upstairs regions, five of them carrying secret instructions to watch lest Sadie get out of the house. The madam and Luce's mother sat in the dimly lighted parlor, near the coffin, in silence.

The street outside was unusually quiet, for it. The boss could hear the policeman's heels striking on the cement sidewalk as he paced up and down in front of the stoop. Three or four of the dingy children whose parents still permitted themselves to live in this neighborhood in spite of its changing character were playing one-eyed cat. Now and then one of them screamed a hoarse and strident adult malediction across the street at a companion, which Mag hoped Luce's mother did not hear. A street piano played the *Lucia* sextet, and, receiving no silver or nickel or copper encouragement, moved out of the street, westward across Seventh Avenue. But the madam, straining at the sounds at this comparatively quiet time, did not find anything in them to frighten her.

About nine o'clock, however, she heard, coming nearer and nearer, an unmistakable band of young college cutups who had begun the night early. They were drunk enough to make much noise, sober enough to escape arrest. They were going from place to place, remaining in each anywhere from ten minutes to an hour, according to the warmth of their reception and their first impression of the house they happened to be in. The boss knew the tactics of these bands, and she hoped the sight of the policeman would at once make an unpleasant impression, so that they would pass her place by without attempting an entrance. Tipping to the front windows, she closed them all the way down, opening one in the rear of the parlor for air. Now the dimmed voices of the singers were swallowed up in a house across the street. The madam put the roisterers out of the forward part of her mind, but away back in her head she kept saying, "I hope old French keeps 'em until they get ready to go home," though she seldom wished anything but ill luck to old Frenchy.

She glanced furtively at Luce's mother in the endeavor to find out if she had been listening to and trying to interpret any of the street sounds; and she was satisfied: Luce's mother appeared not to have heard anything suspicious.

The commanding little gray woman said she would sit by the body until midnight, and the madam went quietly out into the hall, meaning to stand guard in hiding near the bottom of the basement stairs, where she could hear almost everything that went on in the house. Looking down, she saw, already on the lowest step, the leader of the band of roisterers, followed by ten or twelve others; she recognized their kind instantly. They had slipped in through the basement door, intending a surprise for the house. The boss could distinguish their self-satisfied grins, could see them rocking in delightful unstable equilibrium.

The big woman threw both hands over her mouth to force back the screaming curses that mobbed her lips. Her seething mind coined curses and laid them upon the name and family of the policeman, who had probably stepped around the corner for a drink. She barely breathed old familiar curses upon the cook, who had left unlocked the iron-grated basement gate and door.

But what to do? The bold-faced brown-haired boy, with a Greek god's nose, was coming up the stairs. She heard Luce's mother in the dimly lighted parlor behind her, softly sobbing. Argument with half-intoxicated and spirited youth was out of the question, she knew; ejectment, even if she could accomplish it, would make even more noise.

Madam Margaretta never lacked resourcefulness, nor wanted a decision long. Gently she tipped down the stairs, holding two fingers on her lips, whispering, "S-sh!" The invaders looked questioningly at one another; then they smiled, thinking that the madam had entered into the spirit of the palpable surprise party and would assist them. Taking hold of the manifest captain's hand, the boss led him up the stairs, led him forward to the edge of the parlor door, and held him from behind, whispering, "Peep in." He peered around the doorjamb and saw, in the quiet semigloom, a little gray-haired woman crying softly over a black coffin. Gasping a quick breath, he fell back, piloted by the madam to the head of the stairs, down which he went with his head hanging. One by one the others, feeling strangely guilty before they had looked in, peered around the doorjamb and silently followed their leader down the stairs and out of the house.

The boss walked behind them until they had reached the sidewalk and watched them until they had turned the corner into Sixth Avenue. Then she hunted up the policeman and gave him a piece of her mind, which was not pleasant just then; after which she waked up the cook and gave her also a piece, withholding her heavy hand only because of Luce's sacred secret. Going quietly back to the parlor, she found Mrs. Painter sitting in a chair near the head of the coffin.

"Who were those young men?" she asked.

"Those young men?" repeated the boss. "Did you hear them?"

"Oh yes. I only felt them at first. They might have come on in if they knew Lucy and she liked them."

"Oh, they *were* friends of Miss Lucy's. They did mean to come in, but they saw you here, and they thought that maybe they would disturb you. They are so timid, those young fellows; they're only boys anyhow."

"I am sorry," said Luce's mother, leaning her head wearily against the coffin; she had not shown any weariness before this. The boss looked at her apprehensively, concluding, after a while, however, that Luce's secret was still out of danger.

At midnight Lil and My Lady relieved the watchers. The madam saw Mrs. Painter securely in bed on the fourth floor, and then fell into her own bed, praying, as nearly as the boss ever prayed, that the next day would not bring more attacks upon Luce's secret than she could repulse.

With the coming in of Thursday New York threw off the thick and oozy gray blankets of fog that it had been suffering under since Monday, and the wind blew up from the bay a breeze that was bracingly chill and salty. The boss was up early with her family, superintending their toilettes. My Lady was induced, for twelve hours only, to lay aside her diamond earrings. The madam herself gave notice that, though she would wear her furs, she had put aside all her jewelry until the funeral was over. After breakfast, having assembled the family in Luce's room for final instructions, she said only this: "Watch that preacher."

He came presently, a young, clean-shaven, preternaturally solemn, lean man, his personality proclaiming initiative and cheerful briskness as one of his consciously assumed duties on such sad occasions as this.

"Are many of the close relatives here?" he asked, rubbing his hands together with tremendous energy and no noise. He and the boss took chairs just inside the parlor door.

"The mother," replied the madam. "Over there, the little woman in black."

"She the only one?"

"Yes. She's from out of town. Down in Louisiana. No others of the family living."

"And those young ladies?"

"Just boarders of mine—stenographers, bookkeepers, all working girls, friends of Miss Lucy's. Miss Lucy herself was——"

"Ah yes, I understand," the minister interrupted, raising his right hand in mild deprecation of his inquisitiveness. "We may as well begin, don't you think? It is nearly ten o'clock."

"Yes, might as well," replied the boss, suppressing the joyful note in her voice with desperate strength.

After low-toned introductions to Luce's mother and the girls, the young preacher took his stand at the head of the coffin and made a few general remarks about people coming up like flowers and being cut down—"like weeds," whispered Olga to Lil. The words he had to utter were soon uttered; the service at the house was concluded. It had all sounded strange and foreign to the boss, in that parlor. Now and then she looked hard at the six young mourners, soberly clad in black; in her mind's eye she could see them in their customary gorgeous and brief attire.

Now the small Italian undertaker picked up the board that was to shut in the face of Luce forever. He held it poised, suggestively. Taking the hint, the madam and her six walked around the head of the coffin and gazed finally upon her they had known as Luce; the mother bent down and kissed finally the brow of her she had always called "Little Lucy." The undertaker laid on the board; he and an assistant set to work busily with the highly ornamented screws. The crunching of these eating into the wood was cruelly suggestive. The mother broke into her first hysterical sobbing. The girls could not restrain themselves; they did not try to. The boss tried hard and failed.

She heard some shuffling of feet and heavy breathing, which she interpreted to mean that the undertaker's assistants were carrying the coffin to the hearse out in front of the stoop. After a while, when she did look up, the young preacher had Luce's mother by the arm and was conducting her to a carriage, speaking very earnestly. The madam, mopping desperately at her eyes, rushed after the couple and got in just before the door closed, thus forgetting her furs.

All the way out to the cemetery the minister talked vehemently to Luce's mother about the temptations of a great city. The big woman yearned to press both her thick hands over his mouth and yell into his right ear, "Shut up." Mrs. Painter looked strainingly out of a window, answering only yes and no; so the boss let him talk on.

When the coffin had at last been lowered into the ground, and that shattering moment of falling clods upon the hollow-sounding casing had passed, the madam sent the minister back to the city in a carriage by himself, breathing a deep, glad sigh of relief when it had rolled away. Once she had seen Luce's mother off to the railway station, she would lie across a bed and scream for the joy of relaxed nerves; moreover, she would order up champagne, in which the dead would be mourned in a proper manner. Yet Mag was glad she had done her best to carry out Luce's last wishes.

The tension of the two days was somewhat relieved at the dinner table. There was a little low-toned laughter. But in the situation there was still danger. Kittie had to be ruthlessly suppressed with a surreptitious blunderbuss look. Once or twice Olga seemed to be about to explode and erupt wrath over preachers, churches, the present economic system, and respectable society. Sadie ate meagerly and was morose—a bad sign for Sadie.

After dinner the girls scattered through the house. The madam and Mrs. Painter went to Luce's room. The two trunks had been packed and sent away, the railway and Pullman tickets had been bought, and a taxicab ordered for eleven o'clock to catch the midnight train out of the Grand Central Station. The boss could hardly contain her joy over the imminent lifting of the crushingly heavy burden of respectable acting, not to speak of watching over the six less expert actors who relied on her for guidance.

She kept glancing at the clock on the white mantelpiece. She and the little wrinkle-faced electric woman talked easily about all sorts of things, each trying to lead the other's thoughts out of the house and away from its recent sad associations; the hands of the clock were moving upon ten, but slowly. The boss remarked to herself that Luce's mother was "all right"; that was to be expected, being Luce's mother. How lightning-quick she was! How full of gumption! In different circumstances the madam would have wished for an extended visit. The clock hands dragged around to ten-thirty; now they were on the home stretch. The boss was sitting comfortably far back in the rocking chair, her hands folded complacently in her lap.

Suddenly, from down in the front hall, came sounds of a commotion. Mag sat up straight in her chair, her right hand pressed against her cheek, a gesture meaning that she was disturbed and thinking hard and fast. The sounds were familiar to her; they snatched her back from the great content into which she had been slipping. It was Sadie; she had been outside. The watch over her should have been kept up; but it was too late now to think about what *should* have been done.

"Please keep your seat, Mis' Painter," Mag said, smiling in sweetly patient forbearance. "The cook is grumbling again about something, I suppose; she is always grumbling. I'll have to discharge her, I guess, but I hate to do it, because she would have a tough time getting another job, on account of her manners."

Sadie, however, while the boss was preparing for an exit, had been rushing up the stairs, and now she burst into the room before Mag could move her ponderous figure through the door, falling on her knees in front of Mrs. Painter and laying her black crinkly haired head in the little woman's lap.

"I am so sorry," she sobbed. "I am mad at God that He should take away Luce. She was the best of the lot, and this here house ain't worth living in no more."

The big woman, her face writhing in frightened wrath, took two steps toward the kneeling Sadie, her huge hands extended to snatch her to her feet. Luce's mother held up her right hand in protection; the madam stopped still, wilting in despair.

"Luce was the oldest," went on Sadie, who had not raised her head, "but she was the swellest dame in this here house. All the men said so. And she made things sing around this place, Luce did. We been thinking you must have been like her when you were a girl. Was your hair that funny black like hers?"

Sadie broke into hysterical sobbing. The little woman smoothed her hair gently, saying nothing, her eyes closed in apparent pain, soothing the girl into quietness by touch alone.

"If you would kiss me, Luce's mother, I would go to bed," Sadie declared, raising her face, smiling radiantly in the bewildering illogicality of intoxication. Luce's mother having kissed her, she rose and walked out of the room with exaggerated stiffness and steadiness, being received just beyond the door by Lil and My Lady, who seized hold of her arms and conducted her upstairs.

The madam had dropped into her chair after following the girl to the door. She now watched the clock with bold desperation. There were ten more minutes, if the taxicab came according to her time; a few more minutes anyway. How could she get through them? Like a guilty dog, she kept running her eyes over and around Luce's mother, never looking directly at her. The weather was warm, she said. She supposed spring had come long ago in Louisiana, it being so far south. A taxicab snorted in the street—and then went on.

"I'll be putting on my hat and things," stated Mrs. Painter, getting briskly to her feet; and the boss could have hugged her. She rose and stood apprehensively by Luce's mother.

"Mrs. Schwartz," said the little woman in that distressingly clear voice of hers.

"Yes?"

"Don't you be rough with Sadie when I'm gone. She didn't tell me anything; I knew what this house was thirty minutes after I had entered it. Lucy's father took me out of one, in New Orleans, thirty-five years ago."

Mrs. Painter ran a long pin through the hat she wore. The boss's hands fell by her side, her round whitish eyes starting out, the breath blasting out of her cavernous chest.

"But I didn't know about Lucy until I came up here," went on the little woman in a low voice. "I believed her stenography story. I knew she had been a stenographer for a while; I reckoned she was still one. I didn't press her to stay at home; things weren't ever very pleasant there while her father was alive, and when he was dead she was already weaned away.

"And though, as I say, Mrs. Schwartz, I knew about the house, yet I didn't want to let on that I knew anything, on account of you and the girls; you all have acted so fine. It didn't seem like it was fair to hurt you by letting on I knew. But now I am afraid for Sadie, and so I speak. She didn't tell me anything; and so you will be easy with her, won't you?"

"Yes, I will."

A taxicab was coughing and snorting at the door. The bell rang.

"I have told everybody except you good-by, haven't I?" asked Mrs. Painter, putting on her coat.

"Yes."

"And thanked everybody as well as I could, though I couldn't ever do it enough, especially you."

"We was all glad to do what we could, Mis' Painter."

"Lean over, Mag, and let me kiss you. I'm so little."

Then they went downstairs. Luce's mother entered the taxicab, and Mag stood on the high stoop dazedly watching the chauffeur fuss around the front end of his machine. Of a sudden the boss, crying out, "Wait a minute," ran down the steps as fast as she could. Opening the door, she stuck her head into the darkness inside.

"Tell me, Mis' Painter," she said in a hard voice, "did that preacher know too?"

"Yes."

"And you wouldn't have said anything if Sadie hadn't come in like she did?"

"Why, no, Mag."

"Well, good-by, Mis' Painter."

"Good-by, Mag."

The taxicab snorted away. The boss stood on the stoop and followed the red taillight until it had flirted maliciously around the corner of Sixth Avenue, where it had seemed to wink at her in evil glee. With unhurried but terrible deliberation Mag, nearest friend of Luce, marched back inside the house, unscrewed the wooden handle out of the feather duster, and, going upstairs, beat Sadie sober. Then she ordered up champagne for seven.

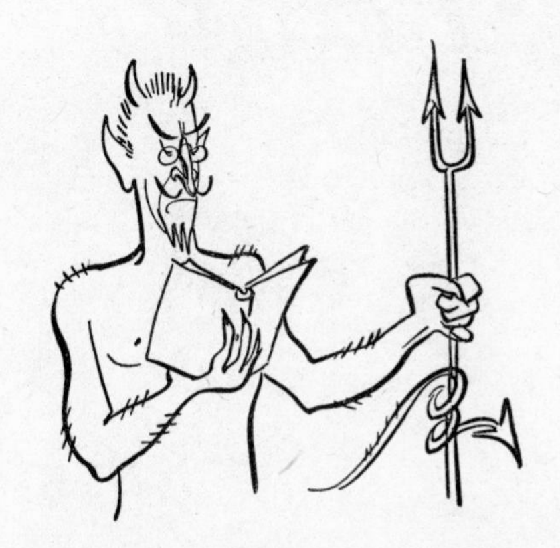

WIELDING THE BLUDGEON

III. WIELDING THE BLUDGEON

AMONG THE LARGER PLEASURES of life, to me at least, is the opportunity of reading vituperative writings. I like the idea of a man getting as indignant as a Republican contemplating Sidney Hillman, wiping a bit of the froth from his mouth, then sitting down and shrieking in print. I don't care what he's sore about, and I don't care how far he departs from reason and logic, just so long as his anger is cosmic and his language suited to the voicing of it.

One day Charles Daggett came to see me off at the Union Station in Los Angeles. He handed me a book and recommended that I read it during the trip to New York. I already had a Raymond Chandler and a Perry Mason but I didn't open either of them on that trip. The book Chuck Daggett gave me was *The Writings of Brann the Iconoclast.*

There was a guy! Up to the time of that train trip he had been no more than a name to me. Back East I tried to find out something about him. Many people to whom I talked never heard of him. He was not in the Dictionary of American Biography, nor in any of the other reference works available in my home or the homes of my friends. Finally I went to the New York Public Library, where they have almost everything, even the works of depraved writers, such as myself. Beyond collections of his own writings, there was but a single item about William Cowper Brann. It was an article in the *South Atlantic Quarterly,* published at Durham, North Carolina, issue of January 1915. The Brann piece was written by a Johns Hopkins professor and was surrounded by fascinating essays on such topics as "North Carolina's Taxation Problem and Its Solution."

Brann was born in Illinois, ran away from home at thirteen, and educated himself. This professor said he was one of the best-educated men of his time. He established his paper, the *Iconoclast,* in Austin, Texas, in 1891. His writing had much the same effect as a fragmentation bomb dropped on the town and after a few issues he ceased publication and went to work on another newspaper. In 1894 he sold his printing press and the title, *Iconoclast,* to a young fellow named W. S. Porter, who later became O. Henry. Subsequently Brann decided to give it another whirl. He got the name back from Porter, who continued with his own paper, the *Rolling Stone*. This time Brann's *Iconoclast* was established in Waco, Texas. He spit on his hands and started ripping the universe to pieces. It must have been fun living in Texas when he was going and if I had been there I'm certain I'd have been standing at the door of the *Iconoclast* offices to get the first copy off the presses.

Brann's assaults on Baylor University, in Waco, split the town into two camps. There were mob scenes in which gangs of students raided the *Iconoclast* offices. The feeling for and against Brann grew more intense with each passing month and in November of 1897 there was a gunfight on the street in Waco in which two men were killed and several wounded. Brann didn't ease up a bit. Then a man named Captain T. E. Davis got sore at him.

On April 1, 1898, Brann and his paper's business manager, named Ward, were walking down a crowded street in Waco. This Captain Davis stepped suddenly out of an office, pistol in hand, and shot Brann in the back. The Apostle, as he called himself, whirled, reaching for his own six-shooter. Ward, the business manager, grabbed at Brann's arm, trying to stop him, but Captain Davis fired again and the bullet shattered Ward's hand. Just like in the movies. Brann, with a bullet through his middle, calmly filled Captain Davis full of uncomfortable bullet holes and then fell over in the street and later on died. So did Captain Davis.

Brann was but forty-three years old when he was shot in the back. His paper had been running a mere two years but almost everybody in the country knew about him. His fame died quickly, however, and today he is all but forgotten. I wish some competent writing man would set himself to work doing a good, honest biography of him. The movies wouldn't dare try it.

Meanwhile I'm content to reprint a few passages from his writings. I've selected them as best illustrating his style. The spectacle of New York society was one of the many things that incensed him.

Here is all that I have the courage to print out of an essay titled:

WILLY WALLY TO WED

By William Cowper Brann

WM. WALDORF ASTOR is a consistent Anglomaniac. Instead of remaining in this blawsted bloomin' country, upon which he looks with the disdain of a well-groomed ass contemplating the *Iliad,* he hied himself to "perfidious Albion" and took up his abode in its foggy metropolis, surrounded by m'luds, whom he so much admires. It could scarce be expected that a country so new and crass as America would harmonize with the triple-plated culchaw and superaestheticism of a man who traces his proud patrician lineage and abundant lucre back to Johann Jakob Astor, the wooden-shod purveyor of green coonskins and odoriferous polecat pelts, Jamaica bug-juice and brummagem jewelry. With a cash capital of one jug of cheap rum and a shirttail full of glass beads, the thrifty Johann Jakob went among the Indians and founded a fortune which enabled him to buy a large slice of Manhattan Island when it was selling at four cents per acre. By feeding himself but once a day, and then with a piece of fat pork anchored to a cotton cord, half-soling his own pants with seaweed and going barefoot in summer to save his shoes, he was able to hang onto his land until the industry and enterprise of others made it worth almost a dollar an acre, when he passed it on to his posterity simply because it wasn't portable.

The unearned increment accumulated from generation to generation in a ratio of geometrical progression, until his spawn became as rich as grease and slung on more unadulterated agony than a Washington nigger with a brass watch. Willy Wally was the flower and fruitage of the Astor family. American vulgarisms grated upon his sensitive soul like a rattail file drawn across a sore tooth, and he arose and fled from us as a Della-Cruscan poetess might chase her shrinking soul from a country hog killing or the pervasive odor of ebullient soft soap. Would to heaven that all the half-baked American slobs who worship at the shrine of European flunkyism, and who say "eyther" and "neyther," would follow in his footsteps. The brainless inanities will breed, and we should encourage them to drop their worthless calves in a foreign country.

Willy Wally has just had the "distinguished honor" of entertaining 'Is Royal 'Ighness, the Prince of Wales. His Nibs has become so well known as a crooked gambler that he can no longer steer the toothsome sucker against his surething games, and he is devoting his talents to the profitable industry of pulling the legs of wealthy plebs in search of social distinction. He is always in need of cash, and even the title-loving English people have tired of paying debts resulting from his debaucheries. It is well understood in England that when he honors a parvenu with his royal presence a fat "loan" is expected, which is in reality his fee for the distinguished social favor. Willy Wally is worth $150,000,000, hence can well afford to tip this social huckster who trades upon his title. Think of the felicity of seeing himself proclaimed in all the Anglomaniacal papers of his native land as the host of imperial highness! I can only wonder that Wales waited so long before tapping the purse of the Astorian plutocrat; but he may have been fighting shy in order to secure a better price.

The prince is heir apparent to nothing but an empty title and the privilege of being supported by the toil of better people. The sovereign of Great Britain is a veritable Toom-ta-bard, a mere figurehead, of about as little real importance in the governmental plan as a sack of sawdust. When the prince succeeds his mother he will be as powerless so far as matters of great moment are concerned as he is at present. He can hock the throne, give the crown jewels to harlots, and divide his time between baccarat and bawdry without throwing one cog in the governmental machinery out of gear.

He is simply a beery old bum who has spent his life cheating at the gaming board, debauching the fool wives of those who hang upon his favors, and doping for the foulest of all diseases. If he pays a woman any attention her reputation is forever ruined. His leery smile would wither the good name of a vestal virgin. Mary Anderson understood this and cut him cold—snubbed him as she might an impudent coon in her native Kentucky. He is the avatar of immorality, the beau ideal of dead beats, a social leper who should be compelled to herd by himself and continually cry, "Unclean! Unclean! He has the heart of a hyena and the instincts of an ape—proving him a true scion of the House of Hanover. He has done absolutely nothing for his country but disgrace it. As if to add insult unto injury, to pile Pelion upon Ossa, he has brought forth a brood of brainless brats to fatten on the public and perpetuate their father's foulness. No self-respecting English gentleman would permit him to enter his mule pasture or associate with his sows were he not "stuck o'er with titles and hung round with strings." When he visits even a peer of the realm he insists upon naming the "ladies" who are to be invited to meet him, and turns the mansion of his host into a harem. That is the feculent cur who has honored the great-grandson of the old Manhattan hide merchant with his imperial presence.

I'M NOT REPRINTING the rest of it—the wedding plans for Willy Wally—for reasons of personal security. Somebody might take offense and ambush me and beat my head flat with a croquet mallet.

The collected writings of Brann are full of explosive

assaults done in the manner of the above excerpt. When he busted loose against a man he pulled out all the stops. He concluded an assault on the editor of the Los Angeles *Times* with this sweet passage:

> I can but wonder what will become of the *Times* editor when the breath leaves his feculent body and death stops the rattling of his abortive brain, for he is unfit for heaven and too foul for hell. He cannot be buried in the earth lest he provoke a pestilence, nor in the sea lest he poison the fish, nor swung in space like Mahomet's coffin lest the circling worlds, in trying to avoid contamination, crash together, wreck the universe, and bring again the noisome reign of Chaos and old Night. The damn rascal seems to be a white elephant on the hands of Deity, and I have some curiosity to know what he will do with it.

There were times, though, when Brann sat down and became almost a pure humorist. Here he is on—

THE CURSE OF KISSING

By William Cowper Brann

EVERY LITTLE WHILE some smart-Alec scientist mounts the bema to inform a foolish world that kissing is a dangerous pastime; that upon the roseate lips of beauty there ever lurks the bacillus, flourishing skull and crossbones—veritable flaming swords to keep poor Adam out of his Eden. According to these learned men the fairest maid is loaded to the muzzle with microbes, her kiss a Judas osculation, betraying the slightest swain who dares to browse upon her dewy lips, to well-nigh certain death. In the "lingering sweetness long drawn out" myriads of disease germs are supposed to pass from mouth to mouth in true reciprocity fashion, and, falling upon new and fecund soil, take root and flourish there until the ecstatic fools pass untimely to that bourne where all faces stand so wide ajar—held so by eternal hosannahs —that an attempted kiss were like dropping Hoosac Tunnel into the Mammoth Cave.

As the duly ordained guide, philosopher, and friend of the

scientists—of the clergy—the *Iconoclast* feels compelled to file a protest. As the Moor of Venice intimated, there's such a thing as knowing entirely too much. Wisdom that knocks the yum-yum out of life, transforms the fond delights of courtship into an armed neutrality, and makes of the sensuous Veil of Cashmere a profitless desert of dead formalities and scientific sanitation, simply to save the life insurance company paying an occasional premium, should be sealed in some Pandora box or genie casket and cast into the sea.

We cannot blame the bacteria for selecting as roosting place the rosebud mouths of the daughters of men, any more than we can blame the bees for hovering with drowsy drunken hum about the fragrant flowers; still we were happier when we knew not of their presence—when we could swoop blithely down upon a pair of ruby lips working like a patent clothes wringer in a steam laundry, and extract Hyblaean honey in great hunks without Death riding his old white skate athwart our pansy bed and freezing the genial current of our soul with his Svengali leer.

We like to quarrel with science, but the tables educed in the currency controversy now epidemic in this unhappy land have made us doubt. Death may lurk in the lover's kiss like a yellow jacket in a Jersey apple; but that scientist who will go about with his compound microscope searching into this tutti-frutti of the soul for miniature monsters is fit for treason, stratagems, and spoils. He's not a credible witness and ought to be abolished. He's the Thersites of modern society, and we hope to see some wrathful Achilles take him out behind the smokehouse and talk with him in a tone of voice that would discourage a book agent or a poor relation. We don't believe a word about his little tale of osculatory woe. During a variegated experience of forty years we've never combed any tuberculosis fungi, mump microbes, or diphtheritic walking delegates out of our white-horse mustache.

Kissing injurious to health, forsooth! Why it's the fount of perennial youth which owl-eyed old Ponce de Leon sought among the savages, instead of filling his sails with sighs of "Gady's soft desiring strain." It's the true Brown-

Sequard elixir, which makes the heart of hoary age beat forever like a boy's. It's the heaven-distilled *eau de vie* which causes the young man to forget a combination of tight boot and soft-boiled corn and makes the grisly octogenarian rise up like William Riley and neigh like a two-year-old. Disease germs, indeed! Why it's nature's remedy for all the ills that flesh is heir to, *facile princeps* of ennui antidotes, infallible cure for that tired feeling.

The latest pseudoscientist to discover that the gentle ripple of the kiss is but a dirge tries to set in the black o'erhanging firmament a bow of promise. He opines that all danger may be avoided if the kissing machines are carefully deodorized before and after using, and recommends that the lips be washed with some chemical compound that will make the most obstinate bacillus sorry he was born. It's a great scheme —but will it work? Will our society belles and beaux now appear equipped, each with a bottle of carbolic acid or a jug of lime water in which to soak their sweetness before effecting that exchange which is no robbery? Or will each parlor be provided with a bowl of bacteria annihilator, which the young man will employ much as the careful cotton planter does Paris green?

The plan of disinfection before permitting the spirits to rush together à la Tennyson at the touch of the lips may work in Boston, perhaps; but out here in the glad free Southwest, where we still have to catch our hare before we cook it, such an arrangement would clog the wheels of progress and perhaps extinguish Hymen's torch. Imagine the Apostle chasing the beauteous Rebecca Merlindy around a log cabin at some husking bee at the metropolis of Harris County, a swab in one hand and a gourdful of carbonated bayou water in the other! Here in Texas a man must take his kiss with the peeling on or go without. He has enough to do to manage the maid without bothering about the bacteria. And, let scientists with their double-geared microscopes say what they may, that man who gets an opportunity to buss a corn-fed beauty whose breath is sweet as that of a brindle calf fed on clover blooms need not worry about bacilli. It is a feast fit for gods, so let him fall to, without waiting to have the bloom sponged off his peach on the foolish hypothesis that its component parts are horned hippogriffs, icthyosauria, and feathered sea serpents such as hover in the gloom of a gold-cure joint at 2 A.M. If his heart fails him—if he be not willing to chance the cold and silent tomb for the felicity of browsing for a few fleeting moments in Elysian Fields—let him follow the example of the great and glorious G. Cleveland, Esq., and hire a substitute. There are cases, however, where it would be well to do considerable deodorizing before risking osculation; better still, to let the doubtful sweets remain unplucked, as not worth the labor.

This great Yankee nation has fallen into the bad habit of promiscuous kissing—a social rite as stale, flat, and every way unprofitable as employing a community toothbrush or an indiscriminate swapping of gum. Whether dangerous diseases may be transmitted thereby I know not; but it is death to sentiment and provocative of nausea. A woman should be almost as chary of her lips as of more gracious favors. A sensitive gentleman would as soon accept a bride from Boiler Avenue as take to wife a vestal virgin whom every lecherous libertine had "mouthed and mumbled."

The practice of "kissing the bride," which still prevails in communities professing not only civilization but the acme of aestheticism, should be abolished by law under severe pains and penalties. Why a modest woman, who has done nothing worse than marry, should be compelled to kiss a company of men and thereby sample everything from the aroma of sour stomachs to masticated codfish, I cannot imagine. The levite who performs the ceremony usually consecrates the first fruits to the Lord, and what he may chance to leave is gleaned by Tom, Dick, and the Devil, until lips that would have tempted angels to assume mortal ills become foul as the Valley of Hinnom—sweet incense to offer a loving lord!

I once attended a church fair in Missouri and there found two local beauties of good family retailing kisses to all comers at two bits apiece—"for the good of the cause!" "D—n a cause," quoth I, "that must be forwarded by such foul means." I bought five dollars worth of the sacred sweetness—then hired an old farmer, who enjoyed a bad case of catarrh and had worn his solitary tooth down to the Pliocene Period chewing plug tobacco and depositing the quotient on his beard, to receive the goods. When half through with the job he struck for a raise of salary!

A kiss should be a sacred thing—the child of a love that is deathless. It is the benediction of a mother, the pledge of a sweetheart, the homage of a wife. Promiscuous kissing is a casting of pearls before swine, a brutal prostitution of the noblest and holiest rite ever practiced by the human race. It is a flagrant offense against all that is noble in man and modest in woman; hence let us hope that it is really conducive to disease—that the wage of sin is death.

Over and above the fact that their last names begin with B, there are parallels worth noting in the careers of Brann the Iconoclast and Ambrose Bierce, who was called "Bitter Bierce." Both came of Middle Western beginnings and both were self-educated; and each of them disappeared from the face of the earth under circumstances such as might have been dreamed up by a hung-over Faith Baldwin. Bierce simply vanished. In 1913, when he was seventy-one, he went to Mexico, for reasons known only to himself, and he never came back. Nor was any definite news of him ever carried back to the United States. There were rumors that Bierce had got himself involved in a revolution and that he had died before a firing squad. In any case his end remains a fascinating mystery and nobody knows even where his bones lie buried.

Bierce's short stories are still widely circulated and saluted and so is his book of witticisms called *The Devil's Dictionary*. It contains much sparkling stuff which, Bierce himself charged, was plagiarized by popular humorists of his day. It is a book I keep around the house for a definite purpose. On rare occasions I find myself on the verge of surrendering to a belief that human behavior and human motives are predominantly noble. Bierce knocks such incipient attacks out of me in a hurry.

I've run through *The Devil's Dictionary* and lifted out some of the definitions I like, bitterly cynical ones along with the comic.

Here they are:

From "THE DEVIL'S DICTIONARY"

By Ambrose Bierce

ABSTAINER, n. A weak person who yields to the temptation of denying himself a pleasure.

ACQUAINTANCE, n. A person whom we know well enough to borrow from but not well enough to lend to.

AMBITION, n. An overmastering desire to be vilified by enemies while living and made ridiculous by friends when dead.

BACCHUS, n. A convenient deity invented by the ancients as an excuse for getting drunk.

BACK, n. That part of your friend which it is your privilege to contemplate in your adversity.

BASTINADO, n. The act of walking on wood without exertion.

BEFRIEND, v.t. To make an ingrate.

BELLADONNA, n. In Italian a beautiful lady; in English a deadly poison. A striking example of the essential identity of the two tongues.

BORE, n. A person who talks when you wish him to listen.

CABBAGE, n. A familiar kitchen-garden vegetable about as large and wise as a man's head.

CANNON, n. An instrument employed in the rectification of national boundaries.

CAT, n. A soft, indestructible automaton provided by nature to be kicked when things go wrong in the domestic circle.

CIRCUS, n. A place where horses, ponies, and elephants are permitted to see men, women, and children acting the fool.

CLAIRVOYANT, n. A person, commonly a woman, who has the power of seeing that which is invisible to her patron—namely, that he is a blockhead.

CLARINET, n. An instrument of torture operated by a person with cotton in his ears. There are two instruments that are worse than a clarinet—two clarinets.

CONNOISSEUR, n. A specialist who knows everything about something and nothing about anything else.

CONSUL, n. In American politics, a person who, having failed to secure an office from the people, is given one by the Administration on condition that he leave the country.

CONSULT, v.t. To seek another's approval of a course already decided on.

DEFAME, v.t. To lie about another. To tell the truth about another.

DIAPHRAGM, n. A muscular partition separating disorders of the chest from disorders of the bowels.

DISTANCE, n. The only thing that the rich are willing for the poor to call theirs, and keep.

EDIBLE, adj. Good to eat, and wholesome to digest, as a worm to a toad, a toad to a snake, a snake to a pig, a pig to a man, and a man to a worm.

EGOTIST, n. A person of low taste, more interested in himself than in me.

FAITH, n. Belief without evidence in what is told by one who speaks without knowledge, of things without parallel.

GOOSE, n. A bird that supplies quills for writing. These, by some occult process of nature, are penetrated and suffused with various degrees of the bird's intellectual energies and emotional character, so that when inked and drawn mechanically across paper by a person called an "author," there results a very fair and accurate transcript of the fowl's thought and feeling. The difference in geese, as discovered by this ingenious method, is considerable: many are found to have only trivial and insignificant powers, but some are seen to be very great geese indeed.

GUILLOTINE, n. A machine which makes a Frenchman shrug his shoulders with good reason.

HARBOR, n. A place where ships taking shelter from storms are exposed to the fury of the customs.

HERS, pron. His.

HISTORIAN, n. A broad-gauge gossip.

HISTORY, n. An account, mostly false, of events, mostly unimportant, which are brought about by rulers, mostly knaves, and soldiers, mostly fools.

HONORABLE, adj. Afflicted with an impediment in one's reach. In legislative bodies it is customary to mention all members as honorable; as, "the honorable gentleman is a scurvy cur."

IDIOT, n. A member of a large and powerful tribe whose influence in human affairs has always been dominant and controlling.

IGNORAMUS, n. A person unacquainted with certain kinds of knowledge familiar to yourself, and having certain other kinds that you know nothing about.

INK, n. A villainous compound of tannogallate of iron, gum arabic, and water, chiefly used to facilitate the infection of idiocy and promote intellectual crime.

MARRIAGE, n. The state or condition of a community consisting of a master, a mistress, and two slaves, making in all two.

MAUSOLEUM, n. The final and funniest folly of the rich.

MEDICINE, n. A stone flung down the Bowery to kill a dog in Broadway.

MIND, n. A mysterious form of matter secreted by the brain. Its chief activity consists in the endeavor to ascertain its own nature, the futility of the attempt being due to the fact that it has nothing but itself to know itself with.

MIRACLE, n. An act or event out of the order of nature and unaccountable, as beating a normal hand of four kings and an ace with four aces and a king.

MYTHOLOGY, n. The body of a primitive people's beliefs concerning its origin, early history, heroes, deities, and so forth, as distinguished from the true accounts which it invents later.

NIHILIST, n. A Russian who denies the existence of anything but Tolstoy. The leader of the school is Tolstoy.

NOVEL, n. A short story padded.

OCCIDENT, n. The part of the world lying west (or east) of the Orient. It is largely inhabited by Christians, a powerful subtribe of the Hypocrites, whose principal industries are murder and cheating, which they are pleased to call "war" and "commerce." These, also, are the principal industries of the Orient.

OCEAN, n. A body of water occupying about two thirds of a world made for man—who has no gills.

ONCE, adv. Enough.

OPTIMIST, n. A proponent of the doctrine that black is white.

PEACE, n. In international affairs, a period of cheating between two periods of fighting.

PHRENOLOGY, n. The science of picking the pocket through the scalp.

POSITIVE, adj. Mistaken at the top of one's voice.

PRAY, v. To ask that the laws of the universe be annulled in behalf of a single petitioner confessedly unworthy.

QUILL, n. An implement of torture yielded by a goose and commonly wielded by an ass.

REPRESENTATIVE, n. In national politics, a member of the Lower House in this world, and without discernible hope of promotion in the next.

SCRIPTURES, n. The sacred books of our holy religion, as distinguished from the false and profane writings on which all other faiths are based.

SERIAL, n. A literary work, usually a story that is not true, creeping through several issues of a newspaper or magazine. Frequently appended to each installment is a "synopsis of preceding chapers" for those who have not read them, but a direr need is a synopsis of succeeding chapters for those who do not intend to read *them*. A synopsis of the entire work would be still better.

SUCCESS, n. The one unpardonable sin against one's fellows.

TEETOTALER, n. One who abstains from strong drink, sometimes totally, sometimes tolerably totally.

TREE, n. A tall vegetable intended by nature to serve as a penal apparatus.

TWICE, adv. Once too often.
UN-AMERICAN, adj. Wicked, intolerable, heathenish.
WEDDING, n. A ceremony at which two persons undertake to become one, one undertakes to become nothing, and nothing undertakes to become supportable.
WHITE, adj. and n. Black.

WESTBROOK PEGLER was a sort of hero around my house for a long time. Then he got goofy and the gilt washed off him. One thing, however, remained. The guy was a whiz of a writer, as far back as I can remember, and he remains a whiz of a writer. Most of the people I know who grow furious over Pegler's reactionary mulishness permit their emotions to obliterate their good sense. "Pegler a good writer?" they say. "Why, that stinking son of a bitch is the lousiest writer on earth."

In other words they hate Pegler right straight down the line. Suppose he had an excellent reputation for table manners. They'd deny it and say he ate like a hog. They'd say his table manners are so atrocious and revolting that he should be compelled to wolf his food off the kitchen floor. If he had nice blue eyes they'd say it was the sorriest shade of blue on earth.

It is my thought that if Westbrook Pegler hadn't started feeling noggin-throbs he could have become one of the greatest humorists in the land. Maybe the greatest. It's a rare thing nowadays for him to take a day off from baiting liberals or snorting at labor, but when he does it he becomes a small god again. I never met him, but recently I had a telephone talk with him. He sounded okay on the phone—didn't growl or shriek a bit. I sort of hinted that it would be a good thing for me to come up and visit him in his Connecticut lair, in order that I might write something about his home life and shaving habits. He didn't take the bait. That was disappointing because I'd like to be able to give people a picture of Pegler at home. Most people imagine that he sits around on his country estate biting the heads off Buff Orpingtons; that he writes a paragraph and then gets up and clouts his cat a couple of good ones; that he greets the letter carrier with a fusillade of horse apples. I suppose that in reality he leads a quiet life, although I've often heard that he shatters furniture during the production of a difficult column. I know one anecdote about him. The late Bob Bender of the United Press used to have his country home adjoining that of Pegler. When he first got the place it had no indoor toilets and the Benders and their guests used two privies set on a hillside some distance from the house. Once they had a houseful of week-end guests and with the coming of dawn people started journeying toward these outhouses. They couldn't get to them, however. Pegler was up early. He was sitting on the porch of his house with a .22 rifle. He sat there all morning, placidly firing bullets through those two privies. The Benders and their guests gave up, finally, and took to the hills.

I'm using several Pegler pieces in this book. One of them seems to fit into this division. It is:

MYRIAD–MINDED US

By Westbrook Pegler

Of all the fantastic fog shapes that have risen off the swamp of confusion since the big war, the most futile and, at the same time, the most pretentious, is the deep-thinking, hair-trigger columnist or commentator who knows all the answers just offhand and can settle great affairs with absolute finality three days or even six days a week.

Being one of these myself, I have been trying to figure out how we came to be. Some, I know, have been pontificating for twenty years and have come to regard themselves as intellectual landmarks and American institutions as permanent as baseball.

But I am one of the green crop, come up after the panic,

and my confidence in the vast public importance of my opinions, to say nothing of their sanity, has not become a fixed habit.

It takes gall to sit down to a typewriter at a certain hour every afternoon to confront a long mile of white paper and presume to tell the people what it is all about to the extent of from five hundred to a thousand words.

Tell them what what is all about? says you. Oh, just anything and everything.

What is it that you would like to be told all about by your favorite myriad-minded commentator? Economics, pig prevention, the Constitution, the law, politics, war, history, labor, the C.I.O. and the A.F. of L., housing, international relations, birth control, the infield fly rule, Fascism, Nazism, and Communism, inflation, agriculture, or phrenology? Name me something we can't tell you all about with absolute, irrefutable authority and no two, perhaps, in agreement on any single point.

We include experts on the budget who can't balance an expense account; economic experts who can't find the five-fifteen on a suburban timetable much less read a balance sheet, labor experts who never did a lick of work in their lives, pundits on the mechanical age who can't put a fresh ribbon on their own typewriters, and resounding authorities on the problem of the farmer who never even grew a geranium in a pot.

We are, in short, the berries of the Fourth Estate, so passionate and self-important these last few years that some of our number, not content with telling the world what and why so on paper, must even rear back at public meetings and snort and sweat in the faces of our fellow citizens in outbursts of courthouse forensics intended to make them think, or anyway think they do.

Not only that, but these oral remarks are sometimes deemed to be of such priceless originality and wisdom as to justify reprinting in full next day, lest some immortal truth be gone with the wind when the cleaners air out the joint.

What causes us? Well, as nearly as I can figure it out, this trade began as a sort of journalistic vaudeville intended to entertain the customers and exert a little circulation pull of a slightly higher tone than that of the comics. Actually, even now at our grimmest, we aren't one, two, six with a real good strip in which some man is plotting to put out a little girl's eyes or throw a little boy into a blast furnace, a reassuring fact, if you are considering the good sense of the nation, as the syndicate managers, in their nasty way, are always reminding us.

In the days of the wham-sock strips our trade was just olives, requiring a cultivated taste, and as the comics veered off into tragedy and we drifted into isms and causes, the salesmen on the road found, as they continue to find today, that it was much easier to peddle serious funnies than funny seriousness. The comic artists still ride in the big cars and spend their winters shooting in the eighties down South, while we drive the light models and interview ourselves day after solemn day on the state of the nation and the wrongs of a woeful world.

You might think that once in a great while we would run out of intelligence, and I often marvel at my own inexhaustible fund of knowledge, but it just keeps on bubbling up. Nowadays numbers of our set even get into acrimonious clothesline spats, figuring, like the old-time fight promoters, that a grudge fight is good for the gate. And the one sure way to drive a small competitor nuts, as Mr. Lippmann has demonstrated in several instances where efforts were made to smoke him out, is to ignore him as though he didn't exist.

Maybe I shouldn't be writing like this, revealing secrets of the trade and all, but I just got to thinking it over and, honest to God, it is getting plumb ridiculous.

My workroom, in which on rare occasions I work, is a fairly large chamber with a big desk, some bookcases, a couple of tables, a pencil sharpener into which none of my pencils will fit, a jug of glue that Alton Cook once gave me for Christmas, a small telescope which I use for something that is none of your dern business, three thousand miscellaneous items that ought to be thrown away, a totem pole, and a studio couch which I use for heavy concentration with the eyes shut. On the walls are nothing but maps, a Rollin Kirby cartoon, and one photograph. The single picture is of H. L. Mencken.

I'm including two pieces by Mencken. They came steaming out of his battered old portable back in the middle 1920s when I didn't even know there was such a person as H. L. Mencken on earth. In those days, whenever Mencken took ball bat in hand and went to work on a human or group of humans, the landscape was soon cluttered with fragments of throbbing flesh and the Anglo-American language was weak-kneed from the remarkable things that had been done with it.

As master of ceremonies in this literary vaudeville show, let me present one of our best acts—with an encore.

CLARION CALL TO POETS

By H. L. Mencken

ONE OF THE CRYING NEEDS of the time in this incomparable Republic—the goal and despair of all other and hence lesser states—is for a suitable burial service for the admittedly damned. I speak as one who has of late attended the funeral orgies of several such gentlemen, each time to my aesthetic distress. The first of these gentlemen, having a great abhorrence of rhetoric in all its branches, left strict orders that not a word was to be said at his obsequies. The result was two extremely chilly and uncomfortable moments: when six of us walked into his house in utter silence and carried out his clay, and when we shoved it, in the same crawling silence, into the yawning firebox of the crematory. The whole business was somehow unnatural and even a shade indecent: it violated one of the most ancient sentiments of *Homo sapiens* to dispatch so charming a fellow in so cavalier a fashion. One felt almost irresistibly impelled to say good-by to him in some manner or other, if only, soldier fashion, by blowing a bugle and rolling a drum. Even the mortician, an eminent star of one of the most self-possessed of professions, looked a bit uneasy and ashamed.

The second funeral was even worse. The deceased had been a socialist of the militantly anti-clerical variety, and threatened, on his deathbed, to leap from his coffin with roars if a clergyman were hired to snuffle over him. His widow accordingly asked two of his socialist colleagues to address the mourners. They prepared for the business by resorting to a bootlegger, and in consequence both of them were garrulous and injudicious. One of them traced the career of Karl Marx in immense detail, and deduced from it a long series of lessons for ambitious American boys. The other, after first denouncing the New York *Times,* read twenty or thirty cantos of execrable poetry from the *Freethinker.* If the widow had not performed a series of very realistic sobs—leaning for support, I may add, upon a comrade who soon afterward succeeded to the rights of the deceased in her person and real estate—the ceremony would have been indistinguishable from a session of the House of Representatives.

The third funeral was conducted by Freemasons, who came in plug hats and with white aprons over their cowcatchers. They entered the house of mourning in a long file, with their hats held over their left breasts in the manner of a President reviewing an inaugural parade, and filed past the open coffin at a brisk parade march. As each passed he gave a swift, mechanical glance at the fallen brother: there was in it the somewhat metallic efficiency of an old hand. These Freemasons brought their own limousines and took a place in the funeral procession ahead of the hearse. At the cemetery they deployed around the grave, and as soon as the clergyman had finished his mumbo-jumbo, began a ceremonial of their own. Their leader, standing at the head of the grave with his plug hat on, first read a long series of quasi-theological generalities—to the general effect, so far as I could make out, that Freemasons are immune to hell, as they are notoriously immune to hanging—and then a brother at the foot of the grave replied. After that there was a slight pause, and in rather ragged chorus the rest of the brethren said, "So mote it be!" This went on almost endlessly; I was heartily glad when it was over. The whole ceremony, in fact, was tedious and trashy. As for me, I'd rather have been planted by a Swedenborgian, whiskers and all. Or even by a grand goblin of the Ethical Culture Society.

What is needed, and what I bawl for politely, is a service that is free from the pious and unsupported asseverations that revolt so many of our best minds, and yet remain happily graceful and consoling. It will be very hard, I grant you, to concoct anything as lasciviously beautiful as the dithyrambs in the Book of Common Prayer. Who wrote them originally I don't know, but whoever did it was a poet. They put the highly improbable into amazingly luscious words, and the palpably not true into words even more caressing and disarming. It is impossible to listen to them, when they are intoned by a High Church rector of sepulchral gifts, without harboring a sneaking wish that, by some transcendental magic, they could throw off their lowly poetical character and take on the dignity and reliability of prose—in other words, that the departed could be actually imagined as leaping out of the grave on the Last Morn, his split colloids all restored to their pristine complexity, his clothes neatly scoured and pressed, and every molecule of him thrilling with a wild surmise. I have felt this wish at the funerals of many virtuous and earnest brethren, whose sole sin was their refusal to swallow such anecdotes as the one in II Kings 11: 23–24. It seems a pity that men of that sort should be doomed to hell, and it seems an even greater pity that they should be laid away to the banal chin music of humorless Freemasons and stewed socialists.

But, as far as I know, no suitable last rites for them have ever been drawn up. Between the service in the Book of Common Prayer (and its various analogues, nearly all of them greatly inferior) and the maudlin mortuary dialogues of the Freemasons, Ku Kluxers, Knights of Pythias, and other such assassins of beauty there is absolutely nothing. Even the professional agnostics, who are violently literary, have never produced anything worthy to be considered; their best is indistinguishable from the text of a flag drill or high-school pageant. Thus the average American skeptic, when his time comes to return to earth, is commonly turned off with what, considering his prejudices, may be best described as a razzing. His widow, disinclined to risk scandal by burying him without any ceremonies at all, calls in the nearest clergyman, and the result is a lamentable comedy, creditable neither to honest faith nor to honest doubt. More than once, in attendance upon such an affair, I have observed a sardonic glitter in the eye of the pastor, especially when he came to the unequivocal statement that the deceased would infallibly rise again. Did he secretly doubt it? Or was he poking fun at a dead opponent, now persuaded of the truth of revelation at last? In either case there was something unpleasant in the spectacle. A suitable funeral for doubters, full of lovely poetry but devoid of any specific pronouncement on the subject of a future life, would make such unpleasantness unnecessary.

We have the poets for the job, and I incline to suspect that their private theological ideas fit them for it. Skepticism, in fact, runs with their cynical trade. Most Americans, as everyone knows, give their ecclesiastical affiliations in Who's Who in America—especially congressmen, pedagogues, bank presidents, and uplifters. But not the poets. The sole exception, so far as I can make out, is Vachel Lindsay, who reports that he is a member of the Christian (Disciples) Church, a powerful sect in the No-More-Scrub-Bulls Belt, with a private hell of its own, deep and hot. Even Edgar Albert Guest is silent on the subject, though he mentions the fact that he is a thirty-third-degree Mason. Frost, Robinson, Sandburg, and Masters keep suspiciously mum. I suggest that they meet in some quiet saloon and draw up the ritual I advocate. Let Masters be chairman of the committee: he is a lawyer as well as a poet, and may be trusted to keep within the statutes. And let Edna St. Vincent Millay be added to give the thing a refined voluptuousness, and James Weldon Johnson to put music into it, and it may be intoned without getting the celebrant out of breath. Here Holy

Church shows the way. Its funeral service is a great deal less forensic than operatic.

There is some need, too, for a marriage service for the damned, and at different times attempts have been made to supply it. But all such works seem to emanate from radicals showing a characteristic lack of humor—and humor is as necessary to a marriage service as poetry is to a funeral service: a fact that the astute authors of the Book of Common Prayer did not overlook. However, the need here is not pressing, for in most American states civil marriage is sufficient, and heretics may be safely united without going before a sorcerer at all. Court clerks and police magistrates perform the job, mumbling unintelligibly out of a mysterious book, perhaps only a stolen Gideon Bible, excavated to hold cigarettes. The main thing is to pay the fee. Marriages after midnight cost double, and if the bridegroom has the fumes of wine in his head, he is apt to lose his watch as well as his liberty.

As I say, the marriage services drawn up by antinomians for the use of unbelievers lack humor. Worse, they are full of indignation—against the common theory that a wife is bound to give some care to her husband's goods, against the convention that she shall adopt his surname, and so on. It is hard to give serious attention to such grim notions at a time immemorially viewed as festive and jocose. One hears frequently of wedding guests getting drunk and fighting—not long ago a Methodist pastor in Missouri was protesting against it publicly—but when they are drawn into sociological controversy it is too much. Such revolutionary marriage services, in point of fact, have never gained much popularity. Now and then a pair of socialists resorts to one, but even socialists appear to prefer the harsh, mechanical offices of a court clerk.

Nor is there any active demand for a non-theological baptismal service. I am constantly amazed, as a bachelor, by the number of children growing up, in these iconoclastic modern days, without any formal naming at all. Not only do heretics spurn the ceremony; even professing Christians often neglect it. In my own nonage practically all babies, at least of the more respectable tribes of the race, were christened. There was a general feeling that failing to put them through the sacrament was, in some obscure way, a tort against them —that it would bring them bad luck, and perhaps lead to difficulties in after life. It is so believed to this day nearly everywhere in Europe, and for sound reasons. Whenever a citizen in those decaying lands comes into contact with the state, which is very often, its agents demand his baptismal certificate as well as his birth certificate. So far the imbeciles at Washington have not come to that, but it must be plain that they will come to it soon or late, and when the time is finally upon us there will be trouble for all those Americanos whose naming is now trusted to acclamation. They will have to dig up senile aunts and uncles, and produce affidavits that they were known to everyone as so-and-so at some date far in the past, just as they now have to get such affidavits, more often than not, when they want passports. The bureaucracy grinds slowly, but it grinds exceeding fine. Recruited from the mentally deficient, it runs to circular insanities. Let it be proved tomorrow that some John Doe, suspected of favoring the recognition of Russia, was actually baptized Johannes, and it will be sufficient excuse for a regulation requiring all of us to prove that we are legally entitled to the names we sign to checks.

But all these are side issues. The main thing is that the poets, though most of them seem to have departed from the precincts and protection of Holy Church and her schismatic colonies—since when has a first-rate American poet written a hymn?—have failed, so far, to rise to the occasion when, even among heretics, poets are most pressingly needed. I have suggested that they meet in some convenient speakeasy and remedy the lack gloriously, but I don't insist, of course, that their service for the doubting dead be wholly original. The authors of the Book of Common Prayer, though they were poets of great talent, certainly did not trust only to their private inspiration. They borrowed copiously from the old missals, and they borrowed, too, directly from Holy Writ. What they concocted finally was a composite, but it was very discreetly and delicately put together, and remains impregnable to this day, despite many furious efforts to undo it.

All I propose is that the committee of poets imitate them, but with an avoidance of strophes objectionable in doctrine. Isn't there material enough in the books? There is enough, and to spare. I point to the works of Walt Whitman, now at last passing freely through the mails—to those parts, of course, of a non-erotic and non-political nature. I point to certain memorable stanzas of William Cullen Bryant. I point to Blake, Tennyson, Milton, Shelley, Keats, even Swinburne; what gaudy stuff for the purpose is in "Ave Atque Vale," "Tristram of Lyonesse," and "Atalanta in Calydon"! There is here a sweet soothing, a healing reassurance, a divine booziness—in brief, all the stuff of A number 1 poetry. It would bring comfort, I believe, to many a poor widow who now groans as the Freemasons intone their balderdash, or flounces her veil, fidgets, and blushes as a socialist orator denounces Omnipotence for permitting stock dividends—it would bring her a great deal more comfort, certainly, than the positive statement, made defiantly by the unwilling rector of the parish, that her departed John, having been colloidal and as the beasts, has now become gaseous and immortal. Such a libretto for the inescapable last act would be humane and valuable. I renew my suggestion that the poets spit upon their hands and confect it at once.

CHIROPRACTIC

By H. L. Mencken

THIS PREPOSTEROUS QUACKERY is now all the rage in the back reaches of the Republic, and even begins to conquer the less civilized of the big cities. As the old-time family doctor dies out in the country towns, with no trained successor willing to take over his dismal business, he is followed by some hearty blacksmith or ice-wagon driver, turned into a chiropractor in six months, often by correspondence. In

Los Angeles the Damned there are more chiropractors than actual physicians, and they are far more generally esteemed. Proceeding from the Ambassador Hotel to the heart of the town, along Wilshire Boulevard, one passes scores of their gaudy signs: there are even many chiropractic "hospitals." The morons who pour in from the prairies and deserts, most of them ailing, patronize these "hospitals" copiously, and give to the chiropractic pathology the same high respect that they accord to the theology of Aimée McPherson and the art of Cecil De Mille. That pathology is grounded upon the doctrine that all human ills are caused by the pressure of misplaced vertebrae upon the nerves which come out of the spinal cord—in other words, that every disease is the result of a pinch. This, plainly enough, is buncombe. The chiropractic therapeutics rest upon the doctrine that the way to get rid of such pinches is to climb upon a table and submit to an heroic pummeling by a retired piano mover. This, obviously, is buncombe doubly damned.

Both doctrines were launched upon the world by an old quack named Andrew T. Still, the father of osteopathy. For years his followers merchanted them, and made a lot of money at the trade. But as they grew opulent they grew ambitious, i.e., they began to study anatomy and physiology. The result was a gradual abandonment of Papa Still's ideas. The high-toned osteopath of today is a sort of eclectic. He tries anything that promises to work, from tonsillectomy to the vibrations of the late Dr. Abrams. With four years' training behind him, he probably knows more anatomy than the average graduate of the Johns Hopkins Medical School, or, at all events, more osteology. Thus enlightened, he seldom has much to say about pinched nerves in the back. But as he abandoned the Still revelation it was seized by the chiropractors, led by another quack, one Palmer. This Palmer grabbed the pinched-nerve nonsense and began teaching it to ambitious farm hands and out-at-elbow Baptist preachers in a few easy lessons. Today the backwoods swarm with chiropractors, and in most states they have been able to exert enough pressure on the rural politicians to get themselves licensed. Any lout with strong hands and arms is perfectly equipped to become a chiropractor. No education beyond the elements is necessary. The whole art and mystery may be imparted in a few months, and the graduate is then free to practice upon God's images. The takings are often high, and so the profession has attracted thousands of recruits—retired baseball players, plumbers, truck drivers, longshoremen, bogus dentists, dubious preachers, village school superintendents. Now and then a quack doctor of some other school—say homeopathy—plunges into it. Hundreds of promising students come from the intellectual ranks of hospital orderlies.

In certain states efforts have been made, sometimes by the medical fraternity, to make the practice of chiropractic unlawful. I am glad to be able to report that practically all of them have failed. Why should it be prohibited? I believe that every free-born man has a clear right, when he is ill, to seek any sort of treatment that he yearns for. If his mental processes are of such a character that the theory of chiropractic seems plausible to him, then he should be permitted to try chiropractic. And if it be granted that he has a right to do so, then it follows clearly that any stevedore privy to the technique of chiropractic has a right to treat him. To preach any contrary doctrine is to advocate despotism and slavery. The arguments for such despotism are all full of holes, and especially those that come from medical men who have been bitten by the public-hygiene madness, i.e., by the messianic delusion. Such fanatics infest every health department in the land. They assume glibly that the whole aim of civilization is to cut down the death rate, and to attain that end they are willing to make a sacrifice of everything else imaginable, including their own sense of humor. There is, as a matter of fact, not the slightest reason to believe that cutting down the death rate, in itself, is of much benefit to the human race. A people with an annual rate of forty a thousand might still produce many Huxleys and Darwins, and one with a rate of but eight or nine might produce nothing but Coolidges and Billy Sundays. The former probability, in truth, is greater than the latter, for a low rate does not necessarily mean that more superior individuals are surviving; it may mean only that more of the inferior are surviving, and that the next generation will be burdened by their get.

Such quackeries as Christian Science, osteopathy, and chiropractic work against the false humanitarianism of the hygienists and to excellent effect. They suck in the botched, and help them on to bliss eternal. When these botched fall into the hands of competent medical men they are very likely to be patched up and turned loose upon the world, to beget their kind. But massaged along the backbone to cure their lues, they quickly pass into the last stages, and so their pathogenic heritage perishes with them. What is too often forgotten is that nature obviously intends the botched to die, and that every interference with that benign process is full of dangers. Moreover, it is, like birth control, profoundly immoral. The chiropractors are innocent in both departments. That their labors tend to propagate epidemics, and so menace the lives of all of us, as is alleged by their medical opponents—this I doubt. The fact is that most infectious diseases of any seriousness throw out such alarming symptoms and so quickly that no sane chiropractor is likely to monkey with them. Seeing his patient breaking out in pustules, or choking, or falling into a stupor, he takes to the woods at once, and leaves the business to the nearest medical man. His trade is mainly with ambulant patients; they must come to his studio for treatment. Most of them have lingering diseases; they tour all the neighborhood doctors before they reach him. His treatment, being entirely nonsensical, is in accord with the divine plan. It is seldom, perhaps, that he actually kills a patient, but at all events he keeps many a worthy soul from getting well.

Thus the multiplication of chiropractors in the Republic gives me a great deal of pleasure. It is agreeable to see so many morons getting slaughtered, and it is equally agreeable to see so many other morons getting rich. The art and mystery of scientific medicine, for a decade or more past, has been closed to all save the sons of wealthy men. It takes a small fortune to go through a Class A medical college, and by the time the graduate is able to make a living for himself he is entering upon middle age, and is commonly so disillusioned that he is unfit for practice. Worse, his fees for looking at tongues and feeling pulses tend to be cruelly high. His predecessors charged fifty cents and threw in the pills; his own charges approach those of divorce lawyers, consulting engineers, and the higher hetaerae. Even general practice, in our great Babylons, has become a sort of specialty, with corresponding emoluments. But the chiropractor, having no such investment in his training, can afford to work for more humane wages, and so he is getting more and more of the trade. Six weeks after he leaves his job at the filling station or abandons the steering wheel of his motor truck he knows all the anatomy and physiology that he will ever learn in this world. Six weeks more, and he is an adept at all the half nelsons and left hooks that constitute the essence of chiropractic therapy. Soon afterward, having taken postgraduate courses in advertising, salesmanship, and mental mastery, he is ready for practice. A sufficiency of patients, it appears, is always ready, too. I hear of no complaint from chiropractors of bad business. New ones are being turned out at a dizzy rate, but they all seem to find the pickings easy. Some time ago I heard of a chiropractor who, having once been a cornet player, had abandoned chiropractic in despair, and gone back to cornet playing. But investigation showed that he was really not a chiropractor at all, but an osteopath.

The osteopaths, I fear, are finding this new competition serious and unpleasant. As I have said, it was their Hippocrates, the late Dr. Still, who invented all of the thrusts, lunges, yanks, hooks, and bounces that the lowly chiropractors now employ with such vast effect, and for years the osteopaths had a monopoly of them. But when they began to grow scientific and ambitious their course of training was lengthened until it took in all sorts of tricks and dodges borrowed from the regular doctors, or resurrection men, including the plucking of tonsils, adenoids, and appendices, the use of the stomach pump, and even some of the legerdemain of psychiatry. They now hurry their students furiously, and turn them out ready for anything from growing hair on a bald head to frying a patient with the X rays. All this new striving, of course, quickly brought its inevitable penalties. The osteopathic graduate, having sweated so long, was no longer willing to take a case of sarcoma for two dollars, and in consequence he lost patients. Worse, very few aspirants could make the long grade. The essence of osteopathy itself could be grasped by any lively farm hand or night watchman in a few weeks, but the borrowed magic baffled him. Confronted by the phenomenon of gastrulation, or by the curious behavior of heart muscle, or by any of the current theories of immunity, he commonly took refuge, like his brother of the orthodox faculty, in a gulp of laboratory alcohol, or fled the premises altogether. Thus he was lost to osteopathic science, and the chiropractors took him in; nay, they welcomed him. He was their meat. Borrowing that primitive part of osteopathy which was comprehensible to the meanest understanding, they threw the rest overboard, at the same time denouncing it as a sorcery invented by the medical trust. Thus they gathered in the garage mechanics, ashmen and decayed welterweights, and the land began to fill with their graduates. Now there is a chiropractor at every crossroads, and in such sinks of imbecility as Los Angeles they are as thick as bootleggers.

I repeat that it eases and soothes me to see them so prosperous, for they counteract the evil work of the so-called science of public hygiene, which now seeks to make morons immortal. If a man, being ill of a pus appendix, resorts to a shaved and fumigated longshoreman to have it disposed of, and submits willingly to a treatment involving balancing him on McBurney's Point and playing on his vertebrae as on a concertina, then I am willing, for one, to believe that he is badly wanted in heaven. And if that same man, having achieved lawfully a lovely babe, hires a blacksmith to cure its diphtheria by pulling its neck, then I do not resist the divine will that there shall be one less radio fan in 1967. In such matters, I am convinced, the laws of nature are far better guides than the fiats and machinations of the medical busybodies who now try to run us. If the latter gentlemen had their way, death, save at the hands of hangmen, Prohibition agents, and other such legalized assassins, would be abolished altogether, and so the present differential in favor of the enlightened would disappear. I can't convince myself that that would work any good to the world. On the contrary, it seems to me that the current coddling of the half-witted should be stopped before it goes too far—if, indeed, it has not gone too far already. To that end nothing operates more cheaply and effectively than the prosperity of quacks. Every time a bottle of cancer specific goes through the mails *Homo americanus* is improved to that extent. And every time a chiropractor spits on his hands and proceeds to treat a gastric ulcer by stretching the backbone the same high end is achieved.

But chiropractic, of course, is not perfect. It has superb potentialities, but only too often they are not converted into concrete cadavers. The hygienists rescue many of its foreordained customers, and, turning them over to agents of the medical trust, maintained at the public expense, get them cured. Moreover, chiropractic itself is not certainly fatal; even an Iowan with diabetes may survive its embraces. Yet worse, I have a suspicion that it sometimes actually cures. For all I know (or any orthodox pathologist seems to know) it *may* be true that certain malaises are caused by the pressure of vagrom vertebrae upon the spinal nerves. And it *may* be true that a hearty ex-boilermaker, by a vigorous yanking and kneading, may be able to relieve that pressure. What is needed is a scientific inquiry into the matter, under rigid test conditions, by a committee of men learned in the architecture and plumbing of the body, and of a high and incorruptible sagacity. Let a thousand patients be selected, let a gang of selected chiropractors examine their backbones and determine what is the matter with them, and then let these diagnoses be checked up by the exact methods of scientific medicine. Then let the same chiropractors essay to cure the patients whose maladies have been determined. My guess is that the chiropractors' errors in diagnosis will run to at least ninety-five per cent and that their failures in treatment will push ninety-nine per cent. But I am willing to be convinced.

Where is such a committee to be found? I undertake to nominate it at ten minutes' notice. The land swarms with men competent in anatomy and pathology, and yet not engaged as doctors. There are hundreds of roomy and well-heated hospitals, with endless clinical material. I offer to supply the committee with cigars and music during the test. I offer, further, to supply both the committee and the chiropractors with sound prewar wet goods. I offer, finally, to give a bawdy banquet to the whole medical trust at the conclusion of the proceedings.

GETTING BACK to our desert island, I do believe that if the hobgoblins of destiny would allow it, I'd ask them to put me ashore with a crate containing the complete works of Mark Twain. This collection would include the Paine biography and even the *Autobiography*. The last-named work comes pretty close to being the worst job Mark Twain ever did, but it is put up in two stout volumes and could be used for walloping scorpions.

I am what is known as a Mark Twain nut. To me even his poorest stuff is good. I don't think I've ever encountered a person who actually disliked his writing, though I've heard that some people of deep religious bent complain about portions of it.

In this book it is only possible for me to provide a mere whiff of Twain flavoring. He touched upon such a multitude of subjects in his writings that it would be possible to assemble a sort of Mark Twain dictionary containing his observations on matters ranging from Mahomet to the molecule. Snoring, for example. There is a long paragraph in *Tom Sawyer Abroad* in which Huck Finn ruminates on snoring. Huck and Tom and Jim are aboard their airship, and . . . but let Huck tell it.

Jim began to snore—soft and blubbery at first, then a long rasp, then a stronger one, then a half a dozen horrible ones, like the last water sucking down the plug hole of a bathtub, then the same with more power to it, and some big coughs and snorts flung in, the way a cow does that is choking to death; and when the person has got to that point he is at his level best, and can wake up a man that is in the next block with a dipperful of loddanum in him, but can't wake himself up although all that awful noise of his'n ain't but three inches from his own ears. And that is the curiosest thing in the world, seems to me. But you rake a match to light the candle, and that little bit of a noise will fetch him. I wish I knowed what was the reason of that, but there don't seem to be no way to find out. Now there was Jim alarming the whole desert, and yanking the animals out, for miles and miles around, to see what in the nation was going on up there; there warn't nobody nor nothing that was as close to the noise as *he* was, and yet he was the only cretur that wasn't disturbed by it. We yelled at him and whooped at him, it never done no good; but the first time there come a little wee noise that wasn't of a usual kind, it woke him up. No sir, I've thought it all over, and so has Tom, and there ain't no way to find out why a snorer can't hear himself snore.

Anybody who attempts to write on the subject of snoring after that is a fool.

There are simply hundreds of memorable passages in Twain that I'd like to pass along. Among his gay adventures in the Holy Land, as set down in *The Innocents Abroad,* is the touching episode in which the American finds himself at Adam's tomb. It goes like this:

From
"THE INNOCENTS ABROAD"

By Mark Twain

IF EVEN GREATER PROOFS than those I have mentioned are wanted, to satisfy the headstrong and the foolish that this is the genuine center of the earth, they are here. The greatest of them lies in the fact that from under this very column was taken *the dust from which Adam was made.* This can surely be regarded in the light of a settler. It is not likely that the original first man would have been made from an inferior quality of earth when it was entirely convenient to get first quality from the world's center. This will strike any reflecting mind forcibly. That Adam was formed of dirt procured in this very spot is amply proven by the fact that in six thousand years no man has ever been able to prove that the dirt was *not* procured here whereof he was made.

It is a singular circumstance that right under the roof of this same great church, and not far away from that illustrious column, Adam himself, the father of the human race, lies buried. There is no question that he is actually buried in the grave which is pointed out as his—there can be none—because it has never yet been proven that this grave is not the grave in which he is buried.

The tomb of Adam! How touching it was, here in a land of strangers, far away from home, and friends, and all who cared for me, thus to discover the grave of a blood relation. True, a distant one, but still a relation. The unerring instinct of nature thrilled its recognition. The fountain of my filial affection was stirred to its profoundest depths, and I gave way to tumultuous emotion. I leaned upon a pillar and burst into tears. I deem it no shame to have wept over the grave of my poor dead relative. Let him who would sneer at my emotion close this volume here, for he will find little to his taste in my journeyings through Holy Land. Noble old man—he did not live to see me—he did not live to see his child. And I—I—alas, I did not live to see *him*. Weighed down by sorrow and disappointment, he died before I was born—six thousand brief summers before I was born. But let us try to bear it with fortitude. Let us trust that he is better off where he is. Let us take comfort in the thought that his loss is our eternal gain.

ANOTHER BIT I find myself returning to, time after time, is found in *A Tramp Abroad*. It is Mark Twain's assault on ants. It recalls to mind a remark I heard my father make years ago. Somebody was telling him about ants, emphasizing their great industry. "Maybe so," said Pop, "but it seems like they sure make a lot of picnics."

The ants which had the misfortune (for their entire race) to fall beneath the gaze of Mark Twain, setting him to thinking about their reputation, were encountered in the Black Forest. Mr. Clemens gives them their lumps:

From
"A TRAMP ABROAD"
By Mark Twain

NOW AND THEN, while we rested, we watched the laborious ant at his work. I found nothing new in him—certainly nothing to change my opinion of him. It seems to me that in the matter of intellect the ant must be a strangely overrated bird. During many summers, now, I have watched him, when I ought to have been in better business, and I have not yet come across a living ant that seemed to have any more sense than a dead one. I refer to the ordinary ant, of course; I have had no experience of those wonderful Swiss and African ones which vote, keep drilled armies, hold slaves, and dispute about religion. Those particular ants may be all that the naturalist paints them, but I am persuaded that the average ant is a sham. I admit his industry, of course; he is the hardest-working creature in the world—when anybody is looking—but his leather-headedness is the point I make against him. He goes out foraging, he makes a capture, and then what does he do? Go home? No—he goes anywhere but home. He doesn't know where home is. His home may be only three feet away—no matter, he can't find it. He makes his capture, as I have said; it is generally something which can be of no sort of use to himself or anybody else; it is usually seven times bigger than it ought to be; he hunts out the awkwardest place to take hold of it; he lifts it bodily up in the air by main force, and starts; not toward home but in the opposite direction; not calmly and wisely but with a frantic haste which is wasteful of his strength; he fetches up against a pebble, and instead of going around it, he climbs over it backward, dragging his booty after him, tumbles down on the other side, jumps up in a passion, kicks the dust off his clothes, moistens his hands, grabs his property viciously, yanks it this way, then that, shoves it ahead of him for a moment, turns tail and lugs it after him another moment, gets madder and madder, then presently hoists it into the air and goes tearing away in an entirely new direction; comes to a weed; it never occurs to him to go around it; no, he must climb it; and he does climb it, dragging his worthless property to the top—which is as bright a thing to do as it would be for me to carry a sack of flour from Heidelberg to Paris by way of Strasbourg steeple; when he gets up there he finds that that is not the place; takes a cursory glance at the scenery and either climbs down again or tumbles down, and starts off once more—as usual, in a new direction. At the end of half an hour he fetches up within six inches of the place he started from and lays his burden down; meantime he has been over all the ground for two yards around, and climbed all the weeds and pebbles he came across. Now he wipes the sweat from his brow, strokes his limbs, and then marches aimlessly off, in as violent a hurry as ever. He traverses a good deal of zigzag country, and by and by stumbles on his same booty again. He does not remember to have ever seen it before; he looks around to see which is not the way home, grabs his bundle, and starts; he goes through the same adventures he had before; finally stops to rest, and a friend comes along. Evidently the friend remarks that a last year's grasshopper leg is a very noble acquisition, and inquires where he got it. Evidently the proprietor does not remember exactly where he did get it, but thinks he got it "around here somewhere." Evidently the friend contracts to help him freight it home. Then, with a judgment peculiarly antic (pun not intentional), they take hold of opposite ends of that grasshopper leg and begin to tug with all their might in opposite directions. Presently they take a rest and confer together. They decide that something is wrong, they can't make out what.

Then they go at it again, just as before. Same result. Mutual recriminations follow. Evidently each accuses the other of being an obstructionist. They warm up, and the dispute ends in a fight. They lock themselves together and chew each other's jaws for a while; then they roll and tumble on the ground till one loses a horn or a leg and has to haul off for repairs. They make up and go to work again in the same old insane way, but the crippled ant is at a disadvantage; tug as he may, the other one drags off the booty and him at the end of it. Instead of giving up, he hangs on, and gets his shins bruised against every obstruction that comes in the way. By and by, when that grasshopper leg has been dragged all over the same old ground once more, it is finally dumped at about the spot where it originally lay, the two perspiring ants inspect it thoughtfully and decide that dried grasshopper legs are a poor sort of property after all, and then each starts off in a different direction to see if he can't find an old nail or something else that is heavy enough to afford entertainment and at the same time valueless enough to make an ant want to own it.

There in the Black Forest, on the mountainside, I saw an ant go through with such a performance as this with a dead spider of fully ten times his own weight. The spider was not quite dead, but too far gone to resist. He had a round body the size of a pea. The little ant—observing that I was noticing—turned him on his back, sunk his fangs into his throat, lifted him into the air, and started vigorously off with him, stumbling over little pebbles, stepping on the spider's legs and tripping himself up, dragging him backward, shoving him bodily ahead, dragging him up stones six inches high instead of going around them, climbing weeds twenty times his own height and jumping from their summits—and finally leaving him in the middle of the road to be confiscated by any other fool of an ant that wanted him. I measured the ground which this ass traversed, and arrived at the conclusion that what he had accomplished inside of twenty minutes would constitute some such job as this—relatively speaking—for a man; to wit: to strap two eight-hundred-pound horses together, carry them eighteen hundred feet, mainly over (not around) boulders averaging six feet high, and in the course of the journey climb up and jump from the top of one precipice like Niagara, and three steeples, each a hundred and twenty feet high; and then put the horses down, in an exposed place, without anybody to watch them, and go off to indulge in some other idiotic miracle for vanity's sake.

Science has recently discovered that the ant does not lay up anything for winter use. This will knock him out of literature, to some extent. He does not work, except when people are looking, and only then when the observer has a green, naturalistic look, and seems to be taking notes. This amounts to deception, and will injure him for the Sunday schools. He has not judgment enough to know what is good to eat from what isn't. This amounts to ignorance, and will impair the world's respect for him. He cannot stroll around a stump and find his way home again. This amounts to idiocy, and once the damaging fact is established, thoughtful people will cease to look up to him, the sentimental will cease to fondle him. His vaunted industry is but a vanity and of no effect, since he never gets home with anything he starts with. This disposes of the last remnant of his reputation and wholly destroys his main usefulness as a moral agent, since it will make the sluggard hesitate to go to him any more. It is strange, beyond comprehension, that so manifest a humbug as the ant has been able to fool so many nations and keep it up so many ages without being found out.

THE SPORTING LIFE

IV. THE SPORTING LIFE

TWO OF THE GREATEST MEN produced out of baseball have not been players, managers, coaches, ground keepers, or even bat boys. One of the two is Walter Lanier Barber, the old redhead. Mr. Barber's technique in broadcasting a ball game is so superlative that other sports announcers suffer horribly when placed alongside him. For several years now he has been associated with the fortunes of the Brooklyn Dodgers and his hog-jowl accent is as familiar to the people of Brooklyn as the bellowing of subway guards. Alone and singlehanded Red has corrupted the most corrupt dialect in America. His employment of distinctly Southern metaphor is having its effect on Brooklynese, and in Flatbush nowadays people are beginning to use cracker talk and one frequently hears such Barberian expressions as "tearin' up the pea patch" or "sittin' in the cat-bird seat."

My wife considers baseball to be the most boresome of all human pursuits. She could not distinguish a called strike from a left fielder, yet she often sits for hours listening to Red Barber. She just likes to hear him talk.

The other great contribution of baseball toward better living conditions in the United States was Ring Lardner. It has been a difficult job to select one of his pieces for this collection. Among the last things he wrote was a short book called *Lose with a Smile,* in which he went back to his old device of an exchange of letters between a boy and a girl, the boy in this case being a Brooklyn rookie. To me that book is the funniest thing he ever wrote, but I can't include it here because of its length and I wouldn't undertake to cut it by so much as one sentence. My Lardner selection is not, however, a baseball story, but—

MR. FRISBIE

By Ring W. Lardner

I AM Mr. Allen Frisbie's chauffeur. Allen Frisbie is a name I made up because they tell me that if I used the real name of the man I am employed by that he might take offense and start trouble though I am sure he will never see what I am writing as he does not read anything except the American Golfer but of course some of his friends might call his attention to it. If you knew who the real name of the man is it would make more interesting reading as he is one of the 10 most wealthiest men in the United States and a man who everybody is interested in because he is so famous and the newspapers are always writing articles about him and sending high salary reporters to interview him but he is a very hard man to reproach or get an interview with and when they do he never tells them anything.

That is how I come to be writing this article because about two weeks ago a Mr. Kirk had an appointment to interview Mr. Frisbie for one of the newspapers and I drove him to the station after the interview was over and he said to me your boss is certainly a tough egg to interview and getting a word out of him is like pulling turnips.

"The public do not know anything about the man," said Mr. Kirk. "They know he is very rich and has got a wife and a son and a daughter and what their names are but as to his private life and his likes and dislikes he might just as well be a monk in a convent."

"The public knows he likes golf," I said.

"They do not know what kind of a game he plays."

"He plays pretty good," I said.

"How good?" said Mr. Kirk.

"About 88 or 90," I said.

"So is your grandmother," said Mr. Kirk.

He only meant the remark as a comparison but had either of my grandmothers lived they would both have been over 90. Mr. Kirk did not believe I was telling the truth about Mr. Frisbie's game and he was right though was I using real names I would not admit it as Mr. Frisbie is very sensitive in regards to his golf.

Mr. Kirk kept pumping at me but I am used to being pumped at and Mr. Kirk finally gave up pumping at me as he found me as closed mouth as Mr. Frisbie himself but he made the remark that he wished he was in my place for a few days and as close to the old man as I am and he would then be able to write the first real article which had ever been written about the old man. He called Mr. Frisbie the old man.

He said it was too bad I am not a writer so I could write up a few instance about Mr. Frisbie from the human side on account of being his caddy at golf and some paper or magazine would pay me big. He said if you would tell me a few instance I would write them up and split with you but I said no I could not think of anything which would make an article but after Mr. Kirk had gone I got to thinking it over and thought to myself maybe I could be a writer if I tried and at least there is no harm in trying so for the week after Mr. Kirk's visit I spent all my spare time writing down about Mr. Frisbie only at first I used his real name but when I showed the article they said for me not to use real names but the public would guess who it was anyway and that was just as good as using real names.

So I have gone over the writing again and changed the name to Allen Frisbie and other changes and here is the article using Allen Frisbie.

When I say I am Mr. Frisbie's chauffeur I mean I am his personal chauffeur. There are two other chauffeurs who drive for the rest of the family and run errands. Had I nothing else to do only drive I might well be turned a man of leisure as Mr. Frisbie seldom never goes in to the city more than twice a week and even less oftener than that does he pay social visits.

His golf links is right on the place an easy walk from the house to the first tee and here is where he spends a good part of each and every day playing along with myself in the roll of caddy. So one would not be far from amiss to refer to me as Mr. Frisbie's caddy rather than his chauffeur but it was as a chauffeur that I was engaged and can flatter myself that there are very few men of my calling who would not gladly exchange their salary and position for mine.

Mr. Frisbie is a man just this side of 60 years of age. Almost 10 years ago he retired from active business with money enough to put him in a class with the richest men in the United States and since then his investments have increased their value to such an extent so that now he is in a class with the richest men in the United States.

It was soon after his retirement that he bought the Peter Fischer estate near Westbury, Long Island. On this estate there was a 9 hole golf course in good condition and considered one of the best private 9 hole golf courses in the United States but Mr. Frisbie would have had it plowed up and the land used for some other usage only for a stroke of chance which was when Mrs. Frisbie's brother came over from England for a visit.

It was during while this brother-in-law was visiting Mr. Frisbie that I entered the last named employee and was an onlooker when Mr. Frisbie's brother-in-law persuaded his brother-in-law to try the game of golf. As luck would have it Mr. Frisbie's first drive was so good that his brother-in-law would not believe he was a new beginner till he had seen Mr. Frisbie shoot again but that first perfect drive made Mr. Frisbie a slave of the game and without which there would be no such instance as I am about to relate.

I would better explain at this junction that I am not a golfer but I have learned quite a lot of knowledge about the game by cadding for Mr. Frisbie and also once or twice in company with my employer have picked up some knowledge of the game by witnessing players like Bobby Jones and Hagen and Sarazen and Smith in some of their matches. I have only tried it myself on a very few occasions when I was sure Mr. Frisbie could not observe me and will confide that in my own mind I am convinced that with a little practise that I would have little trouble defeating Mr. Frisbie but will never seek to prove same for reasons which I will leave it to the reader to guess the reasons.

One day shortly after Mr. Frisbie's brother-in-law had ended his visit I was cadding for Mr. Frisbie and as had become my custom keeping the score for him when a question arose as to whether he had taken 7 or 8 strokes on the last hole. A 7 would have given him a total of 63 for the 9 holes while a 8 would have made it 64. Mr. Frisbie tried to recall the different strokes but was not certain and asked me to help him.

As I remembered it he had sliced his 4th. wooden shot in to a trap but I had recovered well and got on to the green and then had taken 3 putts which would make him a 8 but by some slip of the tongue when I started to say 8 I said 7 and before I could correct myself Mr. Frisbie said yes you are right it was a 7.

"That is even 7s," said Mr. Frisbie.

"Yes," I said.

On the way back to the house he asked me what was my salary which I told him and he said well I think you are worth more than that and from now on you will get $25.00 more per week.

On another occasion when 9 more holes had been added to the course and Mr. Frisbie was playing the 18 holes regular every day he came to the last hole needing a 5 to break 112 which was his best score.

The 18th. hole is only 120 yards with a big green but a brook in front and traps in back of it. Mr. Frisbie got across the brook with his second but the ball went over in to the trap and it looked like bad business because Mr. Frisbie is even worse with a niblick than almost any other club except maybe the No. 3 and 4 irons and the wood.

Well I happened to get to the ball ahead of him and it laid there burred in the deep sand about a foot from a straight up and down bank 8 foot high where it would have been impossible for any man alive to oust it in one stroke but as luck would have it I stumbled and gave the ball a little kick and by chance it struck the side of the bank and stuck in the grass and Mr. Frisbie got it up on the green in one stroke and was down in 2 putts for his 5.

"Well that is my record 111 or 3 over 6s," he said.

Now my brother had a couple of tickets for the polo at Meadowbrook the next afternoon and I am a great lover of horses flesh so I said to Mr. Frisbie can I go to the polo tomorrow afternoon and he said certainly any time you want a afternoon off do not hesitate to ask me but a little while later there was a friend of mine going to get married at Atlantic City and Mr. Frisbie had just shot a 128 and broke his spoon besides and when I mentioned about going to Atlantic City for my friend's wedding he snapped at me like a wolf and said what did I think it was the xmas holidays.

Personally I am a man of simple tastes and few wants and it is very seldom when I am not satisfied to take my life and work as they come and not seek fear or favor but of course there are times in every man's life when they desire something a little out of the ordinary in the way of a little vacation or perhaps a financial accomodation of some kind and in such cases I have found Mr. Frisbie a king amongst men provide it one uses discretion in choosing the moment of their reproach but a variable tyrant if one uses bad judgment in choosing the moment of their reproach.

You can count on him granting any reasonable request just after he has made a good score or even a good shot where as a person seeking a favor when he is off his game might just swell ask President Coolidge to do the split.

I wish to state that having learned my lesson along these lines I did not use my knowledge to benefit myself alone but have on the other hand utilized same mostly to the advantage of others especially the members of Mr. Frisbie's own family. Mr. Frisbie's wife and son and daughter all realized early in my employment that I could handle Mr. Frisbie better than anyone else and without me ever exactly divulging the secret of my methods they just naturally began to take it for granted that I could succeed with him where they failed and it became their habit when they sought something from their respective spouse and father to summons me as their adviser and advocate.

As an example of the above I will first sight an example in connection with Mrs. Frisbie. This occurred many years ago and was the instance which convinced her beyond all doubt that I was a expert on the subject of managing her husband.

Mrs. Frisbie is a great lover of music but unable to perform on any instrument herself. It was her hope that one of the children would be a pianiste and a great deal of money was spent on piano lessons for both Robert the son and Florence the daughter but all in vain as neither of the two showed any talent and their teachers one after another gave them up in despair.

Mrs. Frisbie at last became desirous of purchasing a player piano and of course would consider none but the best but when she brooched the subject to Mr. Frisbie he turned a deaf ear as he said pianos were made to be played by hand and people who could not learn same did not deserve music in the home.

I do not know how often Mr. and Mrs. Frisbie disgust the matter pro and con.

Personally they disgust it in my presence any number of times and finally being a great admirer of music myself and seeing no reason why a man of Mr. Frisbie's great wealth should deny his wife a harmless pleasure such as a player piano I suggested to the madam that possibly if she would leave matters to me the entire proposition might be put over. I can no more than fail I told her and I do not think I will fail so she instructed me to go ahead as I could not do worse than fail which she had already done herself.

I will relate the success of my plan as briefly as possible. Between the house and the golf course there was a summer house in which Mrs. Frisbie sat reading while Mr. Frisbie played golf. In this summer house she could sit so as to not be visible from the golf course. She was to sit there till she heard me whistle the strains of "Over There" where at she was to appear on the scene like she had come direct from the house and the fruits of our scheme would then be known.

For two days Mrs. Frisbie had to console herself with her book as Mr. Frisbie's golf was terrible and there was no moment when I felt like it would not be courting disaster to summons her on the scene but during the 3rd. afternoon his game suddenly improved and he had shot the 1st. 9 holes in 53 and started out on the 10th. with a pretty drive when I realized the time had come.

Mrs. Frisbie appeared promptly in answer to my whistling and walked rapidly up to Mr. Frisbie like she had hurried from the house and said there is a man at the house from that player piano company and he says he will take $50.00 off the regular price if I order today and please let me order one as I want one so much.

"Why certainly dear go ahead and get it dear," said Mr. Frisbie and that is the way Mrs. Frisbie got her way in regards to a player piano. Had I not whistled when I did but waited a little longer it would have spelt ruination to our schemes as Mr. Frisbie took a 12 on the 11th. hole and would have bashed his wife over the head with a No. 1 iron had she even asked him for a toy drum.

I have been of assistance to young Mr. Robert Frisbie the son with reference to several items of which I will only take time to touch on one item with reference to Mr. Robert wanting to drive a car. Before Mr. Robert was 16 years of age he was always after Mr. Frisbie to allow him to drive one of the cars and Mr. Frisbie always said him nay on the grounds that it is against the law for a person under 16 years of age to drive a car.

When Mr. Robert reached the age of 16 years old however this excuse no longer held good and yet Mr. Frisbie continued to say Mr. Robert nay in regards to driving a car. There is plenty of chauffeurs at your beckon call said Mr. Frisbie to drive you where ever and when ever you wish to go but of course Mr. Robert like all youngsters wanted to drive himself and personally I could see no harm in it as I personally could not drive for him and the other 2 chauffeurs in Mr. Frisbie's employee at the time were just as lightly to wreck a car as Mr. Robert so I promised Mr. Robert that I would do my best towards helping him towards obtaining permission to drive one of the cars.

"Leave it to me" was my bequest to Mr. Robert and sure enough my little strategy turned the trick though Mr. Robert did not have the patience like his mother to wait in the summer house till a favorable moment arrived so it was necessary for me to carry through the entire proposition by myself.

The 16th. hole on our course is perhaps the most difficult hole on our course at least it has always been a variable tartar for Mr. Frisbie.

It is about 350 yards long in lenth and it is what is called a blind hole as you can not see the green from the tee as you drive from the tee up over a hill with a direction flag as the only guide and down at the bottom of the hill there is a brook a little over 225 yards from the tee which is the same brook which you come to again on the last hole and in all the times Mr. Frisbie has played around the course he has seldom never made this 16th. hole in less than 7 strokes or more as his tee shot just barely skins the top of the hill giving him a down hill lie which upsets him so that he will miss the 2d. shot entirely or top it and go in to the brook.

Well I generally always stand up on top of the hill to watch where his tee shot goes and on the occasion referred to he got a pretty good tee shot which struck on top of the hill and rolled half way down and I hurried to the ball before he could see me and I picked it up and threw it across the brook and when he climbed to the top of the hill I pointed to where the ball laid the other side of the brook and shouted good shot Mr. Frisbie. He was overjoyed and beamed with joy and did not suspect anything out of the way though in realty he could not hit a ball more than 160 yards if it was teed on the summit of Pike's Peak.

Fate was on my side at this junction and Mr. Frisbie hit a perfect mashie shot on to the green and sunk his 2d. put for the only 4 of his career on this hole. He was almost delirious with joy and you may be sure I took advantage of the situation and before we were fairly off the green I said to him Mr. Frisbie if you do not need me tomorrow morning do you not think it would be a good time for me to learn Mr. Robert to drive a car.

"Why certainly he is old enough now to drive a car and it is time he learned."

I now come to the main instance of my article which is in regards to Miss Florence Frisbie who is now Mrs. Henry Craig and of course Craig is not the real name but you will soon see that what I was able to do for her was no such childs play like gaining consent for Mr. Robert to run a automobile or Mrs. Frisbie to purchase a player piano but this was a matter of the up most importance and I am sure the reader will not consider me a vain bragger when I claim that I handled it with some skill.

Miss Florence is a very pretty and handsome girl who has always had a host of suiters who paid court to her on account of being pretty as much as her great wealth and I believe there has been times when no less than half a dozen or more young men were paying court to her at one time. Well about 2 years ago she lost her heart to young Henry Craig and at the same time Mr. Frisbie told her in no uncertain turns that she must throw young Craig over board and marry his own choice young Junior Holt or he would cut her off without a dime.

Holt and Craig are not the real names of the two young men referred to though I am using their real first names namely Junior and Henry. Young Holt is a son of Mr. Frisbie's former partner in business and a young man who does not drink or smoke and has got plenty of money in his own rights and a young man who any father would feel safe in trusting their daughter in the hands of matrimony. Young Craig at that time had no money and no position and his parents had both died leaving nothing but debts.

"Craig is just a tramp and will never amount to anything," said Mr. Frisbie. "I have had inquirys made and I understand he drinks when anyone will furnish him the drinks. He has never worked and never will. Junior Holt is a model young man from all accounts and comes of good stock and is the only young man I know whose conduct and habits are such that I would consider him fit to marry my daughter."

Miss Florence said that Craig was not a tramp and she loved him and would not marry anyone else and as for Holt he was terrible but even if he was not terrible she would never consider undergoing the bands of matrimony with a man named Junior.

"I will elope with Henry if you do not give in," she said.

Mr. Frisbie was not alarmed by this threat as Miss Florence has a little common sense and would not be lightly to elope with a young man who could hardly finance a honeymoon trip on the subway. But neither was she showing any sign of yielding in regards to his wishes in regards to young Holt and things began to take on the appearance of a dead lock between father and daughter with neither side showing any signs of yielding.

Miss Florence grew pale and thin and spent most of her time in her room instead of seeking enjoyment amongst her friends as was her custom. As for Mr. Frisbie he was always a man of iron will and things began to take on the appearance of a dead lock with neither side showing any signs of yielding.

It was when it looked like Miss Florence was on the verge of a serious illness when Mrs. Frisbie came to me and said we all realize that you have more influence with Mr. Frisbie than anyone else and is there any way you can think of to get him to change his status towards Florence and these 2 young men because if something is not done right away I am afraid of what will happen. Miss Florence likes you and has a great deal of confidence in you said Mrs. Frisbie so will you see her and talk matters over with her and see if you can not think up some plan between you which will put a end to this situation before my poor little girl dies.

So I went to see Miss Florence in her bedroom and she was a sad sight with her eyes red from weeping and so pale and thin and yet her face lit up with a smile when I entered the room and she shook hands with me like I was a long lost friend.

"I asked my mother to send you," said Miss Florence. "This case looks hopeless but I know you are a great fixer as far as Father is concerned and you can fix it if anyone can. Now I have got a idea which I will tell you and if you like it it will be up to you to carry it out."

"What is your idea?"

"Well," said Miss Florence, "I think that if Mr. Craig the man I love could do Father a favor why Father would not be so set against him."

"What kind of a favor?"

"Well Mr. Craig plays a very good game of golf and he might give Father some pointers which would improve Father's game."

"Your father will not play golf with anyone and certainly not with a good player and besides that your father is not the kind of a man that wants anyone giving him pointers. Personally I would just as leaf go up and tickle him as tell him that his stance is wrong."

"Then I guess my idea is not so good."

"No," I said and then all of a sudden I had an idea of my own. "Listen Miss Florence does the other one play golf?"

"Who?"

"Young Junior Holt."

"Even better than Mr. Craig."

"Does your father know that?"

"Father does not know anything about him or he would not like him so well."

Well I said I have got a scheme which may work or may not work but no harm to try and the first thing to be done is for you to spruce up and pretend like you do not feel so unkindly towards young Holt after all. The next thing is to tell your father that Mr. Holt never played golf and never even saw it played but would like to watch your father play so he can get the hang of the game.

And then after that you must get Mr. Holt to ask your father to let him follow him around the course and very secretly you must tip Mr. Holt off that your father wants his advice. When ever your father does anything wrong Mr. Holt is to correct him. Tell him your father is crazy to improve his golf but is shy in regards to asking for help. There is a lot of things that may happen to this scheme but if it should go through why I will guarantee that at least half your troubles will be over.

Well as I said there was a lot of things that might have happened to spoil my scheme but nothing did happen and the very next afternoon Mr. Frisbie confided in me that Miss Florence seemed to feel much better and seemed to have changed her mind in regards to Mr. Holt and also said that the last named had expressed a desire to follow Mr. Frisbie around the golf course and learn something about the game.

Mr. Holt was a kind of a fat pudgy young man with a kind of a sneering smile and the first minute I saw him I wished him the worst.

For a second before Mr. Frisbie started to play I was certain we were lost as Mr. Frisbie remarked where have you been keeping yourself Junior that you never watched golf before. But luckily young Holt took the remark as a joke and made no reply. Right afterwards the storm clouds began to gather in the sky. Mr. Frisbie sliced his tee shot.

"Mr. Frisbie," said young Holt, "there was several things the matter with you then but the main trouble was that you stood too close to the ball and cut across it with your club head and besides that you swang back faster than Alex Smith and you were off your balance and you gripped too hard and you jerked instead of hitting with a smooth follow through."

Well, Mr. Frisbie gave him a queer look and then made up his mind that Junior was trying to be humorous and he frowned at him so as he would not try it again but when we located the ball in the rough and Mr. Frisbie asked me for his spoon young Holt said Oh take your mashie Mr. Frisbie never use a wooden club in a place like that and Mr. Frisbie scowled and mumbled under his breath and missed the ball with his spoon and missed it again and then took a midiron and just dribbled it on to the fairway and finally got on the green in 7 and took 3 putts.

I suppose you might say that this was one of the quickest

golf matches on record as it ended on the 2d. tee. Mr. Frisbie tried to drive and sliced again. Then young Holt took a ball from my pocket and a club from the bag and said here let me show you the swing and drove the ball 250 yards straight down the middle of the course.

I looked at Mr. Frisbie's face and it was puffed out and a kind of a purple black color. Then he burst and I will only repeat a few of the more friendlier of his remarks.

"Get to hell and gone of my place. Do not never darken my doors again. Just show up around here one more time and I will blow out what you have got instead of brains. You lied to my girl and you tried to make a fool out of me. Get out before I sick my dogs on you and tear you to pieces."

Junior most lightly wanted to offer some word of explanation or to demand one on his own account but saw at a glance how useless same would be. I heard later that he saw Miss Florence and that she just laughed at him.

"I made a mistake about Junior Holt," said Mr. Frisbie that evening. "He is no good and must never come to this house again."

"Oh Father and just when I was beginning to like him," said Miss Florence.

Well like him or not like him she and the other young man Henry Craig were married soon afterwards which I suppose Mr. Frisbie permitted the bands in the hopes that same would rile Junior Holt.

Mr. Frisbie admitted he had made a mistake in regards to the last named but he certainly was not mistaken when he said that young Craig was a tramp and would never amount to anything.

Well I guess I have rambled on long enough about Mr. Frisbie.

As YOU PROBABLY KNOW, Westbrook Pegler first became famous as a sports writer. I've picked out a couple of his pieces touching on the sports scene.

COLLOQUY AT SECOND

By Westbrook Pegler

At one world series several years ago I happened to sit next to Johnny Evers for several days up there in the working press and got nicely acquainted with the spidery little man who, in his playing days, had been known to one and all as the Crab because of his many conflicts with the umpires, who often found it necessary in the interests of decorum to heave him out of ball games. Mr. Evers was such a pleasant and friendly person that at one point in the proceedings, when some athlete came out of the dust around second wagging his jaw at the umpire in apparent rage over a close decision, I flicked him lightly on what I thought might be a sensitive subject, namely his own temper.

Mr. Evers laughed and said that yes, of course, he had had some wrangles in his time but went on to say that after he had acquired his reputation as the Crab he sometimes imposed on the customers just to make them howl. Pointing out to the player who was just now stamping and jerking his arms at the umpire at second, Johnny said it was no sure thing that he was protesting at all, although the patrons were booing him on the assumption that he was.

Sometimes, Mr. Evers said, he would go into the bag in a slide, knowing he was out from here to yonder, and pop up like a terrier and stick his chin out in Hank O'Day's face and with sharp, jerky motions of his head yell: "Henry, you're dead right. I was out a mile."

Mr. O'Day would turn his back in that majestic way of umpires, walk a few steps with Johnny pursuing him, and then whirl on him with a measuring gesture of his arms and say, "Yes, John, he had you by that much."

Evers would stomp the ground and, with wider gestures of his arms, yell in Henry's face: "Oh, more than that, Hank. At least twice that. I didn't have a chance."

By this time the crowd would be all over Johnny for his

very poor sportsmanship in crabbing over a decision which, even to the naked eye of the customers and from a distance, was obviously fair.

Johnny would start away, dusting himself off, and then whirl and walk back to Henry.

"Hank," he would say, "how's the folks? Everybody well, I hope."

"Fine, fine, couldn't be better," Henry would say, towering over John and shaking his head. "Everybody okay with you?"

"No complaint, no complaint, thank the good Lord," Johnny would say.

John would start away again, stop, pick up a little dirt from the base line, wheel and, flinging the dirt to the ground, again would stick his chin into Hank's face and say, "Mighty glad your folks are well, Hank. Mighty glad to hear it."

Running out of small talk, Mr. Evers presently would drag himself back to the bench, turning once or twice on the way to yell back at Henry little remarks about the folks and the correctness of the decision on him just now.

Johnny said it was very funny the way a crowd could be monkeyed with and touched off into rages without cause. The customers, especially in New York, would want him thrown out of the game for crabbing, but Henry, or whoever the umpire was, couldn't very well heave a man for agreeing on a decision and inquiring after the family in the friendliest way. The umpire might turn his back and try to shrug him off but a player must be allowed a little latitude on the field and the mere turning of the back wouldn't stop Mr. Evers' courteous praises and inquiries. The alternative was to enter into the spirit of the thing and jaw back at him in the same cordial vein as thousands jeered. McGraw was in on the play but I don't believe he ever joined in because in a ball game he was always strictly a fighter and fraternizing with the enemy was outside his code.

My only excuse for writing all this is that it is coming into world series time again and Johnny, as I read lately, is very sick at his home in Albany and I don't believe this inner story of some of his scraps with the umpires which contributed to his reputation as a crab has ever been written before.

I don't believe it has any social significance, either. Does everything have to have social significance?

SIX-DAY RACE

By Westbrook Pegler

Of all the events on the calendar of sport, the only one which moves the patrons to serious thought is the vulgar six-day bike race, formerly the hoodlum's old home week but in recent years a festival of somewhat wider social scope. In the years that I know of only by hearsay the six-day bike races at the old Garden were reunions of picturesque thugs from the Bowery and other unpleasant parts of town, according to the reminiscences, usually delivered with a sigh, of my informants among the generation that is beginning to dodder and pine. I suspect that they exaggerate largely in several departments of their recollections, because one of the men whom they name to me as a very bad man of the old six-day bicycle races is still present about the bikes and the fights and is proprietor of a cheap little drum in Greenwich Village, catering to the out-of-town trade, for whom he poses as an underworld character. A professional underworld character is something like a circus Indian, however, and if you press any of the older generation to name you one man that this character ever killed or one instance of his having stood up trading gunfire with anybody, they cannot name you one or remember any particular incident that earned his reputation for him. I would not deny him his reputation, however, for that is his living now, that and his elephant ears, acquired when he was a preliminary fighter in the old sawdust clubs, and a nose with warts on it as big as a dill pickle. Ignorant, frowsy, and harmless, he looks bad, but so does Man Mountain Dean, and the pair of them work at it.

In my time the old social character of the six-day bike race has changed, and now it is changing again. Tex Rickard wrought the first great change when he promoted slumming parties of the new crop of stock-market aristocrats to attend the shows in the little hours of the morning, when there was nowhere to go but home. It was an affectation on their part in the first place, just as their love of the prize fights was an affectation, but they remained to be fascinated, because, I tell you, the six-day bike race is something to make even brokers sink up to their ankles in philosophical reflections and think and think and think.

The six-day bike race has always been a routine sport-page story, to be covered with a pretty fair lick on opening night, then dropped down to a little head for a couple of days and then brought up again to a climax on closing night. But along toward midweek it was customary to assign some feature writer from the city side to get at the real hidden meaning of the thing, the significance, as it were, which the sport writers, being just a lot of graduate office boys, could not detect. There is a city-side type of writer who reads fifty-cent magazines with dirty words and no pictures in them who can see things in their relation to life and civilization and all such, and they took many a hack at the six-day bike race to interpret it to the better class of readers. Finally, in the happy days when there was plenty of city-room budget, some of the editors took to hiring great big middle-name magazine writers to do extra-special interpretations.

And what do you think the bike race did to them?

It made them think too.

It made them think the same sort of thoughts that Rickard's dudes thought, and the fight managers and professional underworld characters and song pluggers and the naïve plagiarists who write the songs, generally stealing them from one another, but sometimes, with rare industry, going back to the masters for their material. It made them think that the six-day bike race, scoff at it though you may, is just a mocking, ironic caricature of life itself. Your life, my life, the life of everyone who goes to the office or the job, day after day, year after year, until, at last, the bell rings. Then where are you? The six-day bike racer is just where he began. He has traveled a long way, hustling furiously at times, but when it is all over he hasn't gone anywhere.

So we had many an extra-special significance piece with three names over it, like Empringham Osborne Which, famous magazine writer, or Emmeline Jasmine What, celebrated novelist, telling us exactly what all the boys of all the social groups at the six-day bike race had been thinking all along, which was a general idea that we come from nowhere and positively must go back there and, therefore, what is the big hurry?

I have seen this theme thought of the six-day bike race done into pieces that were billed as stark, human documents, and recognized it as precisely the same idea that the regular sport-page hands had muttered back and forth through the cigarette smoke and garlic fumes as they sat with their feet on the rail after the copy had cleared for the office, long after midnight. Everybody thinks it. It cannot be escaped, because there it goes on before you, and it is always alike. People riding around and around, jamming, hurting themselves, grinding themselves to get where? Well, where do you think all this jamming and suffering and grinding is going to get you? People sit and look at the bikes hour after silent hour.

The theme thought of the bike race may not be very profound, but it is thought nevertheless, and people do not think at football games or fights or whatever else on the sport program. So, as an intellectual event, it stands alone in the sport business, the show that makes people think.

In recent years Frank Sullivan hasn't been working very energetically at the trade of humorist, though there was a time when he was pretty close to the top of the heap. Nowadays Mr. Sullivan is a sort of crusader. He is a crusader on the correct team, but that doesn't alleviate the distress some of us feel when we think about him. Writing a column in the newspaper *PM*, he comes up now and then with an attempt to recapture the old zing, but it ain't there. Apparently depressing shadowgraphs of people like Hamilton Fish and Clare Luce and Burton K. Wheeler keep flashing before his eyes as he sits at his typewriter, obliterating the old light touch. It's too bad, but it seems to happen time and again. The years accumulate and the funnyman gets to pondering over Life and Mankind and the next thing you know he's stumbling along in the wake of Dorothy Thompson, heaving rubber-headed javelins at the foe.

Back in the days when he was a humorist untroubled by cosmic indignations, Frank Sullivan turned out some classic stuff. Some of his cockeyed essays are so familiar to book readers ("The Vanderbilt Convention," for example) that I wouldn't consider reprinting them here. The story that follows is not, I believe, as well known as many of his shorter pieces.

LOVE MAKES THE FILLY GO

A Race-Track Story to End All Race-Track Stories

By Frank Sullivan

ZULEIKA'S HEAD drooped and she gazed upon the world with a jaundiced eye. Stifling a sob, she nibbled a shred of wood from a stanchion. It soothed her lately to eat wood.

It would have seemed to the casual observer that no filly at Saratoga had less reason to chew wood than Zuleika. Everything that makes for the happiness of the average horse was hers. She was only two, yet she was the bright particular star, the expectancy and rose of the stable of Eric Dwindle, youthful heir to the Dwindle headache-powder millions. Fame, fortune, family, beauty, youth, health—all were hers. Except the one thing she wanted more than anything else in the world.

Love was denied Zuleika.

On the racing programs she was described as a "Br f, 2," but so dazzling a creature as Zuleika cannot be dismissed by calling her a "Br f, 2," and letting it go at that. "Br f, 2" gave no hint of the sheen of her coat, a coat the color of a cup of coffee—very best grade—to which a tablespoon of heavy cream had been added, or possibly two tablespoonfuls. It gave no idea of the bewitching curve of her jugular groove, throat latch, and windpipe. It gave no hint of the elegance of her neatly turned fetlock, nor did it convey one whit of the charm of her muzzle, kneepan, hock, gaskin, or croup.

Not only in love but in love beneath her station. Not only in love beneath her station but vainly in love beneath her station. Spurned by a harrow puller. That was the pass to which the proud filly who was the favorite in the approaching Posterity Stakes had come. She sighed and took another nibble of soft pine.

A month previously Zuleika had come to Saratoga heart-whole and fancy-free. It was on a morning shortly after her arrival that she first saw Dan. She was having her usual morning workout. He was pulling a harrow around the track.

She paid no attention to him. He was just another horse. Perhaps not even that, for Zuleika, in the unthinking arrogance born of the knowledge of her own superior position in the social scale, might at that moment have questioned the right of a harrow puller to be termed a horse in the finer sense of the word, as exemplified by herself and the members of her set.

The second time she saw Dan he struck her eye. She noticed that he stood out from all the other horses on the racecourse, and not a few of the men. There was something fine and clean and true about him. The third time she saw him their eyes met. An electric something passed from her fetlock to her withers, and she knew that she was hopelessly in love.

After that day she was disturbingly aware of Dan's nearness when he was near, and of his farness when he was far. They spoke no word to each other, yet such is the magical telegraphy of love, she knew that he knew, and she knew that he knew that she knew. And he knew too.

Zuleika broke the ice one July morning by nodding. Dan bowed courteously in return. Slowly their love ripened into friendship. Every morning a little chat, quite formal, confined to trivia about the weather, the condition of the track, and suchlike small talk. It wasn't much, but it was better than nothing.

Her new-found happiness showed in her work. She skimmed about the course like a bird, breaking track records as casually as though they were champagne goblets crashed into the fireplace by hussars toasting the czar. Uncle Bill Spellacy, her trainer, was beside himself with joy, although not aware of the cause of her delirium. A lovable old fellow, Uncle Bill had been around horses almost since the invention of the spavin, and he knew them backward. He had his heart set on Zuleika winning the Posterity, not only for her sake but because he wanted it to be a proper swan song for his own career. He planned to retire at the close of the Saratoga meeting and devote his remaining years to his hobby, automobile racing. Above all, he wanted Zuleika to show her heels in the Posterity to the Vamp, the champion that had swept all before her in the West and had now come East to scalp Zuleika.

After a time Zuleika began to find friendship rather dull stuff. Courteous whinnies about the condition of the track are all right as far as they go, but they don't go far when a filly is in love. The condition of the track was a matter of indifference to Zuleika at the moment. What she wanted was to pillow her muzzle on Dan's broad withers and hear him whisper into her ear the three words that would make her the happiest equine in the world.

The trouble was he would never say them. He was a harrow puller, but he was proud. He knew his place. In a month Zuleika would be leaving Saratoga, moving on to fresh triumphs at Belmont Park. She might never see him again. Perish this intolerable thought! She decided to act.

One morning after a night spent pacing her stall, she faced Dan on the track.

"Dan," she said.

"Zuleika."

Her name, on his lips. Her heart leaped into her windpipe.

"Dan, I have something to say to you."

"Zuleika." He made as if to interrupt.

"Dan," she hurried on, pawing the earth nervously, "we—you—I—things can't go on like this."

"Zuleika, please."

"No, hear me out, Dan. I love you." She hung her head in pretty confusion. "There. You have made me say it." She smiled up at him. "I knew you never would, so I pocketed my pride."

"Zuleika."

"Yes, Dan."

"I wish you had not spoken."

"Why?"

"It can never be."

For a moment there was silence. It was she who spoke first.

"You mean there is another?" asked Zuleika quietly.

Dan seemed to be in the throes of a severe inward struggle. He pawed the earth. His eyes rolled. He twitched and shuddered, and his tail swished violently. He spoke.

"Yes," he said, "there is."

Zuleika's color changed from brown to bay.

"I see," she said, keeping a stiff upper lip. "I'm sorry—I—your actions had led me to believe—I thought that we——"

"Zuleika," said Dan.

Suddenly she turned on him.

"Stop calling me Zuleika!" she cried. "I hate you! I hate you!" With that she fled.

"Zuleika!" cried Dan.

In her workout the next morning Zuleika did six furlongs in 3.26 ⅖, which was a new unofficial track record for the slow-motion pictures. Uncle Bill Spellacy followed her to her stall in dismay.

"Gosh all Friday, Zuleika, what's the matter with you?" he cried.

For answer she pillowed her head on his comfortable shoulder and burst into a storm of weeping.

"Oh, Uncle Bill, I'm so miserable."

"Tell Uncle Bill about it," said Mr. Spellacy, for, as we have seen, he understood horses.

She told him about Dan. Uncle Bill whistled softly.

"Mr. Dwindle must not hear a word of this," he said.

"Who?"

"Mr. Dwindle. Your owner."

"You mean the little fellow with no chin? The one that's afraid of us horses?"

"Yes."

"Oh, him."

Zuleika had known that someone owned her and the rest of the stable, but had never given the matter much thought.

"He'll be furious if he finds out," said Uncle Bill. "He's socially ambitious, you know, and he's at a point now where mésalliance on the part of himself or any of his horses might bar the doors of Newport, Tuxedo, and Palm Beach to him forever. And you pick this moment to fall in love with a harrow puller!"

"I'll not hear a word against Dan," said Zuleika with spirit.

"I understand, honey," said Uncle Bill. "I've been in love myself. I can see now. It was back in '78. She was as fair——"

"Uncle Bill," said Zuleika, "do you think by any chance it's the Vamp he's in love with?"

"Oh posh!" said Uncle Bill. "He don't even know her."

"Is that so? Well, I've seen them talking together several times since she got here."

"It's probably platonic. I'll find out. Now, Zuleika, don't you worry. Everything will come out all right. The important thing now is for you to go out there Saturday and win that Posterity, Dan or no Dan."

"I'm sorry, Uncle Bill; I shan't win the Posterity."

"Not win the Posterity! Zuleika, what are you saying?"

"I can't help it, Uncle Bill. I don't feel it—here."

She bent her lovely head toward her heart.

"I don't think I shall ever win anything again," she said sadly.

Uncle Bill saw there was no use trying to reason with her at the moment. He withdrew.

"Drat!" he swore to himself as he left her stall. "Won't win the Posterity. Chewing wood. In love with a harrow puller. And he spurns her." Uncle Bill began to get mad! "Why, the insufferable bounder! What does he mean by spurning Zuleika? Where is he? I'll see about this!"

Uncle Bill went in search of Dan. He found him trudging down the backstretch, pulling his harrow. There was the hint of a droop to the splendid shoulders, a weary look in the fine eyes.

"May I have a word with your horse?" Uncle Bill asked Dan's driver.

"Certainly, certainly," said the driver, recognizing the famous trainer.

"In private, if you don't mind," Uncle Bill requested.

"Oh, pardon me," said the driver, withdrawing to a discreet distance.

"Your name is Dan?" asked Uncle Bill.

"Yes sir, it is."

"I am William Spellacy, the famous trainer."

"I know."

There was a simple dignity about the horse that impressed Uncle Bill in spite of himself.

"I'm not going to mince matters, Dan," said Uncle Bill. "I'll be brief and to the point. Is what I hear about you and my Br f, 2, Zuleika, true?"

"Yes, it is."

"You turned her down, eh?"

"I wouldn't put it that way, Mr. Spellacy."

"Ain't she good enough for you?"

"Not good enough for me! Zuleika!"

Dan laughed, a hollow, mocking laugh of despair.

"By Jove," thought Spellacy, "here is a horse that has suffered."

"Mr. Spellacy, I love Zuleika."

"Then why——"

"She is dearer to me than life itself."

"But you told her——"

"I made up that story on the spur of the moment. I did it for her sake. There is no other filly. There never has been. There never will be. There never could be. There never——"

"I know," said Uncle Bill. "You decided she and you were as far apart as the poles and that your love could lead only to tragedy."

"Yes. I couldn't give her all—that." With a swish of his tail Dan indicated the palatial Dwindle stables in the distance.

Uncle Bill found himself liking the harrow puller a great deal.

"I understand, Dan," he said, and there was a suspicious dewiness in his eye. "I was in love myself once. It was in '78. She——"

"Zuleika is destined for great things, Mr. Spellacy," said Dan. "While I am only a harrow puller."

"She loves you."

"I know," said Dan brokenly.

"Don't take it too hard, Dan. I remember, that time I was in love——"

"I thought I was acting for the best," said Dan sadly. "I tried to do the decent thing. But I see it all now. I was wrong in my stubborn pride. I have been a fool—a fool. Has she mentioned my name, Mr. Spellacy?"

"Yes, she has."

"What did she say?" asked Dan eagerly.

"If she never sees you again it will be too soon, she says."

Dan smiled.

"Even in her despair at what she thinks is the loss of my love she has not forgotten her sense of humor," he said.

"She keeps chewing wood," said Uncle Bill, "and she says she won't win the Posterity!"

"Zuleika not win the Posterity! Nonsense! Why, she's got to win the Posterity!"

"Allows as how she won't," said Uncle Bill. "Says she don't feel it—here. You're to blame, of course."

Dan groaned.

"She thinks you're in love with the Vamp," said Uncle Bill.

"Me, in love with the Vamp! Why, I scarcely know her. Just pass the time of day with her occasionally. . . . Say!"

Suddenly Dan became lost in thought. He remained there for a moment. When he reappeared he was excited.

"Mr. Spellacy, Zuleika is going to win the Posterity. Listen."

"It won't work," said Uncle Bill when Dan had finished detailing his plan.

"It will," said Dan. "I know Zuleika, and it will work."

"Do you really think so?"

"I know so, Mr. Spellacy."

"Well, what can we lose?" mused Uncle Bill.

"I tell you we won't lose."

"Dan, I'll do it."

"Good for you, Mr. Spellacy. Now you'll have to arrange matters so that I can do my part. My time isn't my own, as you know. I am more or less a slave to this harrow. We haven't much time. Three days. The Posterity is being run Saturday."

"I'll fix everything," said Uncle Bill. "I'll arrange to get you Saturday afternoon off."

Uncle Bill and Dan went about their mysterious plans and Zuleika remained in the wood-chewing trance in which we found her at the beginning of our story.

Saturday afternoon found a tremendous crowd assembled at the famous old racecourse. One writer, describing the scene, stated without hesitation that it was a record-breaking throng. A second, not to be outdone, characterized the event as a gala occasion. Racing was freely referred to as the sport of kings.

The grandstands, paddocks, and lawns were filled with devotees of the sport of kings in holiday mood. The clubhouse was crammed with the cream of society. In one box alone—that of Mrs. C. Dettrington Tufft, the soap heiress—there were four princesses, each one of them every inch a princess, too; so that, assuming the height of the average well-nourished princess to be five feet eight and a half inches, you had two hundred and seventy-four inches of simon-pure princess in that one box alone. The situation was almost as exciting in other boxes.

A half hour before the Posterity post time Zuleika was led to the copse in the paddock where she was to be saddled. She had always been a great favorite of the crowd because of her born showmanship. She liked the acclaim of the multitude, and usually showed it by prancings, curvettings, spirited neighings, and graceful postures, interspersed with an occasional kick, often planted—with a disregard for authority which was part of her charm—on the person of some august racing official.

Today it was obvious that she was not herself. Her head drooped. She surveyed the gay scene with an aloof melancholy and her tail hung listlessly at its mooring. Not once did she kick anyone, although several splendid opportunities presented themselves. At one moment Tommy Spree, the millionaire playboy, was having his picture taken with his seventh financée for that year, within three feet of Zuleika's hoofs, and she never rose to the bait. On seeing this, many of her fans shook their heads sorrowfully and rushed off to wager their all on the Vamp.

Uncle Bill Spellacy hovered about nervously. He seemed to be waiting for something to happen.

In the clump of birches where the Vamp was being saddled the scene was quite different. Here all was gaiety and confidence. The Vamp was a handsome filly, and a large crowd had gathered about her as she held court in her clump. And among those prominent in the crowd was Eric Dwindle! Race fans were electrified when they heard him say, distinctly and with enthusiasm, "By Jove, she looks like a winner to me. Yesterday I didn't think she had a chance."

Instantly the word spread throughout the racecourse that Eric Dwindle had conceded the defeat of Zuleika. Pandemonium reigned, and the stewards were considering an official rebuke to Dwindle for such unsportsmanlike and premature surrender, when it developed that Mr. Dwindle had joined the Vamp's court under the impression that she was Zuleika.

"All horses look alike to me; I never could tell one from another," he explained, laughing, as he was led over to Zuleika's copse.

Uncle Bill continued nervous. He was standing first on one leg, then on another, like a stork waiting for a call. He cast frequent glances toward the Vamp's clump. Then he suddenly saw something that moved him violently. The crowd around the Vamp had cleared momentarily. Uncle Bill's face lit up. He turned hastily to Zuleika and whispered, quickly but casually, "Wonder who that handsome work horse is, talking to the Vamp?" He had to say it twice before Zuleika lifted her head and gazed languidly toward the Vamp's corner.

She stiffened. Something seemed to have happened to Zuleika; something not unlike, let us say, a thousand volts of electricity.

"It's Dan!" she managed to snort in Uncle Bill's ear.

"Is that Dan?" said Uncle Bill innocently. "He's not a bad-looking horse, for a harrow puller. I guess you were right about the Vamp, Zuleika."

Zuleika's answer was to look about her carefully, get the range, and plant a carefully aimed kick on Mr. Dwindle with such force that only an intervening wallet saved him from a permanent dent. Uncle Bill was overjoyed. It was the first sign of animation Zuleika had shown since the day of her showdown with Dan.

The bugle sounded for the parade to the post. The Vamp passed, escorted by and engaged in animated conversation with Dan. Zuleika tossed her head unconcernedly and looked straight through them both. Uncle Bill winked at Dan, who winked at Uncle Bill.

On the way to the post Zuleika was suddenly her old gay self. Eric Dwindle trained his field glasses on her, decided she must be the Vamp, and whispered to Uncle Bill a concession of Zuleika's defeat. Uncle Bill smiled. Sports lovers who had wagered their all on the Vamp after noting Zuleika's failure to kick Mr. Spree gazed upon the rejuvenated Zuleika with delight and scurried off to rewager their all on her. Her odds dropped like a barometer before a monsoon.

At the post she was the life of the party. She would show Dan how little she cared. She popped her jockey off twice, with a graceful arching of her back. She kicked the assistant starters whenever possible, and plunged the starter, Mr. Delehanty, into a frenzy by her antics. She broke away once and capered halfway around the course. See if she cared!

At last that tenth of a second came when they were all quiet for a fifteenth of a second. Mr. Delehanty hastily pressed a button and shouted, "W-o-o-mp!" or something that sounded like that. The barrier flew up. The gong sounded. And the age-old cry of the turf rang through the historic park: "They're off!"

And so they were. All except one. Zuleika. She had been left at the post.

A groan went up from the record-breaking throng. But it was too late now for them to re-rewager their all on the Vamp. Zuleika stood, cool as a cucumber. A cloud of dust in the distance indicated the rest of the horses. A slight commotion in front of the clubhouse marked the spot where Uncle Bill Spellacy had sunk to the ground in a swoon. Other Zuleika fans joined him almost immediately. Dan had ceased winking.

"Who's that left at the post?" inquired Mr. Dwindle.

"The Vamp," replied a tactful, though mendacious, friend.

Mr. Delehanty had been mopping his brow in relief. He emerged from behind the bandanna and saw Zuleika. He had thought he had got them all off to a good clean start She leered at him mischievously. With a cry of baffled rag Mr. Delehanty seized a club, leaped from the starter's plat form, and made for her, but she was too quick for him. Wit a flirt of her tail she was off. Her jockey, taken unaware had just time to grab her mane and hang on for dear life. A roar went up from the crowd. Approximately a hundre more race fans swooned.

"She's off!" "She's gaining!" "Come on, you Zuleika "She's caught 'em!" and then, "She's passed 'em!" as Zuleik with no great effort, overtook her colleagues and, passin wide on the turn, saluted the Vamp with a smile of scor

In another few seconds Zuleika was out in front, running alone.

"She's leading by a furlong!" shouted a fan.

"Who is?" demanded Eric Dwindle anxiously.

"The Vamp," lied a disgruntled sports lover in the next box, and it must have been a petty gratification he derived from the ensuing spectacle of poor Mr. Dwindle sliding from his chair in a syncope. Others continued to faint as the excitement waxed.

Zuleika, a furlong and a half ahead of her rivals, spied a bed of fresh young daisies. With a suddenness that sent her jockey sliding into her mane, she stopped, thrust her head inside the rail, and began to munch daisies leisurely. A roar went up from the crowd. The rest of the field swept by. Zuleika nodded casually at them and threw a wickedly sweet smile at the Vamp. The Vamp threw back a look that should have cremated Zuleika.

Emory Minton, the racing expert who was broadcasting the event, was rapidly coming to a boil.

"What a race, ladies and gentlemen," he told the vast radio audience. "Oh boy! I wish you folks could just see this race. Probably never been a race like this in the history of the American turf. It's more like the type they have in Eng-and. Oh boy! Zuleika's stopped. The rest of the field is a urlong ahead. Looks like the rest of the field would win asy. What's that? Zuleika's off. Yes, there she goes. She's ff. Look at the colt—I mean that mare—I mean that filly—o! What a race! People are fainting around here like flies.)-o-p, there goes Mrs. Sneeden Twedd, of Newport. What nose dive she took! There goes Alicia Serrington Caulfield, e twine heiress, out like a light, followed by her financé, ord Twigg of Twigg. Let's see what's going on out there the track. Where's Zuleika?"

Zuleika, replete with daisies, had started after her com-des again and was tearing around the turn into the back-etch. The Vamp, well ahead of the field, cast troubled nces behind to locate Zuleika. The rest of the horses emed confused but kept on running. At the turn into the etch Zuleika was again abreast of the pack. A second later she was neck and neck with the Vamp. The crowd roared.

"WHat a race!" screamed the broadcaster. "I wish you folks could see this race. I don't know what's happening. They're in the stretch. Zuleika and the Vamp are neck and neck. It's a duel. Hup, what's that? Zuleika's down! The Vamp tripped her! Zuleika's jockey has landed safely on top of a furlong pole. Folks, it looks like the Vamp's race. Zuleika's up! No, she's down! She's up! She's down! She's up! She's gone back to get her jockey. He's up! He's on! She's off! She's running on three legs! She's gaining! She's caught 'em! She's neck and neck with the Vamp again. They're fighting it out down the last furlong. There will now be a brief pause for station announcements. . . ."

"Bing, bo-ong, bo-o-ong. Ladies and gentlemen, this is Station WWT at Saugerties, New York. This program is also broadcast internationally by W3Z2M. The time is now eleven seconds before five, by courtesy of the McGrath Sun Dial Company. We now return you to the Saratoga race track, where Emory Minton is broadcasting a description of the sixty-fourth annual running of the historic Posterity Stakes."

". . . And here they come, folks! Zuleika and the Vamp fighting it out at the finish—a-a-nd the winner is——"

The vast radio audience heard no more from Emory Minton that day. The strain had been too much. He had fainted.

As Zuleika and the Vamp crossed the finish line no roar went up from the record-breaking throng. No roar could. The most exciting race that had ever taken place in the history of the American turf had taken its toll. Everyone had fainted.

Everyone except Uncle Bill Spellacy and a few peculiar men who had sat all through the race with their backs to the horses, doing crossword puzzles. They were the members of the famous Keep Your Shirt On Club, stoics who made it a practice to attend all major sports events without getting hysterical. At championship prize fights they were invariably to be found in ringside seats arranging their stamp collections while the reigning heavyweight champ was being knocked out. At world series games it was their custom ıire two or three of the best boxes and play chess during the :rucial innings.

Only Uncle Bill actually saw the finish. Having been the ırst to swoon, he was the first to revive, just in time to see ᷊uleika sweep across the finish line a length ahead of the /amp.

He rushed to the track as Zuleika limped back.

"Zuleika!" he shouted. "You did it, old girl! . . . Why, ᷊uleika, you're hurt!"

"It's nothing," said Br f, 2, sliding quietly to the ground ı a faint.

When she came to, Dan was bending over her.

"You!" she said weakly but scornfully.

"Zuleika, I can explain everything," interposed Uncle Bill astily. And he did. He told her the true state of Dan's feel-ıgs toward her, and of the harrow puller's willingness to ·crifice himself for her. He told her how Dan's interest the Vamp had been simply a clever ruse to play on uleika's jealousy and goad her into winning the Posterity.

"And you must admit it worked," said Uncle Bill happily.

"Is all this true?" said Zuleika, lifting her great brown eyes Dan.

"It is, Zuleika."

"Then you do love me?"

"You are more to me than life itself."

"Oh, Dan, I am the happiest horse in the world."

"Mr. Dwindle," said the veterinarian who had been ex-ıining Zuleika's leg during this scene, "this filly will never :e again. Bowed tendon. You won't have to shoot her, but u'll have to turn her out to grass for the rest of her days."

"That's all right with me," said Mr. Dwindle cordially. m never going to race again either. What's the use? I can't l one horse from another. They don't like me. They're vays biting me, or kicking me, or neighing right in my :e. They call it neighing but I call it laughing. And there's nething about a horse's neigh that sends cold shivers up spine, like people cracking their knuckles, or rubbing ıcils across glass. At the races I never can tell who's win-ıg; I'm always looking through the wrong end of these confounded field glasses. The game just isn't worth the candle as far as I'm concerned. . . . Spellacy, you said you were going in for automobile racing when you got back to New York."

"That was my intention, sir."

"I'm going along with you. At least automobiles don't whinny."

"Uncle Bill," said Zuleika, "does this mean I won't have to race again?"

"I'm afraid it does, honey."

"You're afraid?"

"Yes. When the Vamp tripped you I guess she finished your racing career, all right."

"And I can stay here in Saratoga with Dan forever and a day?"

"I don't see why not."

"Well then, all I can say is, bless the Vamp's kind old heart. Dan!"

"Yes, dear!"

"Where's that harrow of ours?"

And the record-breaking throng, which by this time wa practically one hundred per cent revived, roared.

HERBERT ASBURY is one of the most competent research me in the writing business. His wonderful books about the gang of New York, old New Orleans, Chicago, and San Fran cisco suggest that he loves nothing better than library prow ing.

The following article comes from a book of his short pieces and it is one of those things that I find myself goin back to read again and again. It is an account of one of th great practical jokes of all time. I don't know why I inclu it in the Sports Department. It fits here as well as anyplac and some people might consider practical joking to be spo

THE SAWING OFF OF MANHATTAN ISLAND

By Herbert Asbury

ONE OF THE MOST extraordinary hoaxes ever perpetrated in New York originated a little more than a hundred years ago in the fertile imagination of a little dried-up old man named Lozier, who had amassed a competence as a carpenter and contractor and had then retired to enjoy life. For almost two months during the summer of 1824 Lozier's fantastic activities, which he carried on with the enthusiastic assistance of John DeVoe, a retired butcher better known as Uncle John, kept a considerable portion of middle- and lower-class New York in a veritable frenzy of excitement. In later years Uncle John's nephew, Thomas F. DeVoe, an honored member of the New York Historical Society and himself a prosperous butcher of Civil War days, incorporated an account of the hoax in his two-volume work: *The Market Book, Containing a Historical Account of the Public Markets in the Cities of New York, Boston, Philadelphia, and Brooklyn, with a Brief Description of Every Article of Human Food Sold Therein, the Introduction of Cattle in America and Notices of Many Remarkable Specimens, et cetera, et cetera, et cetera.*

In those early days, when the present American metropolis was a comparatively small city of not more than a hundred and fifty thousand population, a favorite loafing place was the old Centre Market at Grand, Baxter, and Centre Streets. A dozen long benches lined the Grand Street side of the market, and every afternoon from spring to winter they were filled with amateur statesmen, principally retired butchers and other such small businessmen, most of whom combined scant knowledge with excessive gullibility. Chief among them were Lozier and Uncle John DeVoe, and of these two venerable jokesters, Lozier was the leader. He did most of the talking at the daily forums in front of the market and was invariably able to produce a definite and apparently practicable remedy for every conceivable financial, political, or economic ill. He was always listened to with enormous respect, for he was wealthy, he possessed more education than his fellows and was therefore better able to express himself, and he was a recognized traveler, having made several voyages to Europe as a ship's carpenter. There was no lack of subjects to talk about, for those were wondrous times. The first great wave of Irish immigration had begun to beat against American shores as a result of the potato famine of 1822; Brazil and Mexico had thrown off the shackles of Portugal and Spain; the first steamship had crossed the Atlantic only a few years before; President James Monroe had just promulgated the Monroe Doctrine; and Mrs. Monroe had almost precipitated a revolution in New York and Washington society by announcing that as the first lady of the land she would no longer return social calls. The gifted Lozier professed to know the inside stories of all these momentous events, and so convincing was he that there were many who believed that he was high in the confidence not only of the President but of foreign potentates as well.

Early in July 1824 Lozier was absent from his accustomed bench for several days, an unparalleled occurrence which aroused much comment. When he returned he refused to join in the flow of conversation and even declined to settle arguments. He talked only to Uncle John DeVoe, and for the most part sat alone, brooding, obviously concerned with weighty matters. When his friends asked where he had been, and sought diligently to learn what mighty thoughts troubled his mind, he would at first divulge no information. At length, however, he admitted that he had been at City Hall in consultation with Mayor Stephen Allen. No one doubted the truth of this statement, which caused even more talk than had his absence. In those days the mayor of New York was a personage of impressive dignity; he was not so approachable as now, and a man who had been summoned by His Honor automatically became a person of considerable importance. For almost a week Lozier kept his friends and admirers on tenterhooks of curiosity. Finally, one day when all the market benches were occupied and he was thus assured of an audience worthy of his talents, he made a full and complete explanation.

It appeared that Lozier and Mayor Allen had had a long conversation about Manhattan Island and had reached the conclusion that it was much too heavy on the Battery end, because of the many large buildings. The situation was rapidly becoming dangerous. Already the island had begun to sag, as was plain from the fact that it was all downhill from City Hall, and there were numerous and alarming indications that it might break off and sink into the sea, with appalling losses of life and property. Lozier and the mayor had decided, therefore, that the island must be sawed off at Kingsbridge, at the northern end, and turned around, so that the Kingsbridge end would be where the Battery end had been for ages. The Battery end, of course, if it did not fall off in transit, would take the place of the Kingsbridge end. Once the turn had been made, the weaker end of the island would be anchored to the mainland, thus averting the danger of collapse.

When the conferences at City Hall began, it further appeared, Lozier and Mayor Allen were not in complete agreement as to the best method of accomplishing the mighty task. The mayor thought that before Manhattan could be turned around it would be necessary to detach Long Island from its moorings and tow it out of the way, returning it later to its proper place. Lozier finally convinced him, however, that there was ample space in the harbor and the bay. It was at length decided, therefore, simply to saw Manhattan Island off, float it down past Governors and Ellis islands, turn it around, and then float it back to its new position. For political reasons Mayor Allen wished the job to appear as a private undertaking and had turned the whole project over to Lozier, instructing him to employ the necessary labor and to superintend the work.

Such were the force of Lozier's personality, the power of his reputation, and the credulity of his generation that practically none who heard him thought of questioning the feasibility of the scheme. The few who were inclined to scoff were soon silenced, if not actually convinced, by his earnestness, and by the acclaim which had greeted the announcement of the project. Everyone realized at once that it was truly a gigantic plan, but they had Lozier's word for it that it could be accomplished. Moreover, as Lozier pointed out, the construction of the famous Erie Canal, which was then nearing completion, had once been called impossible even by competent engineers, and much derision had greeted the prediction that steamships would one day cross the ocean. If man could run a river through the very heart of a mountain, and if he could cause a simple steam engine to propel a gigantic boat, why couldn't he saw off an island? Nobody knew the answer, and Lozier's story was swallowed in toto, hook, line, and sinker.

Sawing Manhattan Island off soon became the principal subject of argument and conversation at Centre Market, and elsewhere as news of the great project spread. Neither then nor later, however, did the few newspapers of the period pay any attention to Lozier's activities. It is doubtful if the editors ever heard of him, for in those days the only way of transmitting intelligence was by word of mouth, or by letter, which was even more uncertain. Important happenings in one part of the city did not become generally known for weeks or months, and frequently not at all. And Grand Street then was as far uptown as the farthest reaches of the Bronx are today.

A few days after he had started the ball rolling Lozier appeared at Centre Market with a huge ledger, in which he proposed to record the names of all applicants for jobs, pending an examination to determine their fitness. This and other clerical work which developed during the progress of the hoax was the special care of Uncle John DeVoe, who ceremoniously set down the names, ages, and places of residence of all who applied. Work was none too plentiful that year, and laborers, many of them recently arrived Irishmen, answered Lozier's call in such numbers that the big ledger soon bore the names of some three hundred men, all eager to begin the great work of sawing off Manhattan Island.

Lozier further aroused confidence in his scheme by notifying various butchers of his acquaintance to begin assembling the enormous herds of cattle, droves of hogs, and flocks of chickens which would be necessary to feed his army of workmen. He estimated that he would require at once five hundred head of cattle, an equal number of hogs, and at least three thousand chickens. He was especially anxious to obtain as many fowls as possible, for he had definitely promised that all who obtained jobs would have chicken dinners twice a week. There was great excitement among the butchers, the immediate effect of which was an increase in the prices of all sorts of meat. One enterprising butcher had in his pens fifty fat hogs awaiting slaughter, and to make certain of a sale to Lozier he drove them north and penned them near Kingsbridge, where he fed them for almost a month at considerable expense.

With his food supply assured, Lozier engaged a score of small contractors and carpenters to furnish lumber and to superintend, under his direction, the building of the great barracks which were to house the workmen during the sawing operations. A separate building, to be constructed of the best materials, was ordered for the convenience of the twenty or thirty women, wives of laborers, who had been employed to cook and wash for the entire crew. Several of these contractors let their enthusiasm get the better of their judgment and actually hauled a dozen loads of lumber to the northern end of the island and dumped them near Kingsbridge. They implored Lozier to let them begin building, but he said that actual construction must wait until he had engaged all the men he would need and had assembled all his materials. It was his intention, he announced, to muster his workmen at a central meeting place when everything was ready and march them in a body to Kingsbridge. He assured the contractors that by using a new method of building which he had devised, but which he declined to disclose in advance, they could easily erect the necessary buildings within a few hours.

The excitement was now at fever heat, and Lozier added fuel to the flame by producing elaborate plans for the various appliances which were to be used in the project. First there were the great saws with which Manhattan Island was to be cut loose from the mainland. Each was to be one hundred feet long, with teeth three feet high. Fifty men would be required to manipulate one of these giant tools, and Lozier estimated that he would need at least a score. Then there were twenty-four huge oars, each two hundred and fifty feet long; and twenty-four great cast-iron towers, or oarlocks, in which the oars were to be mounted, twelve on the Hudson River shore and twelve on the East River. A hundred men would bend their backs at each oar, and row Manhattan Island down the bay after the sawyers had finished their work, then sweep it around and row it back. Great chains and anchors were to be provided to keep the island from being carried out to sea in the event that a storm arose. Lozier gave the plans and specifications of these Gargantuan implements to a score of blacksmiths, carpenters, and mechanics, who retired forthwith to their shops and feverishly began to estimate the cost and the quantities of material that must go into their manufacture.

Lozier now turned his attention to the unskilled laborers whose names Uncle John DeVoe had set down as potential sawyers and rowers. He sent word for them to report at Centre Market for examination and announced that he would pay triple wages to those who performed the hazardous work of sawing off that part of the island which lay under water. The longest-winded men would be awarded these dangerous but desirable jobs. Laborers swarmed to the market, and every day for a week Lozier sat enthroned on a bench while man after man stepped forward and held his breath. As each displayed his prowess, Uncle John DeVoe timed them and entered the result in his ledger.

Lozier kept delaying the commencement of actual work by professing dissatisfaction with the estimates on the oars and towers and by insisting that he had not hired nearly enough men to do the job properly. At last, however, "the numbers became so thick and pressing," as DeVoe put it in *The Market Book,* that Lozier was compelled to fix a date for the grand trek northward. He hurriedly awarded th contracts for manufacturing the saws, oars, and towers and ordered them rushed to completion. He then instructed all who were to have a hand in the great work to report at the Bowery and Spring Street, where they would be met by a fife-and-drum corps which he had thoughtfully engaged to lead the march to Kingsbridge. The exact number who appeared at the rendezvous is unknown, of course, but DeVoe says that "great numbers presented themselves," and there were probably between five hundred and a thousand persons. Laborers were there by the score, many accompanied by their wives and children; the contractors and carpenters drove up in style, escorting wagons laden with lumber and tools; the butchers were on hand with cattle and hogs, and carts loaded with crated chickens. Practically everyone who had ever heard of the project was there, in fact, excepting Lozier and Uncle John DeVoe. When several hours had elapsed and they still had failed to appear a volunteer delegation went to Centre Market in search of them. They found a message that both Lozier and Uncle John had left town on account of their health.

The crowd at Bowery and Spring Street milled about uncertainly for another hour or two, while the hogs grunted, the cattle mooed, the chickens cackled, the children squalled, and the fife-and-drum corps industriously dispensed martial music. At length, for the first time in weeks, if not in years, some of the more intelligent of Lozier's victims began to think, and the more they thought, the less likely it appeared that Manhattan Island would ever be sawed off. Gradually this conviction spread, and after a while the crowd began shamefacedly to disperse. A few of the more hotheaded went looking for Lozier, vowing that if they couldn't saw Manhattan off they could at least saw Lozier off, but they never found him. Lozier and Uncle John DeVoe had fled to Brooklyn as soon as Lozier had issued his final instructions, and had sought refuge in the home of a friend. There was much talk of having them arrested, but no one seemed willing to make a complaint to the authorities and so admit that he had been duped, and both Lozier and Uncle John went scot-free. However, it was several months before they again appeared at Centre Market and when they did Lozier found himself an oracle without a temple. The Centre Market statesmen had had enough.

James street has been a neighbor of mine and a friend of long standing. Our wives are as thick as thieves, spending long hours discussing whether one bay leaf would be best in a lamb stew, or two bay leaves, or no bay leaves. Mr. Street has more children than I have, more hair, more phonograph records, and infinitely more sense. Yet he has put up with me for something over ten years. Once he and I snuck away from our homes and went to the tip end of Long Island for the purpose of writing a play together. We got about twenty pages written and then a cow walked up to the window of our cottage and looked in at us. We never wrote the play, but we acted one out from that moment on. That's a long story and I intend to put it in a book one of these days, provided Mr. Street doesn't beat me to it.

We have a good system for maintaining our friendship. He never asks me to read his stuff, and I never ask him to read mine. We don't talk much about each other's masterpieces, except for such casual remarks as, "Brother, your stuff sure stinks."

The addition of Mr. Street to this collection is a last-minute tip-in. I hadn't considered that any of his shorter pieces met my peculiar qualifications. Then along came this story and the moment I finished reading it I knew it had to go into the book.

THE GOLDEN KEY

By James Street

Mr. hill's real name was Earl Van Dorn Hill, but folks around here called him Ol' Down Hill because it looked like he was always going that way. They poked fun at him every chance they got, and even the kids played jokes on him.

I liked him, though. He told me he'd seen Christy Mathewson pitch, and that he used to be a brakeman, a cannonball man on the best railroads. "I was an A No. 1 brakeman," he told me. "A boomer. I just rambled from place to place, having myself a time and seeing some sights."

Mr. Twofer Evans said Mr. Hill couldn't hold a job on a logging line, much less a real railroad, and that he hadn't been sober since he kicked the slats out of his cradle. Folks laughed every time Mr. Twofer said that, and then he always got them to laughing harder by saying, "Ol' Down Hill would climb a greasy pole to tell a lie when he could sit in a rocker and tell the truth." So when Mr. Hill had anything to say, they just put it down as another big lie.

Mr. Twofer was the important man in our town of Pine Hill, Mississippi. I never heard him called anything but Mr. Twofer. That's because he smoked twofers—two-for-a-nickel cigars—and raised Cain when he couldn't get them. He owned a little peckerwood sawmill and a butcher shop and slaughter pen, and lots of land and stock and stuff that he bought in for taxes.

Mr. Hill worked out at Mr. Twofer's slaughter pen, fattening shoats and beeves and killing them for the butcher shop. It was the best job he could get and he had to work for Mr. Twofer because he owed him money. Mr. Hill was born here, but went away when he was a young'un, and folks forgot about him. He was nothing but skin and bones when he showed up about a year ago and told everybody he aimed to hang around awhile just to see his folks and friends.

His papa and mother died while he was away, and all of his kinfolks went to Texas, and nobody around here remembered him except Mr. Twofer and Mr. Reddock down at the store. Mr. Hill got drunk the first night he was back and ran up and down the street, ringing a cowbell and hissing like a steam engine and singing *Casey Jones*.

The town marshal locked him in the jailhouse, and Mr. Twofer bailed him out and paid his fine, then gave him a job down in his sawmill to pay off the money. Mr. Hill never got out of debt to Mr. Twofer. Just as he'd get about even he'd bust loose and get in jail again and Mr. Twofer'd bail him out and keep him in debt.

Finally he worked his way downhill until he wound up at the slaughter pen and was staying pretty sober until the *Titanic* went down last spring. I don't know what the *Titanic* had to do with Mr. Hill. He didn't know anybody on her. But he told me he'd aimed to be in New York this summer and might have taken himself a trip on that boat and she might have sunk then instead of when she did. "It sure was a narrow escape," he said and shook his head real slow. "And all them women and children. It just goes to show you that when the Big Engineer throws on the air brakes, it's too late to jump."

He went off and got drunk and sat on the churchhouse steps, singing *Nearer My God to Thee* and bawling about all the women and children who went down with the *Titanic*. The preacher tried to help him, but Mr. Twofer said he'd insulted the church and had him locked up again, then bailed him out and sent him back to the slaughter pen.

The summer passed, and I had forgotten the *Titanic* and was thinking about baseball that day when I went over to the slaughter pen to visit with Mr. Hill and see if he had any I'm-the-guy buttons or baseball pictures. He saved I'm-the-guy buttons for me. They were blue buttons with pins on them like political-campaign buttons, and every one of them had a funny saying like, "I'm the guy that put the skids under skiddoo." They came in packages of jelly beans and he got 'em by swapping around.

When he had money enough to buy ready-rolled cigarettes, he smoked the kind that had baseball pictures in 'em and he saved 'em for me, too. I had more I'm-the-guy buttons and baseball pictures than any boy in town.

Mr. Hill was standing out in the lot near the slaughter pen when I walked up. He was just staring into space, rubbing the neck of a bull yearling. An old scrub cow was scratching her side against the fence and they were the only beeves in the lot. He'd named the yearling Sante Fe and had raised him since he was weaned. I was right upon Mr.

Hill before he saw me and then he quit petting Sante Fe and said, "Hello, Cub."

He always called me Cub. My name is Horace and the other boys called me Tubby. I used to be sort of fat and didn't like to be called Tubby and that's why Mr. Hill called me Cub.

I said hello to him and looked at him real close to see if he had been drinking. He hadn't. His eyes were just as clear and sort of twinkled. He was a lanky man, thin as a two-by-four, and he had a long jaw and creases in his face.

"Got any I'm-the-guys?" I asked.

"Nope. But I got a Rube Marquard and two Carrigans."

Marquard was a pitcher for the Giants and Carrigan was a catcher for the Boston Red Sox. The Giants and the Red Sox had won the pennants and were fixing to go at it in the World Series. Our town was hog-wild about baseball, specially the men who hung around Mr. Reddock's store. They didn't talk about nothing except crops and politics and baseball. I thought Marquard was a humdinging good pitcher, good as Christy Mathewson. But Mr. Hill said I was crazy. He thought Christy Mathewson and William Jennings Bryan were the greatest men in the country.

I was rightly glad to get the Marquard picture and said, "Maybe they'll use the Rube in the first game."

"Maybe," Mr. Hill said. Then he looked away like he wasn't looking at anything, but just thinking, and said, "I saw the Rube pitch against the Pirates one day."

Mr. Twofer would have said that Mr. Hill was making up a tale, but I didn't doubt his word. Maybe he had seen the Rube. Maybe he'd been a brakeman on the Sante Fe and the Rock Island and the Union Pacific like he said. I always sort of thought that story of his about being in San Francisco during the earthquake was laying it on pretty thick. But I didn't hold that against him. When you're cooped up in a little town like Pine Hill, there ain't no harm in thinking out loud about the things you'd like to do. One time I told some of the boys that I'd been plumb to Memphis. I'd never been out of the county and I just told that to show off, so who was I to make fun of Mr. Hill about some of his tales.

We were still talking baseball when we moseyed out of the lot and down back of the slaughter pen, where the G. & S. I. Railroad ran through a cut and by a siding and water tower before it got to the depot. The G. & S. I. was the Gulf & Ship Island, but we called it the God Save Ireland. Two passenger trains came through every day and two freights. It wasn't much railroad if you stacked it against some of those big lines. It suited us, though.

It was about time for the northbound freight, and me and Mr. Hill sat on the bank of the cut and watched the rails running way off up yonder and getting narrower and narrower until they went out of sight. Heat waves were pouring up from the tracks and bitter weeds were growing along the right-of-way.

We heard the train a-blowing and Mr. Hill's ears seemed to come up like a mule's and he said, "Listen to them gondolas rolling. She's an 0-6-0 and she's balling the jack."

The train wasn't even in sight, but Mr. Hill could tell me all about her just by listening to her roll. An 0-6-0 engine is a six-wheeler without any front and trailing truck wheels. The train came huffing by and disappeared up the line, heading for Jackson, and from there maybe some of the cars would go to St. Louis, even Chicago.

I watched her out of sight and the smoke was laying close to the tracks and I was making believe that I was riding her away from there. Mr. Hill looked at me and grinned and said: "Me and you both, Cub. I was thinking the same thing. Out on the Sante Fe I've seen 2-10-2 engines, two front truck wheels, ten drivers, and two trailing truck wheels. I used to brake behind one of them engines."

"Yes siree, bobtail," I said, sort of heading him off from a long story about the Sante Fe. "Sure wish I was on that train going up to see the Red Sox beat the Giants."

"You're crazy." Mr. Hill's Adam's apple began jumping up and down. "Boston ain't got a chance. Matty will tie 'em in knots." Then he went into facts and figures and began spouting averages and things like that. He had it figured that the whole thing was going only five games, like it did two years ago when the Athletics beat the Cubs in the 1910 Series.

I argued with him just to hear him talk, and we were walking back to the slaughter pen, still talking baseball, when we saw Mr. Twofer standing in the lot. He was as mad as a wet hen when he saw us, and yelled: "Hey, Down. Where the blazes have you been? Thought I told you to slaughter these two beeves."

Mr. Hill opened the lot gate and latched it after he went through. He ambled up to his boss and said: "Aimed to talk to you about them beeves, Twofer. They are mighty pore beeves. Fit'n only for tallow and hides, and tallow ain't selling much right now."

"Tallow my hind leg," Mr. Twofer snorted. "This beef is for the road gang and it don't have to be much 'count. Get them critters killed and dressed before I bust you wide open."

Mr. Hill's eyes got real pale and watery and his Adam's apple bounced up and down like a cork on a fishing line. He swallowed two or three times and then said, "I ain't aiming to slaughter that yearling and that old cow."

I nearly jumped a foot. First time I ever heard Mr. Hill talk up to anybody.

Mr. Twofer was put out and was boiling over. "Have you gone crazy?"

"Nope. I just ain't going to kill 'em."

"How come? It's your job, ain't it?" Mr. Twofer was rubbing the stubble on his chin.

Mr. Hill leaned against the gate and looked at the yearling, then at his boss. "I raised that little fellow, Twofer. I've been mighty close to him and that old cow. I just can't knock 'em in the head."

"That's the darnedest thing I ever heard of." Mr. Twofer was goggle-eyed.

"Maybe so. Now if I'd had twenty or thirty head out here I wouldn't mind killing 'em. A man can't get close to twenty or thirty head. There ain't nothing personal or friendly about a herd of cattle. But two." He shook his head slowly.

"You can get mighty fond of just two head. I can walk into that slaughterhouse and little Sante Fe and the cow follow me. Nope, I can't do it."

I thought Mr. Twofer was going to explode. He started cussing something awful and grabbed that yearling and pulled him into the slaughterhouse. Then he reached for the sledge and knocked him in the head.

Mr. Hill turned away and went out of the gate and didn't latch it. He walked down the road toward the swamp and left me standing there.

Mr. Twofer came out and told me, "Hey, kid, help me get that old cow inside and I'll give you a dime."

I was sort of sick at my stomach and shinnied over the gate and ran home. I forgot that the gate was unlatched.

Mr. Hill wasn't around the rest of that day and I began looking for him. I reckoned he was drunk out in the swamp. Everybody down at Mr. Reddock's store was laughing about how chickenhearted he was. They didn't pay me no mind and I was just sitting there thinking about Mr. Hill when they got to talking about the World Series. Then I heard the news.

Mr. Twofer and several other men had put up money to get a telegraph operator to come to Pine Hill and take the games play by play. It was the biggest thing that ever happened in our town and the folks were a heap more excited than the time President Taft came through in a private car.

I sure did want Mr. Hill to hear about it, so I just sat there listening, aiming to tell him about it, when he showed up. I never had seen a telegraph operator and somehow it was hard to believe that a man could sit at a desk and listen to the World Series way up in New York.

Back when there were a couple of big sawmills and lots of business around here we had a telegraph operator at the depot. That was before my day, but the wires and things were still in the depot. Mr. Twofer and the other men had it all figured out. They had put up a hundred dollars to get an operator from Jackson and he was going to sit right there in the depot and tell us everything that happened in the World Series.

I took in every word they said and was drinking a lemon

pop when I heard the boys laughing and yelling out in the street. I ran out and there was Mr. Hill staggering and falling down. He was bellowing, "Man the lifeboats!"

One of the kids whooped: "What's the matter, Down? Did you hit an iceberg?"

I almost cried.

The men in Mr. Reddock's store saw him then and Mr. Twofer grabbed a gallon can of molasses and they ran out of the store and tripped Mr. Hill and poured the molasses on his face and in his hair. Mr. Hill was spluttering when they picked him up like a sack of meal and took him over to the horse trough and threw him in. Then they stepped back and laughed fit to kill and Mr. Twofer yelled, "Man overboard."

Mr. Hill looked like a drowned rat when he poked his head up and he was scared and kept hollering, "Women and children first!"

Then he seemed to get a little sober and realized where he was and tried to scramble out of the horse trough. Some of the kids kept pushing him back in and I got me a stick and a couple of clods and ran up and chased them away. I tried to help Mr. Hill get out.

"I'll fix 'em, Cub," he said. "I'll fix 'em if it's the last thing I ever do."

The town marshal came up and instead of grabbing the other men he arrested Mr. Hill and hustled him to jail.

Mr. Twofer said, "I'll let him rot in jail this time."

"But you need him, Twofer," Mr. Reddock said. "You get him for nothing and nobody else will do that work."

"I ain't got no beeves at the slaughter pen," Mr. Twofer said. "And I won't have any for about two weeks. So I'll leave him in jail for a spell. He'll miss the World Series and that'll learn him a lesson."

Mr. Hill's fine was $10 and I didn't have ten cents. I was pretty down in the mouth the next day when I went to the store to see what was going on. Mr. Twofer rode up in his buggy and came in and bought four cigars. He had on his straw katy and a clean shirt. He was on his way to the depot to meet the telegraph operator.

Just about everybody in town was at the train and I saw him step off. I wasn't close enough to get a good look because the menfolks were ganging around him. But the first thing I noticed about him was the golden key.

It wasn't a real key, like a key that unlocks a door. It was a little key shaped exactly like a telegraph operator's key, with a tiny gold bar with a gold button on top at one end. It was shining in the sun. He wore it on a chain across his stomach. I didn't know what it meant at first and then I heard some of the men whispering about it.

"Look at that key," one said. "Pure gold."

"It's his badge," another said. "Like a star is a marshal's badge, that key is his'n."

"Badge your foot," Mr. Reddock said. "That's the trademark of his craft. That shows he's a telegraph operator. Every good operator wears a golden key. They can get in ball games and ride free just by showing the keys. I'd rather have a pure D telegrapher's key than an annual pass."

Mr. Twofer took the operator in his buggy. The rest of us ran back to the store and I was sitting on the front steps when the operator and Mr. Twofer came up. The operator was wearing a derby and his button shoes had brown cloth tops. He was a sport, all right.

Mr. Twofer slapped him on the back and introduced him around. "This here is Ed MacLane," he said.

Most of the men just stared at him, pop-eyed. But a few shook his hand. I wished Mr. Hill was there. I was thinking that Mr. Hill would shake his hand just like he was any other man.

Mr. MacLane walked to the cigar counter and said, "Got any twofers?"

Mr. Reddock nearly busted a trace getting out the cigars and Mr. MacLane smelled one of them and shoved it back. "I meant two for a quarter," he said. He wasn't bragging, either. His voice sounded just like anybody else's. Sort of soft. The best cigar in the store was a five-center. Mr. MacLane took that one and Mr. Reddock nearly broke his arm reaching for a match.

Mr. Twofer lit a cigar, too, and r'ared back. "Me and

Ed—" he called him Ed just as big as you please—"me and Ed have been looking over the depot and he says he'll need a caller to help him with the Series."

"What's a caller?" Mr. Reddock asked.

"You tell 'em, Ed," Mr. Twofer said.

Mr. MacLane looked at the end of his cigar, then said, "That depot is pretty small and I don't want a heap of folks breathing on my neck while I'm copying the Series." He flicked the ash off of his cigar. "The instruments are behind a counter and off to themselves. So I can let only one man behind the counter with me. I'll take it play by play and he'll read it off and call it out."

That was all right with everybody.

"I'll have to have a man who knows baseball," Mr. MacLane said. "My agreement is that all I will do is copy the report and turn it over to the caller. So he will have to know his business."

Mr. Twofer tried to knock off his ash just like Mr. MacLane had done. But he made a mess of it. Then he said: "I know baseball. I'll do the calling."

Mr. MacLane sort of frowned and I had a feeling he wasn't rightly fond of Mr. Twofer. "How many games did Bedient win for Boston this season?"

Mr. Twofer was stumped. "I don't know," he admitted.

"Then you don't know baseball."

I don't know what got into me, but I spoke right up and told him how many games Bedient had won and then showed him my pictures of all the players. Then I got scared, but instead of being mad he looked down at me and grinned.

"Now there's a baseball fan," he said. "Wish you were big enough to call for me. Where did you learn so much?"

I was almost tongue-tied, but I managed to get it out: "From Mr. Hill."

"Where is he?" Mr. MacLane looked around at the crowd.

"Jail," I said. "He got drunk last night."

Mr. MacLane grunted. "Now that's a fine howdy-do. Throwing a man in jail for getting drunk. He'll miss the Series and that's a low-down trick to play on any man."

Mr. Twofer stepped up. "That's just what I was thinking,"

he said. He sure was trying to stay in good with that operator. "Hill works for me and we had to lock him up last night to keep him from hurting himself. I aimed to bail him out today. Might as well go do it right now. If you want him to call for you, it'll be all right with me and I'll make him do it for nothing."

"That's no skin off my back," Mr. MacLane said. "I don't pay my caller. You do. But I've got to have a good man and this Hill sounds like he knows the game."

I hoped Mr. Hill would clean up a bit before he showed up, but he didn't. He and Mr. Twofer were walking side by side and Mr. Twofer was laying the law down to him when they came up to the store. Mr. Hill saw me and grinned and I grinned back. He looked like something that had been drug up by the cats.

Then he saw Mr. MacLane and Mr. MacLane saw him. The operator's cigar almost fell out of his mouth and he said: "Earl Hill! Well, I'll be doggoned."

"Ed!" Mr. Hill said. "Be John Brown if it ain't ol' Ed MacLane."

They shook hands and started pounding each other's back. The men in the store had their mouths open and Mr. Twofer's eyes were about to pop out. You could have knocked me down with a feather, but I looked around at the other kids and grinned.

"So you two know each other?" Mr. Twofer was flabbergasted.

Mr. Hill laughed and Mr. MacLane said: "Lord, yes. I've known Earl Hill for years. We used to work for the same railroad."

"We got around, huh, Ed?" Mr. Hill was the happiest man you ever saw.

"You tell 'em," Mr. MacLane said. "Remember that time in Milwaukee?"

They both laughed and Mr. Hill said, "And how about Denver?"

"And San Francisco," Mr. MacLane said. He glanced around at the crowd. "Earl here braked the first train out of San Francisco after the earthquake."

I was so proud that I nearly busted open. So he hadn't been telling no rat-killing lies. Mr. Twofer and the other men just looked at one another and were pretty put out. They wanted to make a big show before the operator and there was Mr. Hill having all the fun.

"What in the world are you doing here?" Mr. MacLane asked. "Been sick?"

"Naw, Ed. I was born here and came back to see my folks and sort of got down. You know how it is." He looked pretty shamed and then his eyes perked up and he said: "What you doing in this part of the country? Last time I saw you was more'n two years ago. You were dispatching for the U.P."

"I got tired of sitting still. So I got to booming, just knocking around the country. I happened to be up in Jackson and heard I could pick up some spondulix down here."

Mr. Hill didn't say nothing, but looked down at his dusty shoes and Mr. MacLane reached out and patted him on the back. Then he turned to Mr. Twofer and said: "This man will call for me. And he's going to stay at the boardinghouse with me. Fix it up." He was dangling that golden key and his cigar was tilted out of his mouth. I knew then that he was the biggest man in the country; bigger even than William Jennings Bryan.

Mr. Twofer didn't dare say nothing. He was chewing his lower lip and everybody else was gawking at Mr. Hill. The idea of our town drunk being friends with such a big man as Mr. MacLane just beat all. The folks couldn't get over it. They still ain't over it.

Mr. MacLane reached in his pocket and got out two silver dollars and pitched them to me. "Take these wagon wheels, partner, and go get Mr. Hill a clean shirt and some socks. Bring 'em down to the boardinghouse."

It was the first time I'd ever had so much money in my hand and I was clinking those silver dollars when Mr. Hill and Mr. MacLane walked out of the store. Mr. Hill was saying, "But I tell you, Ed, I've been blackballed by every line in the country."

"Forget it. You hit it up too heavy on the Sante Fe and you been hitting it too heavy here. But you ain't blackballed. They're begging for brakemen."

I ran up and bought a blue work shirt and some socks and was plumb out of breath when I got to the boardinghouse. I just walked right on in the house like I was the big rabbit in the turnip patch. Mr. MacLane was mighty glad to see me and gave me four bits. He had taken off his coat and derby. His hair was plastered down and parted on the side. His shirt was pink with a green silk collar.

He saw me staring at the golden key and he took it off of the chain and tossed it over to me. "Look it over, partner. That shows that I'm an A No. 1 telegrapher, drunk or sober."

I held the key in my hand and it seemed that it opened the whole world and I began making believe that I owned a golden key and was sitting in a depot, a green shade over my eyes, and I was talking plumb to San Fran-by-gum-cisco. I handed the key back to him and noticed then that his cuff links were little gold telegraph receiving sets and his stickpin was a little gold telegraph pole.

Mr. MacLane and Mr. Hill treated me just like I was a man and I leaned against the washstand and listened to them talk. I wished the other kids could see me. Mr. Hill was in debt $22 worth, so they agreed to charge $25 for the calling. So we went back up to the store and collected Mr. MacLane's $100 and Mr. Hill's $25.

"I always get paid in advance," Mr. MacLane said.

Right then and there Mr. Hill paid off his debt to Mr. Twofer and had enough money left over for a few cigars. But instead he bought cigarettes and gave me the baseball pictures. He told Mr. MacLane that I was the best kid in town and asked him to save baseball pictures for me.

Mr. MacLane mussed up my hair and I said: "Got any I'm-the-guys? I save them, too."

"Maybe I can find a few," he said. "You know I'm the guy that put the top in Topeka."

Huh, that was an old one. I winked at him and said, "I'm the guy that put the gal in Galveston."

It was blazing hot the day the World Series started and the old folks around here said there hadn't been such a to-do since Dewey won at Manila. Mr. MacLane and Mr. Hill and me went down to the depot and got things ready. The folks were standing around on the cinders outside the depot and kept gawking.

Mr. MacLane sat down and began messing with the receiving set and put a tobacco can behind the sounder to sharpen the clicking. I got him a couple of fresh cigars and moved the cuspidor near his chair. He opened his wire and his sounder began dotting and dashing.

"Cincinnati," Mr. MacLane said. "We're on a Cincinnati-New Orleans wire." He listened closely and said: "That's Heck Newton sending. Remember old Heck?"

"Sure," said Mr. Hill. "Tell him hello for me."

Mr. MacLane broke in and began tapping out a message and when the answer came he got to laughing. "Heck says you owe him $3. Since Denver days. And he says you can get a job in Cincinnati, braking on the B. & O."

The crowd was jamming into the depot and Mr. MacLane told them that they'd have to stay back and give him room. "Nobody is allowed back here except my caller and the boy."

I looked at all the other kids and tried not to show off. Then I began sharpening Mr. MacLane's pencils and put a glass of water near by. He took off his coat and put a pad of paper in front of him and we waited for the game to start.

The line-ups came along and Mr. MacLane copied them and handed the sheet to Mr. Hill. The Giants weren't pitching Mathewson the first day. "Saving him," Mr. Hill said, and then turned toward the crowd and cupped his hands and yelled out the line-ups. The folks were jabbering and getting excited.

I sat on a high stool sort of behind Mr. MacLane and as fast as Mr. Hill read off the plays he passed the pages to me and I put them on a spike. The Giants scored first in the third inning and were rocking along all right until late in the game when Boston overtook them and put the game on ice. It wasn't much of a ball game. Everybody was for the Giants and the folks were pretty blue. Mr. Twofer said the game was crooked. He thought everything was crooked.

The next day the Giants threw Christy Mathewson in there and the Red Sox knocked the stuffing out of him. Mr. Hill got so excited that his Adam's apple stuck in his throat and he just spluttered. That game ended in a tie, 6 to 6, and then Rube Marquard went in the third game and beat Boston, 2 to 1. That evened things up and I couldn't help strutting a bit because I had said all along that the Rube was the man to watch.

Mr. MacLane was taking the whole thing in his stride, but everybody else was on pins and needles. Most everybody had a hunch that Mr. MacLane had some inside dope on the Series and folks fell over themselves asking him out to dinner. They asked Mr. Hill, too, because that was the only way to get Mr. MacLane. You never saw such a change in a town. Mr. Twofer took a back seat and Mr. MacLane became the biggest man around here, with Mr. Hill right behind.

I reckon there never was such a Series as that one and the crowds around the depot got bigger and bigger. Boston won the fourth game and I'll be John Brown if they didn't beat Mathewson in the fifth. I thought sure Mr. Hill was going to get drunk, but he didn't.

The Rube came back in the sixth and pitched the Giants to their second win and then the Giants got sixteen hits in the seventh game and won it hands down and evened the Series.

Even Mr. MacLane was getting mighty excited and everybody else in town was fit to be tied. I couldn't sleep much the night before the last game and was up early that morning and down at Mr. Reddock's store watching the fun. Folks came from miles away to hear the game. They brought their dogs and young-uns and picnic baskets. The preacher said protracted meeting never had drawn such a crowd and by noon there must have been a hundred wagons hitched down near the depot.

Mr. MacLane and Mr. Hill and me had to nudge our way through the crowd to get into the depot. I fixed the pencils just right and then sat back and waited.

Mr. Hill was grinning like a possum when he announced that Mathewson was going in for the Giants, and the folks started whooping.

Then things got so still you could hear the folks breathing and Mr. Hill began calling the game. The Giants scored in the third and the crowd had a fit. But Boston evened it up in the seventh and they were tied at one all when she went into the tenth. I was sweating like a plowhand and Mr. Hill was hoarse from yelling. In the first of the tenth, New York scored again and Mr. Hill was jumping up and down and pulling for Mathewson.

It looked like the Giants had won themselves a World Series until Snodgrass dropped an easy fly and the Red Sox tied the score. Mr. Hill's Adam's apple was having a spasm. Mr. MacLane was hunched over the sounder, sweating and listening for every word. And the crowd was as still as a graveyard.

Then it happened. The sounder began clicking and Mr. MacLane took down the words and looked up at Mr. Hill when he handed him the sheet of paper. Mr. Hill got as white as a ghost and just stood there shaking like a wet puppy.

"What is it, Down?" Mr. Twofer yelled from the crowd. "Read it, you fool."

The idea hit Mr. Hill then. He crumpled the paper up and tore it into little bits and looked at the crowd. "I ain't going to tell you," he said.

I nearly fell off my stool and Mr. Twofer and Mr. Reddock and all the others were struck dumb for a second and then began raising the roof. Mr. Hill just looked at them. He was getting even, all right.

"Cut out the horseplay," Mr. Twofer yelled. "Who won and what happened? You, MacLane, what happened?"

Mr. MacLane closed his wire and lit a cigar. His eyes were shining and he was about to bust out laughing. "I don't remember. I took it down and gave it to Earl. I ain't sure what happened."

I knew he was telling a fib, but there was nothing they could do about it. The whole thing was up to Mr. Hill and he looked first at Mr. Twofer and then at Mr. Reddock and at all the others who had been so mean to him and said real slowlike, "I really ain't telling."

He sure had them and they got to begging. I was dying to know myself what had happened, but I sure was having fun seeing Mr. Hill get even.

They tried to pay Mr. Hill to tell 'em and he just shook his head. Then Mr. Twofer said he'd beat Mr. Hill half to death. But Mr. Hill wasn't scared. He and Mr. MacLane walked right through the crowd and they didn't lay a finger on 'em. The crowd followed 'em up the street, still begging. Mr. Twofer and Mr. Reddock got to squabbling when Mr. Twofer said: "You ought to have a telyphone in your store, Reddock. Then we could phone New Orleans and find out."

"You're loony," Mr. Reddock said. "If anybody in this town needs a telyphone, it's you. You old skinflint."

So they fell out, and just about everybody else got mad at Mr. Twofer. Some of 'em blamed him for bringing Mr. MacLane to town and others blamed him for being so mean to Mr. Hill.

I went to the boardinghouse and watched Mr. Hill and Mr. MacLane pack and there was a lump in my throat. The game had been over more'n an hour, but folks still were hanging around the store. The northbound passenger train got in about eight o'clock and fetched newspapers. Until it got to Pine Hill, though, there was no way for us to know what had happened unless Mr. Hill broke down. But he stuck by his guns and let the whole town stew.

About seven o'clock Mr. Hill and Mr. MacLane and me walked to the water tower and waited for the southbound freight. She came humming along, pulled by a 2-6-0 engine, and stopped for water. Mr. MacLane showed his golden key and the conductor told him and Mr. Hill to get in the caboose.

Mr. MacLane reached down and mussed my hair again and said: "So long, partner. And remember that I'm the guy that took a tuck in Kentucky." He swung up into the caboose.

Mr. Hill was looking away and I think he sort of hated

to leave me. He didn't look at me when he shook my hand. "Matty lost," he said. "The Red Sox won the Series."

Of course I was surprised, but I wasn't thinking so much about the game. When that freight pulled out I'd know something that nobody else in Pine Hill knew.

"The Giants kicked the game away," Mr. Hill said. "Merkle didn't go after an easy pop fly and Boston won three to two. So long, Cub."

I waited until the freight train pulled out and then I balled the jack back to the store. The folks were still cussing and stomping around. I walked through the crowd for a few minutes, strutting a little bit. Nobody paid me any mind and I just couldn't stand it any longer. I was rightly fixing to bust. So I stood in front of Mr. Twofer and said, "I know what happened."

The men and the boys started ganging around me and begging. Mr. Twofer bought me some licorice and the boys gave me all their I'm-the-guy buttons and baseball pictures just to tell 'em, so I told 'em.

But I'll be John Brown if they believed me. They didn't believe me because they just didn't want to believe me. Mr. Twofer said, "This kid has been hanging around Ol' Down Hill so much that he lies too. Just natural."

I was pretty let down and kept yelling, "It's the truth. Merkle pulled a boner and Boston won."

They just ragged me and said I told a whopper to get the I'm-the-guy buttons and baseball pictures.

Just then the whistle blew and they ran down to the station to get the news. I should have been rightly tickled, knowing they'd learn I had known all along. Maybe the next time I told 'em som'n they'd pay me some mind.

But I was down in the mouth, standing there by myself on the porch of the store. I knew that pretty soon the boys would forget about the World Series and it'd be time to swap I'm-the-guy buttons again and there wouldn't be anymore to swap because I had 'em all. So it wouldn't be any fun anymore. On top of that, Mr. Hill was gone and I didn't have anybody to play with.

LIFE'S LITTLE PROBLEMS

V. LIFE'S LITTLE PROBLEMS

ONE DAY a report reached me that Robert Benchley had decided to abandon writing forever. On behalf of mankind I hurried down to his apartment on Forty-fourth Street, backed him into a corner, and said:

"Listen, you. The world will not permit this. You cannot quit us at this stage of the game."

I demanded a reason for Mr. Benchley's decision to quit writing.

"I can't find anything to write about," he said. "Anyway, I wore myself out long ago thinking up clever things to write in the front of books and sending funny telegrams in the funny-telegram era. Back in those days the people in my crowd always sent funny telegrams. Suppose one of us left on a journey. He would receive a funny telegram at every stop the train made. I exhausted myself writing them and now I can't write any more."

While we're on the subject of Mr. Benchley there's another small matter worth reporting. One day my wife caught me in the act of reading a book and laughing at it. I tried to duck it behind me but she saw that it was one of my own books.

"My God," she said, "laughing at your own stuff!"

When she found out I was going to see Mr. Benchley she suggested that I ask him if he ever laughs at his own stuff. She figured the answer would be a forthright no, and that I would realize what an idiot I am.

I said to Mr. Benchley: "Do you ever pick up your own books and read something in them?"

"Oh, certainly," said Mr. Benchley.

"Do you ever catch yourself laughing at your own stuff?"

"Good God, yes!" he said. "It's a source of embarrassment to me. Whenever I pick up one of my own books I look quickly in all directions to be certain nobody is watching me. I can't risk opening one of my books in public at all. Usually I go into a bedroom and lock the door. I just sit and howl! I read some of that stuff and roar, and fall down, and get the hiccups. I read that stuff and I say to myself that *I* couldn't have written that—it's too good, too funny—somebody else wrote it and used my name.

"It's the same thing with movies. I hate to go to see the rough cuts of the movie shorts I make. It is part of my job to see those rough cuts in the studio projection rooms, but I cringe at the prospect. I sit there and roar and scream with delight at myself on the screen. I don't know what the other people in the room think. Actually, I'm not laughing at myself. I'm laughing at old Charlie Benchley—my father. Everything I do on the screen is a projection of old Charlie. And when it's over and I see it on the screen it's not Bob Benchley at all. It's old Charlie."

Mr. Benchley, as essayist, has touched upon most of Life's Little Problems at one time or another. He treats, in the piece that follows, of a matter that has worried me for years.

THE MYSTERY OF BRIDGE BUILDING

By Robert Benchley

I AM NOT MUCH of a one to be writing on bridge building, having never really built a bridge myself, but if the reader (you) will overlook a little vagueness in some of the directions, I myself will overlook the fact that the reader has nc right to criticize, unless, of course, he happens to be a pro fessional bridge builder himself.

It has always seemed to me that the most difficult part o building a bridge would be the start. What does a man dc first when he sets out to build a bridge? Granted he has hi plans all drawn up and enough food and drink to last him month. He is standing on one bank of a river and wants t build a bridge across to the other bank. What is the first thing that he does? (I seem to be asking all the questions.)

I suppose that he takes a shovel and digs a little hole, and has his picture taken doing it. Maybe somebody waves a flag. I have seen photographs of such a ceremony, but they never show what happens next. Frankly, I would be up against it if anyone were to put me on one bank of a river and say: "Build a bridge across to the other bank." I might be able to finish it if someone would start it for me, but as for making the first move, I would be left blushing furiously.

I once heard of a man who was confronted by just this emergency. It had got around somehow that he was an authority on bridgework (as a matter of fact, he was a dentist), and when the people in the neighboring town wanted a bridge built they sent for him. He was an easy-going sort of chap, and after they had given him a big dinner and a good cigar he didn't have the heart to tell them that he really knew nothing about the sort of bridge building that they wanted. He kept meaning to tell them, but they were so nice and evidently had so much confidence in him that he hated to spoil their good time, especially after he had eaten their dinner. So he just sat tight and let things take their course.

Pretty soon he found himself on the left bank of the river, with a brass band huddled around him and a lot of people in frock coats, and after someone had read Lincoln's Gettysburg Address he was given a gold shovel and told to go ahead. Fortunately the people didn't stick around and watch him, as they figured out that he might be embarrassed by so many spectators, so he stuck the shovel in the ground and waved good-by to everyone, and then bent over as if he were going to work. As a matter of fact he was in a terrible state of mind.

He looked across at the other bank and tried to figure out how far it was. Then he looked behind him and tried to figure out how far that was. He thought that maybe the thing to do was to go and get the bridge made somewhere else, bring it to this spot, and stick one end of it in the hole he had dug and then swing it around until the other end was over the other bank, but that didn't seem practical. So he sat down and began writing some letters he had been meaning to write for months. Then he started throwing shovelfuls of dirt into the river, hoping against hope that he might get enough of it piled up on the river bottom to make a kind of bridge in itself, but he couldn't even make it show above the surface in one spot.

Just then a man with a rod and a fish basket happened to stroll by and asked him what he was doing.

"You will just laugh when I tell you," said the bridge builder.

"No, I won't, honestly," said the fisherman.

"Then you don't laugh easily," said the bridge builder. "I'm building a bridge."

"And a very smart thing to be doing, too," replied the fisherman. "One never can have too many bridges." Then he added, "You see, I didn't laugh."

This so endeared him to the bridge builder that he offered the stranger a drink, and one thing led to another until they both were sitting on the river bank talking about old songs they used to sing when they were boys.

"Do you remember one that used to go, 'Hello, ma baby, hello, ma lady, hello, ma ragtime gal'?" asked one.

" 'Send me a kiss by wire, honey, ma heart's on fire'?" added the other. "Is that the one you mean?"

"It sure is," said the other. "And then it went, 'If you refuse me, honey, you lose me, then I'll be left alone.' "

" 'So, baby, telephone and tell me I'se your own,' " they both sang in unison.

Well, this sort of thing went on for months and months until they had exhausted all the old songs they used to know and got to making up new ones. The bridge expert forgot entirely what he was there for and the fisherman had never really known, so he had nothing to forget. People used to come over from the town to see how the bridge was coming on and then would tiptoe away again when they saw the two having such a good time. Finally they got someone else to build the bridge, starting from the other side of the river ınd what was the surprise of the original bridge expert one lay to look up from his game of cribbage with the fisherman ınd find that they were directly in the way of the vehicular raffic from a brand-new bridge. You may be sure that he oined in the laughter, even though the joke was in a way on ıim. But he saw the fun of the thing, and that is better than ıny bridge building. What we need in this world is fewer ›ridges and more fun.

However, the problem of the bridge expert which has just ›een cited doesn't do much to help those of us who don't ınderstand how a bridge is built. What we want to know s how the second man that the town got went about the job. Ie evidently knew something about it, for he got the thing lone.

I think that it is all that stuff in the air over the river that ›uzzles me. I can understand the things they build on the ›anks all right. You go about building those as you would ‚o about building a house, except, of course, for the win- ows and front porch. But all those wires and hangings vhich are suspended from apparently nowhere and yet are trong enough to hold up any number of automobiles and rolley cars that take it into their heads to cross the river. 'here is something very fishy about those. Who supports hem? I don't like the looks of it, frankly.

Of course I suppose that if I had gone a little further in ıathematics in school I would be a little easier in my mind bout bridges. There is evidently something beyond plane eometry which I don't know about and which may hold the ey to this mystery. Maybe it's in plane geometry. I missed couple of days when I had a sore throat, and perhaps those re the days when the geometry class took up bridge build- ıg. Or it is quite possible that I actually studied it and idn't absorb it. I would say that my absorption point in ıathematics was about .007, and I would not be surprised ɔ find out that I had missed the whole point entirely.

However, even though your engineer has it all worked out ıathematically on paper, with figures and digits all over he place, I still don't see how they get those wires up there ı the air or how the wires are induced to hold things up.

I studied physics and I'm no fool. You can't tell me that al
that weight isn't pulling down, and my question is, "Dowr
from what?"

I don't mean to be nasty about this thing, or narrow
minded. Neither do I incline to the theory of witchcraft–
much. There is a man in India, so they tell me, who throw
a rope up in the air and then climbs up it, which is evidentl
the principle of bridge building. But that man in India i
supposed to be a fakir, and, according to some theories, th
spectators are hypnotized into thinking they see him climl
the rope, whereas he is actually not doing it at all. Thi
would be a good explanation of bridges if it were not for th
fact that you can't hypnotize a truck into thinking it is cross
ing a river.

Of course the old-fashioned covered bridge is easy enougl
to understand. People could wade right out into those river
and stick the posts in by hand, or at any rate could ge
planks long enough to reach across. All that was necessar
was to get good planks that would rumble. And, by the way
what has become of the old-fashioned rumbling plank? Yo
never hear planks rumbling today as they used to on thos
old covered bridges. I once spent the night in a farmhous
which I later found out was near a covered bridge. In th
middle of the night I heard what I thought was thunder; s
I got up and shut the window. The room got very hot i
about half an hour, so, hearing no more thunder, I though
that the storm had passed us by, and got up and opened th
window again. In about ten minutes there was another rum
ble; this time very loud. With a bound I was out of bed an
had the window down in a jiffy. Then came half an hou
of stifling again, with a pronounced odor of burning ha
from the mattress. I got up and looked out the window. Th
stars were shining. So up she came again and I went bac
to bed after stepping on both my shoes, which were lyin
upside down by the bed. This went on at intervals of hal
an hour all night, until I finally overcame my fear of thun
derstorms and decided to let the lightning come right in an
get into bed with me if it wanted to, rather than shut th
window again. I have already given away the point of thi

story, so I need hardly say that I found out in the morning that it actually had been thunder that I had heard and that the town on the other side of the mountain had had a bad storm all night. The covered bridge, however, could have been responsible for the rumbling if it had wanted to.

This little anecdote, exciting and amusing as it has been for all of us, I am sure, has drawn us quite a long way from the theme of this treatise, which, you will remember, was, "What sort of trickery goes into the building of bridges?" I don't happen to know many bridge engineers, so I am unable to say whether they are tricksters as a class. In fact the only one that I know built a privately owned toll bridge across a river once, and then found that the township ran a free bridge about half a mile down the river around a bend which he hadn't seen before. So he hung his bridge with Japanese lanterns and limited it to rickshas and spent his vacations fishing from it.

But, aside from possibly taking on a job for building a pontoon bridge, which I could do if I had enough boats, I am distinctly not in the market for a bridge contract until someone explains the principle of the thing more clearly to me.

I once read of a man who was caught in a hotel fire and broke open one of those glass cases containing what is known as a "fire ax." Then, as he stood there, ax in hand, watching little curls of smoke coming up through the floor, he tried to figure out what to do with the ax. He could chop a hole in the floor and let more fire up, or he could chop a hole in the wall and make a nice draft. Aside from those two courses of action he seemed to be saddled with an ax and that was all. After waving it weakly around his head once or twice, thinking maybe to frighten the fire away, he just stood there, making imaginary chopping motions, until the firemen came and carried him out still asking, "What do I do with this?"

Such will be my dilemma when someone puts a shovel in my hand and says: "How about building a bridge?"

Erskine Caldwell is not, so far as I've ever heard, regarded as a humorist. People have told me that his stuff is not to be laughed at, that he writes almost altogether of tragic matters and that anybody who giggles at, say, *Tobacco Road,* is an enemy of mankind. Nuts. I have read *God's Little Acre* eight or ten times and think it's among the funniest books ever written. The same goes for *Journeyman.* This short novel was not very successful and the play somebody made out of it was an immediate flop.

Journeyman is the story of a small group of backwoods people in Georgia and of the havoc created by an itinerant preacher named Semon Dye who arrives among them, raises all manner of hell for a while, then goes away. Clay Horey is host to Preacher Semon Dye while Clay's neighbor Tom Rhodes furnishes most of the drinkin' licker. The social significance of the story, I suppose, is the dreariness of the lives these people lead—existence so dull that they welcome the arrival of such a consummate villain as Semon Dye.

The following episode, illustrating a remarkable method for escaping boredom, is among the bits of "nuisance literature" around my house, called that because I am forever forcing people to take it and read it, or insisting on reading it aloud to them. It is from *Journeyman.*

THE CRACK

By Erskine Caldwell

A hundred yards from Tom Rhodes's house Semon slowed down. He looked at the house and barn and at the outhouses scattered around the place without design.

"What's the matter now?" Clay asked, following his eyes and feeling the car slow down.

"It might not be a bad idea to stop and speak to Tom," Semon said. "I haven't seen him since yesterday."

Without waiting for Clay to reply, he turned into the driveway and drove down to the barnyard gate. He stopped the car, pocketed the key, and got out.

"Now I don't know where Tom might be," Clay said, walking toward the barn. "Sometimes he goes to town on Saturday, and sometimes he don't."

"There's his car in the shed. He ought to be around somewhere."

The Negro who worked around the house and barn came out of an outhouse.

"Where's Mr. Tom?" Clay asked.

"Down in the pasture," Frank said, pointing beyond the garden and orchard. "You can find him down there."

They climbed the barnyard fence at the gate and walked across the garden. The vegetables were up and growing well. Semon stopped and pulled up a carrot. After wiping the soil off with his hands he began eating it, taking big bites, one after the other, and crunching the pulp in his jaws.

Tom was nowhere to be seen in the pasture, but there was a cowshed near the creek. They went toward it, stepping gingerly along the crooked cowpath.

At the door Clay stopped and looked inside. There was Tom, perched on a stool, looking through a crack in the wall of the shed. He had not seen them.

"What in thunder are you doing peeping through that crack, Tom?" Clay said, stepping inside and stopping to look closely at Tom.

Tom jumped to his feet, his face suddenly red. He did not know what to do to hide his embarrassment.

"Nothing," he said, trying to laugh.

Semon went across the shed and bent over at the crack. He peered through it for a few minutes, shutting one eye and squinting the other.

"I don't see a thing but the woods over there," Semon said, standing erect and looking at Tom. But he was still wondering what it was that could be seen through the crack.

Tom did not try to explain.

"What in thunderation's going on over across there, Tom?" Clay asked. He bent over and looked through the crack in the wall. He shut one eye, squinted the other one, but he could still see nothing except the pine trees.

"Is somebody over there, Tom?" Semon asked.

Tom shook his head, trying not to meet the eyes of either
of them.

"I just come down here sometimes and sit," he said, hem
ming and hawing. "I don't have much else to do, so I jus
sit and look through the crack. It used to be that I coul
find plenty to do, but I've got so I'd rather stay down here."

"And look at nothing?" Semon asked in amazement.

"Well, there's nothing but the woods over there, I reckon
There's that, and something else. I don't know what."

"I'll be doggone," Clay said. "I never knew you did tha
before. There ain't much sense in doing it, is there, Tom?"

"No," Tom said. "I don't reckon there's a bit of sense in it
But I just do it anyway."

Semon sat down on one of the stools. He then saw th
jug that had been sitting all that time against the wall.

"I reckon you're going to be neighborly with the jug
won't you, Tom?" he said.

"That's what it's for. Just help yourself."

Semon took a long draft of the corn whisky and set th
jug down none too lightly. There was no floor under th
shed, only the bare earth, and so it did not break. He passe
the back of his hand across his mouth and licked it.

"Help yourself, Clay," Tom said. "That's what I make
for. Wouldn't be no sense in running it off if nobody mad
use of it."

While Clay and Tom were drinking from the jug Semo
moved over to the stool by the wall and bent his head again
the crack. He sat there looking through it with his e
squinted for several minutes. After that he raised his hea
and looked at the others rather sheepishly.

"See anything?" Clay asked.

"Not much."

"Move over, then, and let me take a look through it."

Clay sat down and looked through the crack. There w
nothing much to be seen except the trees on the other si
of the pasture. The fence over there that bordered that si
of the pasture was barbed wire, and the posts were split pi
He saw all that in a glance, and there was nothing else
see, but he continued to look through the crack as thou

he saw something that he had never seen before in his life.

"Where you folks headed for?" Tom asked Semon.

"To the schoolhouse. That's where we started. I don't reckon there's much up there to see, though."

"No," Tom said, moving restlessly on his stool. "No, there ain't much up there. Least, I never could see much up around there."

He turned around to see if Clay had finished looking through the crack. After waiting as long as he could he got up and went over there.

"What's the matter?" Clay asked.

"It's about my turn now."

He pushed Clay away from the stool and sat down to press his face against the wall where the crack was. He moved his head slightly to the left, then lowered it a fraction of an inch. After that he sat motionless.

"See anything, coz?" Semon said.

Tom said nothing.

"I reckon I'll take my other drink now, instead of later," Semon said. He picked up the jug and drank heavily.

After he had finished he handed it over to Clay.

"There wouldn't be much sense in going to the schoolhouse now," Semon said, shaking his head at Clay. "There's nothing much up there to go for."

"It's bound to be just like it was the last time I saw it," Tom agreed.

Semon walked nervously around the cowshed. He came to a stop beside Tom.

"Don't hog it all the time, coz," he said, pushing him. "Let white man take a look once in a while."

Tom got up and looked for the jug.

"I can't seem to remember when I liked to look at a thing so much as I do now," Semon said, adjusting his eye to the crack.

Clay leaned against the wall, taking out his harmonica. He tapped the flakes of tobacco and weed out of it, and drew it swiftly across his mouth. It made a sound like an automobile tire going flat.

He started playing "I've Got a Gal."

Semon, with his eye glued to the crack, began keeping time with his feet on the bare earth.

"That's the God-damnedest little slit in the whole world," Tom said. "I come down here and sit on the stool and look through it all morning sometimes. There's not a doggone thing to see but the trees over there, and maybe the fence posts, but I can't keep from looking to save my soul. It's the doggonest thing I ever saw in all my life."

Semon settled himself more comfortably on the stool.

"There's not a single thing to see," Tom said, "and then again there's the whole world to look at. Looking through the side of the shed ain't like nothing else I can think of. You sit there awhile, and the first thing you know, you can't get away from it. It gets a hold on a man like nothing else does. You sit there, screwing up your eye and looking at the trees or something, and you might start to thinking what a fool thing you're doing, but you don't give a cuss about that. All you care for is staying there and looking."

Semon continued keeping time to the harmonica with both feet. Neither of them made any sound on the bare ground, but he kept it up just the same.

"'She wore a little yellow dress——'"

Clay was playing as though his life depended upon it, and Tom was singing a line every once in a while. He hummed under his breath when he was not singing.

Semon was reaching for the glass jug. His hand was searching in a circle for it, but it was beyond his reach. He would not stop looking through the crack for even a second to see where the jug really was.

"Can't help you out none, Preacher," Tom said. "You'l have to come and get it. It's my time to look some now."

"'—those eyes were made for me to see.'"

Tom sang a line and stopped to talk again.

"You ought to give somebody else a chance to look, ever once in a while, Preacher."

Semon got up from the stool without moving his head. H stood there bent over until Tom shoved him out of his way

"'In the nighttime is the right time——'"

"Shove off, Preacher," Tom said, giving him a final push.

Semon sat down on the other stool, rubbing the strain from his left eye. He blinked several times, resuming the tapping of his feet.

"That's the God-damnedest slit I ever saw in all my life," Semon said. "You can look through there all day and never get tired. And come back the next day, and I'll bet it would look just as good. There's something about looking through a crack that nothing else in the whole wide world will give you."

Clay had warmed up until he could not stop. The song he was playing had long before run out, but the chorus would not end. He could not make himself quit.

Finally the harmonica filled up, and he had to stop. He was sorry the song was over.

Tom was still humming the tune, though, and he ended up with another line from the chorus.

"Coz, do that some more," Semon said. "I want to hear that piece again. I don't reckon I've ever heard a mouth organ play a prettier one."

"It's my time to look through the crack now."

"Here, take another drink, and me and Tom will give you the next two turns, instead of one. Just go ahead and play that pretty little piece some more. It makes me want to cry, it's that good, and I feel like crying over it now."

Clay drank, and jerked the harmonica across his lips. It sounded this time like air going into a tire.

With his head pressed tightly against the shed wall, Tom started humming again. He patted his feet on the ground, swinging into rhythm with the tune Clay was playing.

"There's never been but one gal like that in all the world," Semon said. The tears welled in his eyes and dripped against the backs of his hands. "If I could just look through the crack and see her I wouldn't ask to live no longer. That crack is the God-damnedest thing I ever looked through. I sit there and look, and think about that gal, thinking maybe I'll see her with the next bat of my eye, and all the time I'm looking clear to the back side of heaven."

He strode to the wall and pushed Tom away. Without

waiting to sit down first, he pressed his eye to the slit in the wall. After that he slowly sat down on the stool.

"'—you're the prettiest one and the sweetest one.'"

Tom stooped and picked up the jug. He took his drink and replaced it at Clay's feet. Clay was too busy then to stop for a drink. He could not stop.

"'When I'm loving you, I'm telling you——'"

Semon put his hand to his face and wiped the tears from his cheeks.

"I don't know what I'd do without that crack in the wall," Tom said. "I reckon I'd just dry up and die away, I'd be that sad about it. I come down here and sit and look, and I don't see nothing you can't see better from the outside, but that don't make a bit of difference. It's sitting there looking through the crack at the trees all day long that sort of gets me. I don't know what it is, and it might not be nothing at all when you figure it out. But it's not the knowing about it, anyway—it's just the sitting there and looking through it that sort of makes me feel like heaven can't be so doggone far away."

THE PROBLEM of what to do with fatheads who insist on demonstrating their card tricks in company has never been so adequately handled as by the late Stephen Leacock. Mr. Leacock does the thing neatly and briefly in—

A MODEL DIALOGUE

By Stephen Leacock

THE DRAWING-ROOM JUGGLER, having slyly got hold of the pack of cards at the end of the game of whist, says:

"Ever see any card tricks? Here's rather a good one; pick a card."

"Thank you, I don't want a card."

"No, but just pick one, any one you like, and I'll tell you which one you pick."

"You'll tell who?"

"No, no; I mean, I'll know which it is, don't you see? Go on now, pick a card."

"Any one I like?"

"Yes."

"Any color at all?"

"Yes, yes."

"Any suit?"

"Oh yes; do go on."

"Well, let me see, I'll–pick–the–ace of spades."

"Great Caesar! I mean you are to pull a card out of the pack."

"Oh, to pull it out of the pack. All right–I've got it."

"Have you picked one?"

"Yes, it's the three of hearts. Did you know it?"

"Hang it! Don't tell me like that. You spoil the thing. Here, try again. Pick a card."

"All right, I've got it."

"Put it back in the pack. Thanks." (Shuffle, shuffle, shuffle–flip.) "There, is that it?" (Triumphantly.)

"I don't know. I lost sight of it."

"Lost sight of it! Confound it, you have to look at it and see what it is."

"Oh, you want me to look at the front of it!"

"Why, of course! Now then, pick a card."

"All right. I've picked it. Go ahead."

(Shuffle, shuffle, shuffle–flip.)

"Say, confound you, did you put that card back in the pack?"

"Why, no. I kept it."

"Holy Moses! Listen. Pick–a–card–just one–look at it–see what it is–then put it back–do you understand?"

"Oh, perfectly. Only I don't see how you are ever going to do it. You must be awfully clever."

(Shuffle, shuffle, shuffle–flip.)

"There you are; that's your card, now, isn't it?"

(This is the supreme moment.)

"*No. That is not my card.*" (This is a flat lie, but heaven will pardon you for it.)

"Not that card! Say—just hold on a second. Here now, watch what you're at this time. I can do this cursed thing, mind you, every time. I've done it on Father, on Mother, and on everyone that's ever come around our place. Pick a card." (Shuffle, shuffle, shuffle—flip, bang.) "There, that's your card."

"*No. I am sorry. That is not my card.* But won't you try it again? Please do. Perhaps you are a little excited—I'm afraid I was rather stupid. Won't you go and sit quietly by yourself on the back veranda for half an hour and then try? You have to go home? Oh, I'm so sorry. It must be such an awfully clever little trick. Good night!"

AND HERE IS Mr. Benchley again. This piece is, to my mind, the best thing ever written about the mental state of a man facing a dentist appointment. There is one thing about it, however, for which Mr. Benchley should have his lifeblood spattered on the pavement. I refer to the title.

THE TOOTH, THE WHOLE TOOTH, AND NOTHING BUT THE TOOTH

By Robert Benchley

SOME WELL-KNOWN SAYING (it doesn't make much difference what) is proved by the fact that everyone likes to talk about his experiences at the dentist's. For years and years little articles like this have been written on the subject, little jokes like some that I shall presently make have been made, and people in general have been telling other people just what emotions they experience when they crawl into the old red plush guillotine.

They like to explain to each other how they feel when the dentist puts "that buzzer thing" against their bicuspids, and, if sufficiently pressed, they will describe their sensations on mouthing a rubber dam.

"I'll tell you what I hate," they will say with great relish, "when he takes that little nutpick and begins to scrape. Ugh!"

"Oh, I'll tell you what's worse than that," says the friend, not to be outdone, "when he is poking around careless like, and strikes a nerve. Wow!"

And if there are more than two people at the experience meeting, everyone will chip in and tell what he or she considers to be the worst phase of the dentist's work, all present enjoying the narration hugely and none so much as the narrator who has suffered so.

This sort of thing has been going on ever since the first mammoth gold tooth was hung out as a bait to folks in search of a good time. (By the way, when did the present obnoxious system of dentistry begin? It can't be so very long ago that the electric auger was invented, and where would a dentist be without an electric auger? Yet you never hear of Amalgam Filling Day, or any other anniversary in the dental year. There must be a conspiracy of silence on the part of the trade to keep hidden the names of the men who are responsible for all this.)

However many years it may be that dentists have been plying their trade, in all that time people have never tired of talking about their teeth. This is probably due to the inscrutable workings of Nature, who is always supplying new teeth to talk about.

As a matter of fact the actual time and suffering in the chair is only a fraction of the gross expenditure connected with the affair. The preliminary period, about which nobody talks, is much the worse. This dates from the discovery of the wayward tooth and extends to the moment when the dentist places his foot on the automatic hoist which jacks you up into range. Giving gas for tooth extraction is all very humane in its way, but the time for anesthetics is when the patient first decides that he must go to the dentist. From

then on, until the first excavation is started, should b
shrouded in oblivion.

There is probably no moment more appalling than that i
which the tongue, running idly over the teeth in a momen
of carefree play, comes suddenly upon the ragged edge of
space from which the old familiar filling has disappeared
The world stops and you look meditatively up to the corne
of the ceiling. Then quickly you draw your tongue away an
try to laugh the affair off, saying to yourself:

"Stuff and nonsense, my good fellow! There is nothing
the matter with your tooth. Your nerves are upset after a
hard day's work, that's all."

Having decided this to your satisfaction, you slyly, and
with a poor attempt at being casual, slide the tongue back
along the line of adjacent teeth, hoping against hope that
it will reach the end without mishap.

But there it is! There can be no doubt about it this time.
The tooth simply has got to be filled by someone, and the
only person who can fill it with anything permament is a
dentist. You wonder if you might not be able to patch it up
yourself for the time being—a year or so—perhaps with a
little spruce gum and a coating of New Skin. It is fairly far
back and wouldn't have to be a very sightly job.

But this has an impracticable sound, even to you. You
might want to eat some peanut brittle (you never can tell
when someone might offer you peanut brittle these days),
and the New Skin, while serviceable enough in the case of
cream soups and custards, couldn't be expected to stand up
under heavy crunching.

So you admit that, since the thing has got to be filled, it
might as well be a dentist who does the job.

This much decided, all that is necessary is to call him up
and make an appointment.

Let us say that this resolve is made on Tuesday. That
afternoon you start to look up the dentist's number in the
telephone book. A great wave of relief sweeps over you when
you discover that it isn't there. How can you be expected to
make an appointment with a man who hasn't got a telephone? And how can you have a tooth filled without making

an appointment? The whole thing is impossible, and that's all there is to it. God knows you did your best.

On Wednesday there is a slightly more insistent twinge, owing to bad management of a sip of ice water. You decide that you simply must get in touch with that dentist when you get back from lunch. But you know how those things are. First one thing and then another came up, and a man came in from Providence who had to be shown around the office, and by the time you had a minute to yourself it was five o'clock. And anyway, the tooth didn't bother you again. You wouldn't be surprised if, by being careful, you could get along with it as it is until the end of the week when you will have more time. A man has to think of his business, after all, and what is a little personal discomfort in the shape of an unfilled tooth to the satisfaction of work well done in the office?

By Saturday morning you are fairly reconciled to going ahead, but it is only a half day and probably he has no appointments left anyway. Monday is really the time. You can begin the week afresh. After all, Monday is really the logical day to start in going to the dentist.

Bright and early Monday morning you make another try at the telephone book, and find, to your horror, that sometime between now and last Tuesday the dentist's name and number have been inserted into the directory. There it is. There is no getting around it: "Burgess, Jas. Kendal, DDS. . . . Courtland-2654." There is really nothing left to do but to call him up. Fortunately the line is busy, which gives you a perfectly good excuse for putting it over until Tuesday. But on Tuesday luck is against you and you get a clear connection with the doctor himself. An appointment is arranged for Thursday afternoon at three-thirty.

Thursday afternoon, and here it is only Tuesday morning! Almost anything may happen between now and then. We might declare war on Mexico, and off you'd have to go, dentist appointment or no dentist appointment. Surely a man couldn't let a date to have a tooth filled stand in the way of his doing his duty to his country. Or the social revolution might start on Wednesday, and by Thursday the whole town might be in ashes. You can picture yourself standing, Thursday afternoon at three-thirty, on the ruins of the City Hall, fighting off marauding bands of Reds, and saying to yourself with a sigh of relief: "Only to think! At this time I was to have been climbing into the dentist's chair!" You never can tell when your luck will turn in a thing like that.

But Wednesday goes by and nothing happens. And Thursday morning dawns without even a word from the dentist saying that he has been called suddenly out of town to lecture before the Incisor Club. Apparently everything is working against you.

By this time your tongue has taken up a permanent resting place in the vacant tooth and is causing you to talk indistinctly and incoherently. Somehow you feel that if the dentist opens your mouth and finds the tip of your tongue in the tooth he will be deceived and go away without doing anything.

The only thing left is for you to call him up and say that you have just killed a man and are being arrested and can't possibly keep your appointment. But any dentist would see through that. He would laugh right into his transmitter at you. There is probably no excuse which it would be possible to invent which a dentist has not already heard eighty or ninety times. No, you might as well see the thing through now.

Luncheon is a ghastly rite. The whole left side of your jaw has suddenly developed an acute sensitiveness and the disaffection has spread to the four teeth on either side of the original one. You doubt if it will be possible for him to touch it at all. Perhaps all he intends to do this time is to look at it anyway. You might even suggest that to him. You could very easily come in again soon and have him do the actual work.

Three-thirty draws near. A horrible time of day at best. Just when a man's vitality is lowest. Before stepping in out of the sunlight into the building in which the dental parlor is, you take one look about you at the happy people scurrying by in the street. Carefree children that they are! What do they know of life? Probably that man in the silly-looking hat never had trouble with so much as his baby teeth. There they go, pushing and jostling each other, just as if within ten feet of them there was not a man who stands on the brink of the Great Misadventure. Ah well! Life is like that!

Into the elevator. The last hope is gone. The door clangs and you look hopelessly about you at the stupid faces of your fellow passengers. How can people be so clownish? Of course there is always the chance that the elevator will fall and that you will all be terribly hurt. But that is too much to expect. You dismiss it from your thoughts as too impractical, too visionary. Things don't work out as happily as that in real life.

You feel a certain glow of heroic pride when you tell the operator the right floor number. You might just as easily have told him a floor too high or too low, and that would at least have caused delay. But after all, a man must prove himself a man and the least you can do is to meet Fate with an unflinching eye and give the right floor number.

Too often has the scene in the dentist's waiting room been described for me to try to do it again here. They are all alike. The antiseptic smell, the ominous hum from the operating rooms, the ancient *Digests,* and the silent, sullen group of waiting patients, each trying to look unconcerned and cordially disliking everyone else in the room—all these have been sung by poets of far greater lyric powers than mine. (Not that I really think that they *are* greater than mine, but that's the customary form of excuse for not writing something you haven't got time or space to do. As a matter of fact I think I could do it much better than it has ever been done before.)

I can only say that, as you sit looking, with unseeing eyes, through a large book entitled, *The War in Pictures,* you would gladly change places with the most lowly of God's creatures. It is inconceivable that there should be anyone worse off than you, unless perhaps it is some of the poor wretches who are waiting with you.

That one over in the armchair, nervously tearing to shreds a copy of the *Dental Review and Practical Inlay Worker.*

She may have something frightful the trouble with her. She couldn't possibly look more worried. Perhaps it is very, very painful. This thought cheers you up considerably. What cowards women are in times like these!

And then there comes the sound of voices from the next room.

"All right, Doctor, and if it gives me any more pain shall I call you up? . . . Do you think that it will bleed much more? . . . Saturday morning, then, at eleven. . . . Good-by, Doctor."

And a middle-aged woman emerges (all women are middle-aged when emerging from the dentist's office) looking as if she were playing the big emotional scene in *John Ferguson.* A wisp of hair waves dissolutely across her forehead between her eyes. Her face is pale, except for a slight inflammation at the corners of her mouth, and in her eyes is that faraway look of one who has been face to face with Life. But she is through. She should care how she looks.

The nurse appears and looks inquiringly at each one in the room. Each one in the room evades the nurse's glance in one last, futile attempt to fool someone and get away without seeing the dentist. But she spots you and nods pleasantly. God, how pleasantly she nods! There ought to be a law against people being as pleasant as that.

"The doctor will see you now," she says.

The English language may hold a more disagreeable combination of words than "The doctor will see you now." I am willing to concede something to the phrase "Have you anything to say before the current is turned on?" That may be worse for the moment, but it doesn't last so long. For continued, unmitigating depression, I know nothing to equal "The doctor will see you now." But I'm not narrow-minded about it. I'm willing to consider other possibilities.

Smiling feebly, you trip over the extended feet of the man next to you, and stagger into the delivery room, where amid a ghastly array of death masks of teeth, blue flames waving eerily from Bunsen burners, and the drowning sound of perpetually running water which chokes and gurgles at intervals, you sink into the chair and close your eyes.

But now let us consider the spiritual exaltation that comes when you are at last let down and turned loose. It is all over, and what did it amount to? Why, nothing at all. A-ha-ha-ha-ha-ha! Nothing at all.

You suddenly develop a particular friendship for the dentist. A splendid fellow, really. You ask him questions about his instruments. What does he use this thing for, for instance? Well, well, to think of a little thing like that making all that trouble. A-ha-ha-ha-ha-ha! . . . And the dentist's family, how are they? Isn't that fine!

Gaily you shake hands with him and straighten your tie. Forgotten is the fact that you have another appointment with him for Monday. There is no such thing as Monday. You are through for today, and all's right with the world.

As you pass out through the waiting room you leer at the others unpleasantly. The poor fishes! Why can't they take their medicine like grown people and not sit there moping as if they were going to be shot?

Heigh-ho! Here's the elevator man! A charming fellow! You wonder if he knows that you have just had a tooth filled. You feel tempted to tell him and slap him on the back. You feel tempted to tell everyone out in the bright, cheery street. And what a wonderful street it is, too! All full of nice, black snow and water. After all, life is sweet!

And then you go and find the first person whom you can accost without being arrested and explain to him just what it was that the dentist did to you, and how you felt, and what you have got to have done next time.

Which brings us right back to where we were in the beginning, and perhaps accounts for everyone's liking to divulge their dental secrets to others. It may be a sort of hysterical relief that, for the time being, it is all over with.

DOMESTIC SCIENCE

VI. DOMESTIC SCIENCE

BACK AROUND the finn de sickle (1930) Nunnally Johnson wrote a series of short stories. These stories were bunched together into a book called *There Ought to Be a Law.* Over the years I remembered one of them distinctly but I ran into trouble when I began searching for it.

I don't suppose there was ever in history a short story that fled and skulked before such a posse as went out after this one. Mr. Johnson himself was unable to help me. He only published one book in his life and he didn't have a copy of it; nor did he know anybody on earth who had a copy; nor did he have any idea of where I might find one. I did everything but set the Pinkertons on the trail. I myself began exploring secondhand bookshops in Manhattan and spent one entire day in the stores on lower Fourth Avenue. I flung a human bloodhound named George Gode into action with authority to advertise, tunnel, blast, and dredge. At last he came up with a copy of the book. He telephoned his flash and I hurried to his office. He had it all right and as I took it in my hand I noticed some printing on it. It said, "Doubleday, Doran." I spoke of the Deity at some length. Here I had spent a month in the search and all of that time there was a copy standing on a shelf in the office of my own publishers, and I didn't once think of going there with my problem.

Well, the candle was worth the wick, or however it goes. The story from which the book got its title is—

THERE OUGHT TO BE A LAW

By Nunnally Johnson

I'D SAID there wasn't a comfortable chair in the house, so Margaret had got this one, precisely what I wanted. Placing it on the right side of the fireplace, under a good reading lamp, she shoved its predecessor, a rather smaller armchair, back against the wall, moved two straight chairs upstairs, pushed the love seat toward the radiator, the divan farther out into the room, a chair from the sun parlor into the living room, and rehung three pictures.

"That's fine," I said. "Now we're settled."

Five days later she moved the new chair over to the left side of the fireplace, swapped the reading lamp for one in a guest room, brought the two straight chairs back downstairs, switched the divan and the love seat, and rehung five pictures.

"That's better," I said. "Now we're set."

Exactly a week later, in the evening, I was sitting in the new chair in its new position and reading a very gripping novel, when suddenly a cold chill swept over me, followed by such a shudder as one is said to experience when somebody walks over one's future grave. I looked up, frightened. Margaret stood in the center of the room, a thoughtful hand to her mouth; she was studying the arrangement of the furniture.

"Darling," I said.

"That divan," she said, as though to herself, "is wrong. It ought to be over there. We could put it over there, swap that butterfly table and that arm table, push that large chair over there——"

"I know," I said wearily, "and rehang eight pictures."

"What?"

"Listen, honey," I said, feeling that matters were beginning to call for a bit of talking over. "Why don't you just sit down and relax for a moment?"

"Relax?"

"Just relax. Let the muscles sag naturally. Let the hands droop over the arms of the chair, like little lilies, as it were. Let the head fall back against the pillow. Let all of the air out of the lungs. The truth is, you are overwrought; the purchase of this chair has been too much for you emotionally. You need relaxation."

"That divan," she said, "is wrong."

"Wrong? What's wrong with it?"

"It's in the wrong place."

"It's in practically the only place it hasn't been in this room. But we might try it out in the kitchen, or even in the garage. How would that suit you?"

"I believe it belongs back where it was."

"Look, darling," I said; "did I ever tell you the story of my uncle Alfred, somewhat along these same lines?"

"Is that the barmy one?"

"I wish you wouldn't keep referring to my relatives as barmy," I protested. "Every time I mention somebody related to me you pop up with that same question. Do I ever say anything about that half-witted cousin of yours—the one in Sing Sing?"

"The love seat's not right there either."

"What do you say we put it on the roof?"

"What?"

"Sit down, dear," I repeated. "We've reached the point now where we'll have to speak plainly, with frankness on both sides. Things can go on no longer as they are. We are face to face with a problem—one that's got to be solved immediately. And it may be that Uncle Alfred's experience can help us."

"That spindle-leg table——"

My uncle Alfred—I insisted firmly—did not marry until late in life—that is, late in life as marriage is figured in our family. At thirty-two he was still single, apparently a confirmed bachelor, and living in a comfortable parlor-bedroom-and-bath in the Murray Hill district, where he'd moved ten years before.

It was a very quiet life that he led. Occasionally he went out of an evening; generally in the company of one lady or another of unquestioned propriety. They had dinner in the dining room of a proper hotel and then attended the current Pulitzer-prize-winning play or its equivalent. At home finally, after seeing her to her door, he smoked a last pipe, crawled into bed, and was almost instantly asleep with a clean, clear conscience.

Other evenings he escorted this young lady or that to the apartment of married friends, where bridge was played; or else, in an old dressing gown and pajamas, his feet in felt slippers, he sat beside his fire and read a good book, or just sat and thought out big problems which presented themselves in the editorial pages of newspapers.

Quiet it was, but comfortable, and himself as even-tempered and serene a man as I've ever known. We—the rest of the family—saw him regularly every Sunday afternoon, when he called on Grandmother, and on Grandmother's birthday, Thanksgiving, and Christmas, when we all sat down to dinner together. Sometimes we wondered, naturally, about his marrying, but as the years passed and nothing happened, we finally gave in to the inevitable conclusion that he was too happy in his present state to risk himself in another.

We had just about settled this point to our own satisfaction when Uncle Alfred walked in with his bride. They had met quietly, courted quietly, and wedded quietly, as was Uncle Alfred's way. Her name, he said, was Victorine, and as soon as they got settled in a new apartment he'd leased, he hoped we'd all call on them.

At first glance she was just the girl for him—sweet, gentle of manner, pretty in a demure fashion, and with none of this vo-de-odo-boop-adoop-doop stuff about her. Grandmother and the girls, Uncle Alfred's sisters, took to her on the spot. "A womanly woman," they said. "She'll make a home for Alfred."

I liked her, too, but it seemed to me there was something a little odd there. Nothing you could place your finger on, but a nervous eye—an eye that shifted uncertainly from divan to chair, chair to table, table to picture—and hands that opened and shut eagerly, as though aching to be at something whereof I knew nothing. Too, she licked her lips with her tongue wickedly, once when her eyes rested on a hassock which Grandmother had by her chair. But, as I say, nothing you could place definitely; just a suggestion of something a trifle queer.

They were happy, very happy, that six months. I rarely saw them myself, but the reports were good. The apartment had been found and furnished, the happy couple had adjusted themselves to their new mode of life, and the goose hung high. We were all quite pleased.

Then one morning Uncle Alfred called up George, my brother, who also worked downtown, and they had lunch together. It puzzled George, because it was so unheard of; Uncle Alfred wasn't the lunching-together kind. And the lunch itself was just as queer. It apparently had no point whatever; Uncle Alfred, seemingly somehow worried, just sat and ate and stared thoughtfully at George.

"You and Julie all right?" he asked finally.

"Couldn't be better," George told him.

"That's fine," Uncle Alfred said. Then he sighed deeply. "All—all settled now?"

"Oh sure." Since George and Julie had been married for four years, the question did not seem to have much sense to it. "We're settled all right."

"That's fine," Uncle Alfred said again. "That's mighty fine." Once more he sighed. "I was just thinking of your furniture. Is that all settled too?"

"Of course. Why?"

"Oh, nothing! Nothing at all!" Uncle Alfred hastened to explain. "Just interested, you know—about how you were getting on, and your furniture, and everything. Just wanted to know."

"Yes," George said, "we're all set, I suppose."

"That's fine. That's mighty fine. That's mighty fine indeed."

He started to say something else, George said, but after some form of spiritual struggle he decided not to. But

George noticed, he told me, that Uncle Alfred wasn't quite his old serene self; there was a faint, hunted look in his eyes. He was nervous, too, and at the passing of every female clutched his chair and the table desperately, one with each hand.

"Mighty queer," George added.

"Mighty queer indeed," I agreed.

"Not like the old Uncle Alfred."

"A world of difference."

Silence settled down then over the little love nest, as silence can settle down over a love nest only in New York, and we heard no more from it for three weeks, when once more Uncle Alfred emerged from the murk, this time to confer with his brother, my uncle Frank. And now there was no getting away from it: Uncle Alfred was suffering. Something terrible was obviously gnawing at his vitals.

"Frank," he said, "how do you get along with Madge?"

"Madge who?" asked Uncle Frank, who was absent-minded.

"Madge, your wife."

"Oh, her!" Relieved, Uncle Frank laughed. "Why, we get along first rate. Why? Is there talk?"

"I mean about furniture," Uncle Alfred insisted. "Does she worry you much about furniture?"

"Furniture!" Uncle Frank was naturally astonished. "Why should she worry me about furniture?"

For a minute Uncle Alfred said nothing but just bit his lower lip. Then: "Frank," he said, "under ordinary circumstances I'd be the last man to utter a word about my wife. Under ordinary circumstances a man who did that would be a cad and a bounder. But these are not ordinary circumstances, and there is no use trying to blind myself to the fact any longer: Victorine, Frank, moves furniture!"

"For a living?" exclaimed Uncle Frank, who was also a little slow on the uptake.

"No, no! For fun, I suppose."

Then it all came out. Uncle Alfred had married a living-room-furniture motorman, a divan-and-chair manipulator. Under this surface of sweetness and gentleness there lurked

ı Victorine a demon that just couldn't bear to see a table
ot on the go daily. Her eyes had glittered, her palms itched,
'hen first she entered the new apartment Uncle Alfred had
ot, and from that day on, he explained sadly, he had had
o peace.

"We've all but got the furniture on wheels," he said
ıoodily. "The living room has got ruts and grooves in it
ke a railroad freight yard, and all day and half the night
ıere is a steady rumble of heavy pieces of furniture being
ıoved from this place to that. That's the kind of thing that
psets a man."

Never having noticed his own furniture for some years,
Incle Frank did not know exactly what to say.

"The way I like a piece of furniture," Uncle Alfred went
n, "is that when you leave it on a spot in the morning it
still there on that spot when you get home that evening,
ot up in the attic or out in the nasturtium bed, or some-
'here like that. That big chair of mine that I had before I
'as married was never moved two inches during the whole
n years I had it; about the only way I can sit in it now
sort of hop it as it goes by, hoping it won't be carried up
down any steps."

"Well," Uncle Frank said uncertainly, "did you ever
ıention it to her? I mean about not shoving the hell out of
ıe furniture?"

"Once I said something."

"Well?"

"She didn't hear me; she was moving the piano," Uncle
lfred said sadly. "I didn't want to speak too loudly, be-
ıuse in all other respects she is a very delicate girl."

"Myself," Uncle Frank said, "I'd say something to her, and
l say it good and loud."

"You would?"

"I wouldn't hesitate a second."

"If Madge was that way, would you say something to her?"

"Madge who?"

"Madge, your wife."

"Oh, her! Sure I'd say it to Madge. Why not?"

When these accounts were brought to the family there

developed, I was interested to note, two schools of though male and female. The uncles and nephews were with Unc Alfred to a man; the girls, the aunts and nieces, on the oth hand, claimed to be able to see eye to eye with Victorin "The child," they said, "is simply trying to make a home f a man who has become self-centered and cranky throug living alone so long. How on earth can one tell how thin are going to look until you try them out a bit! Land sak alive!"

Grandmother alone took no side, having for years been t weak for such jolly fun as pushing beds about the hous "But when I was a girl!" she hinted darkly.

Sunday afternoon Uncle Alfred and Victorine called pay their respects, for the first time in some weeks. And the were signs in him of the strain that he was undergoing. H lips were set, and though he smiled when he entered, was only with his mouth. His eyes were hard. Victorin however, was her customary sweet, gentle self, apparent unaware of anything wrong.

"We've just got a new tea table," she said laughingly, "ar it's just thrown the whole place out of proportion! I' experimented and experimented——"

The girls, at a signal from Grandmother, promptly stepp up and surrounded her and, before she knew what was g ing on, had whisked her out of the room, for Uncle Alfr had begun to look as though he were going to explode. Th in itself marked the occasion as one of no little importanc for never before had Uncle Alfred ever looked as thoug he were going to explode. The men, left alone, sat dow uneasily. Uncle Alfred had changed. There was no que tion about it; he had changed greatly.

"Well?" Uncle Frank said tentatively.

"She's still at it." Uncle Alfred spoke morbidly.

"Still at the divan, eh?"

"It's the dining room now," he said. "She's got the tab and the dresser and the bureau and whatever else it spinning around until half the time I'm sitting down to jardiniere or an umbrella stand to eat. Half the time I do know where I'm at."

"Didn't you say anything to her?"

"I'm waiting."

"Waiting for what?"

"She'll reach a point someday."

"What point?"

"I'm not going to do or say anything rashly," Uncle Alfred xplained. "I'm just going to be patient and see what hapens. Maybe she'll shake herself out of it. If she doesn't——" Ie stopped.

"Patience may be the best policy," Uncle Frank said, but I doubt it."

"When the time comes I'll act, and act promptly."

As it happened, the time came only two days later, and vhen I tell you about it, and the consequences, I want you remember that it was all the occasion of much embarassment on the part of the family, which had always prided self on its circumspectness. Never before had such a thing appened to our family and, God willing, Margaret, nothing ike it ever will again.

It seems that on Tuesday night Uncle Alfred had to work ate at the office, taking inventory or something like that. Aidnight had come, with something like fifteen hours of ard work to his credit, when finally he was able to get way. Never, he told me later, had he felt so tired. Ordinarily is trip home from the office was a little depressing; he was vorried usually about the probable whereabouts of his big, omfortable chair, which rarely was to be found in the same lace two nights running. This night it never occurred to im. All he could think of was his bed, his soft feather ed—how warm it was, how comfortable, how delicious it vould be to lay his tired frame on it, pull up the covers, nd drift off to the most welcome sleep he could remember.

Letting himself in softly, he found the apartment in darkess; Victorine had gone to bed. He struck a match, lest the lare of electric lights awaken her, and tiptoed through he living room. He could hear her breathing, softly and egularly, when he entered the bedroom.

Still in the dark, with his hands stretched before him, he found his night chair, and sank into it with a heavy sigh.

For five minutes he rested there, relaxed. Then he began to undress, and as he went about it, slowly, with tired fingers the soft breathing across the room touched him. The thought of her there, so quiet and innocent and sweet and gentle in her sleep, softened him, and he was ashamed of himself for his impatience with her. After all, she was such a child, and she couldn't know all of his peculiarities immediately; and this that had annoyed him was so trifling, so unimportant. He resolved to take a broader view of things.

Feeling his way to the bathroom, where, after he had closed the door, he turned on the lights and brushed his teeth, this thought sank deeper and deeper in him, and tomorrow, he told himself as he switched off the lights and started back to the bedroom, his wife would find the same old tender, understanding Alfred once more.

It was with this kindly thought in mind that he yawned and stretched and shuffled over to his bed—his warm, comfortable bed, where rest would come at last—and so thrilling was the prospect that, turning his back to it, he threw up his arms in pure abandon, and with a happy, ecstatic smile on his face, he fell straight back—back to a soft, warm, luxurious splash in the broad bosom of feathers.

The next instant Margaret, the dark of the room, the still of the night were split with a bellow of pain that cleared the windows and reverberated throughout the neighborhood, followed almost immediately by a shriek of fright, a long, high, superbly sustained screech, as Victorine sat up suddenly in bed and flashed on the light.

Uncle Alfred was scrambling to his feet, one forearm hugging the back of his skull, from the floor where his bed had always been, but now was not, having been shifted during the day in an unannounced rearrangement of the bedroom appointments.

Was Uncle Alfred mad? It is possible to say, without exaggeration, that he was beside himself.

A million stars spattered before his tear-wet eyes, spasms of pain shot through him from head to foot, and before his horrified wife he performed a kind of Indian dance in his bare feet and pajamas, clutching his throbbing head and oaring loud, unintelligible sounds indicative of suffering, ury, and insane determination.

"That's a nice thing to do!" he kept shouting. "That's a nighty nice thing to do!"

"Darling, are you hurt?"

Lights were appearing in windows in near-by apartment ouses, and there was a shout or two of inquiry, none of which my uncle Alfred heard.

"Just wait!" he muttered, sitting down and squeezing his ead with his hands to ease the pain. "Try to kill me, will ou? Try to kill me in my own home! Well, just wait—you ust wait!"

Talk like this alarmed Victorine, who still did not quite nderstand what had happened. Getting hastily out of bed, he donned slippers and dressing gown and ran to the bath-oom for whatever first aid was there. When she returned vith a damp cloth and a bottle of bicarbonate of soda, her avorite remedy for all ails, Uncle Alfred was on his feet urveying the room, and at the expression on his face she lropped the rag and soda and nearly swooned.

"So that's it!" he said thickly. His eyes strayed to the ed, now located at the far end of the room. "So that's it, h! Shifted it and wouldn't tell me! Trying to kill me——"

His eyes lighted now on her, and at the insane demon urking in them as he advanced on her, teeth bared, hands lutching, Victorine went pale and staggered back against he wall.

When the policeman arrived from the corner, summoned nd accompanied by the superintendent, who opened the all door with his passkey, Uncle Alfred had Victorine by he throat with one hand and was pointing violently to the pot where his head had banged the floor.

"That's where the bed belonged!" he was shouting. "That's vhere it always has been and that's where it always ought o be! The next time a bed is moved in this apartment——"

The cop was a family man—as he said later, he respected American womanhood—and his blood boiled at the sight. Needless to say, neither he nor the superintendent, who also espected American womanhood as well as the specimen of

Swedish womanhood that he had married, handled Uncl
Alfred with anything like gentleness. In fact they pushe
him around quite a bit before approaching the formality o
investigating the circumstances leading up to the assault.

"You brute!" the cop said finally. "You get a fine littl
wife like this little lady and you got to choke her! You're a
fine American, you are! A mighty fine American indeed!" H
turned to Victorine. "Don't worry, little lady," he said. "It'l
be a long time before he'll have another chance to chok
anybody." He glared at Uncle Alfred. "What's your name
you bulshevik?"

"Parker," Uncle Alfred said—"Alfred Coolidge Parker.

"Well, Mr. Parker," the cop said, taking out his boo
and beginning to write, "I'll have you in the can for si
months for this, or my name ain't Vladislov Kaminoffski.

"Put me down for witness," the superintendent said. "M
name's Olaf Swenson."

"Now, little lady," Policeman Kaminoffski said, "let'
hear all about it. What happened?"

Still sobbing faintly, Victorine tried to answer. "I don'
know," she faltered. "All I know is he's become unbalanced
I was asleep and I was waked by his shouting, and he go
to dancing around, and then when I went to help him h
choked me." Then she broke down.

Policeman Kaminoffski clenched his fists.

"I'll call the wagon," Superintendent Swenson said.

"Good." Kaminoffski turned back to Uncle Alfred, wh
was beginning to get panicky. "Now, you," he said, juttin
out his chin, "what you got to say for yourself? Spit it out
and be quick about it."

Uncle Alfred told him. Beginning at the beginning, h
told him the whole story, from his heavy day at the office t
his unhappy drop to the floor where his bed should hav
been. And as he talked a curious thing happened. At th
first mention of the shifting of furniture Policeman Kami
noffski started; he looked at Uncle Alfred suspiciously
Then, presently, as Uncle Alfred proceeded, his suspicio
departed, and he began to nod his head sympathetically
Once, at a point that struck him as unusually noteworthy, h

turned to Mr. Swenson with a significant look, and they both nodded their heads. Uncle Alfred, noticing but not understanding, took heart. When he had finished, Policeman Kaminoffski put one hand fraternally on his shoulder.

"My wife," he said, "is just about the same way, only worse. I just want to tell you one instance——"

"Mrs. Swenson moves everything," the superintendent put in. "Half the time I don't know where the whole dining room is, much less the table itself."

"—one instance," insisted Policeman Kaminoffski, taking off his cap and sitting down. "But sit down, Mr. Parker, and you, too, Swenson. I want to tell you about what my wife did the other day."

Swenson drew up two more chairs, which he and Uncle Alfred took, and Victorine, a little bewildered, withdrew across the bedroom.

"I had me a ash-tray stand, one of these smoking stands," the cop went on, "and I always like it at my right elbow, so's I can just flick my cigar without I've got to look for a place to flick it. Well, sir, you can believe me or not, but that ash-tray stand gets shoved around, from the left side to the right side, from the right side to the left side, and back and forth, and it just nearly run me crazy——"

"Have a cigar," interrupted Superintendent Swenson sociably, taking several from his pocket and offering them.

"Don't mind if I do," Policeman Kaminoffski said.

"Thanks," said Uncle Alfred.

"Mrs. Swenson," said Mr. Swenson, lighting up, "don't count her day is complete until she has changed things around a little."

"Don't it beat all?" the cop asked.

"The other day," Mr. Swenson continued, "she got a new little hassock. You know what a hassock is?"

"It's a fish, isn't it?" asked Kaminoffski.

"No, it's a little stool, kind of. Well, what I mean, gentlemen, if it was any of us that got a hassock we would say, 'Well, we have got a hassock and what of it?' and then we'd throw it on the floor and there it would be for whenever we wanted it. But Mrs. Swenson! If that hassock's been one place it's been a thousand. I bet I stumbled over that hassock a million times, without exaggeration."

"I'd like to bet you ten thousand dollars," the cop said to Uncle Alfred, "that this ain't the first time that Mrs. Parker has moved things around a little."

"The first time!" Uncle Alfred exclaimed.

Policeman Kaminoffski nodded. "I knew it," he said to Mr. Swenson. "You can always tell. If they move things once, they'll move them again. With women like that," he added, "nobody would ever get settled, if they lived as long as Methuslem."

"I can tell you another thing about Mrs. Swenson," Mr. Swenson said. "You take the time she got that corner closet——"

The doorbell rang and Policeman Kaminoffski frowned in annoyance. Uncle Alfred went to answer it, and as he opened the door two more policemen leaped in and grabbed him; but at his yelp of fright Policeman Kaminoffski came to his aid and secured his release. The reinforcements, it seemed, had come with the wagon.

"Who sent for any wagon?" Policeman Kaminoffski asked irritably. "We don't need any wagon here."

"Somebody sent," one of the officers insisted. "We wouldn't come without we were sent for."

"It was a mistake," Kaminoffski said. "Take it back."

"No, it was not a mistake either!" Victorine stepped forward, her face white with anger. "That idiot," she said, pointing at Policeman Kaminoffski, "ordered it and he's going to use it. I'm charging my husband with assault and battery, if that's what it is, and you're going to take him."

All the policemen and Uncle Alfred and Mr. Swenson looked at one another, and then back at Victorine, now as furious as Uncle Alfred had been a short time ago.

"I'll arrest her too," Kaminoffski said to Uncle Alfred, "if you say the word."

"What's all this, anyway?" asked one of the cops who had come with the wagon. "Don't you know who you're arresting?"

"He's arresting my husband," Victorine told him. "My

usband attacked me like a fiend, and this idiot"—she eemed bent on making Policeman Kaminoffski uncomfort- ble—"has been sitting around here talking nonsense for fteen minutes. So do your duty."

"Who's the dame?" asked one of the cops.

At a sign from Policeman Kaminoffski the patrol-wagon nen withdrew to one side for an explanation and a con- erence, while Mr. Swenson sought vainly to mollify Vic- orine. Uncle Alfred stood around uncomfortably. Finally hey all assembled again.

"He ain't a bad fellow," Policeman Kaminoffski began ersuasively to Victorine. "If you just get to thinking about t——"

"I'm making a charge," she interrupted coldly. "Are you going to take him, or shall I report you?"

"All right," Kaminoffski said reluctantly, "but it's a shame —a mighty big shame indeed."

"I'd brain her," one of the other cops muttered.

Uncle Alfred spent that night in a cell, to the mortifica- tion of the whole family, and Victorine spent it in tears. He hadn't been gone ten minutes before she was on the phone, trying to undo the damage her emotional spell had done, and later she was in the station house; but it was too late; the charge had been docketed.

As a matter of fact Uncle Alfred spent a reasonably pleas- ant night. His story had been passed on from the patrol- wagon men to the desk sergeant, and from him to the head keeper of the detention cells, and, to his surprise and grati- fication, prison turned out to be not so unbearable after all.

"My only disturbance," he told me later, "was when the head keeper's wife waked us all up about four o'clock. Or maybe it was five. She wanted to get us all out, because she had a new idea as to where the bunks ought to be hung in the cells. Aside from this everything was unexpectedly pleas- ant, and everyone unexpectedly considerate."

Naturally the thing upset the family. The idea of any member, especially Uncle Alfred, becoming involved in a brawl that ended in a police cell put all of them quite out; and all the influence possible was brought to bear on the district attorney to ease up the prosecution. Victorine wa willing, eager, to withdraw, but the district attorney wa adamant. Too many husbands already were playing duck and drakes with their wives, and Uncle Alfred woul serve as an example. Uncle Alfred would get the works.

We were all in court that morning, anxious and worried when Uncle Alfred was brought in and arraigned. From front seat we heard the gibberish necessary in the selectio of a jury and saw ten men and two women finally selecte after many tiresome harangues among the district attorney Uncle Alfred's lawyer, and the judge. And finally we hear Victorine, her eyes red-rimmed from crying, reluctantly giv her testimony under the insistent demand of the distric attorney, who waxed eloquent every now and then, whethe the occasion was plausible or not, on the subject of violence between husband and wife. Then the defense, and Uncle Alfred took the chair as his own witness.

"Now, Mr. Parker," the judge said, "just tell your own story in your own words."

He spoke evenly enough, but his glare showed what he thought of a man who would attack his wife in such wanton fashion. In fact the whole court, the spectators as well as the jurors, leveled cold eyes on him. Nowhere was there sympathy save in the family.

Uncle Alfred began, and spoke so low that he had to be instructed to speak up. He began, by his lawyer's advice, with his courtship of Victorine. He told of their marriage, of their happiness, of the efforts he was making to better their condition. The court, from judge to attendant, listened coldly.

Finally he came to the matter of furniture. He put, obviously, the best construction he could on everything that had happened, but the truth was the truth, and had to be told. He explained his big chair, how he loved it, what sweet comfort it had given him, and how he had always found it, for the first month after his marriage, on the right side of the fireplace. He told of the first time it had not been there.

"I'll bet," the judge interrupted suddenly, "that it was on the left side of the fireplace."

"It was, your honor."

"And half the rest of the furniture in the room," the judge continued, "had been shifted."

"That's quite true, your honor."

"I see!" the judge said, and leaned back, nodding.

"I had a desk on the sun porch——"

"Listen!" The judge suddenly sat forward. "You don't know anything! You think your wife shifted things. Well, I just want to tell you the experience I had with a night table. My wife——"

He related a very long story concerning the perambulations of a night table. He went quite into detail about it, and when he finished he sat back. "Beat that one!" he said.

"Your honor!" Uncle Alfred's lawyer had risen from his seat at the counsel table. "It was not two weeks ago that my wife stood in the center of our living room and——"

"I object, your honor."

"Sit down!" the judge said to the district attorney. "Let us hear what the learned counsel's wife did."

"My wife," Uncle Alfred's lawyer continued, "stood in the center of our living room, and for a picture—for a single picture, mind you—decided to move every single, blessed piece of furniture in the room, regardless!"

"For a single picture!" the judge marveled. "And yet I shouldn't be surprised. I remember one time, ten or twelve years ago, when I was practicing law, before I was elevated to the bench. We had a card table, a kind of folding card table, that I just put up one night and never thought any more about it——"

"We had a card table once," suddenly spoke up Juror Number 7 man. "I'll bet your experience was something like ours."

"Your wife wanted to get a new one because the old one did not go with the rest of the furniture," the judge said quickly.

"Precisely!" exclaimed Juror Number 7.

"Can you beat it!" said the judge.

"She nearly drove me nuts," admitted Juror Number 7.

"Excuse me, your honor," said the court reporter, "but shall I take all this down?"

"No," the judge said; "let's see what Mr. Parker has to say. Continue, Mr. Parker."

Then Uncle Alfred took up the events of the night before. He told of his long day at the office. He explained how tired he was. He told of his weary ride home, and his thoughts of bed. He explained how all resentment against his wife because of her weakness for moving furniture had melted away before an overwhelming love for her, and he remarked that he had not turned on the lights, lest their glare disturb her slumber.

And as he unfolded his story the judge began to nod his understanding of the situation. Presently the court reporter, reminded by the narrative of some familiar episode in his own life, laid down his pen and nodded also his appreciation of the circumstances.

Uncle Alfred's lawyer was, naturally, in agreement with the witness, and it was not long before Juror Number 7, followed almost at once by Jurors Numbers 1, 3, 8, 9, 10, 11, and 12, were likewise signifying their accord by sympathetic nods. One or two black looks were directed at Victorine.

"All I wanted," Uncle Alfred explained simply, "was to go to bed, to rest, to sleep. And there I was, ready for slumber, and there the bed, as I assumed, in its customary place, where it had always been."

"Where it always should be," agreed the judge, clicking his tongue against his teeth as sign of his entire approbation of Uncle Alfred's assumption.

"And so," Uncle Alfred went on, "I went for it. I just decided to fall back, just to get a good swish in the mattress, and when I fell back——"

He stopped, and there was a long silence. You could have heard a pin drop.

Then the judge spoke. "And when you fell back," he said softly, "the bed wasn't there."

"It wasn't."

"It had been moved during the day in a general rearrangement of the furniture."

"It had."

Another long silence, and then the district attorney spoke.

"Your honor," he said, "when I was first married my wife and I furnished an apartment. Well, sir, I thought that that apartment was just about as comfortable as a man could wish. I had a nice easy chair that I loved very much——"

"On the right side of the fireplace?" asked the judge.

"On the right side of the fireplace," the district attorney said, "where a man's big easy chair ought to be."

"My wife thinks it looks better on the left side," spoke up Juror Number 10. "Personally, I can't see any difference in the looks, whether it's on the right side or the left, but——"

"But it feels better on the right," the judge insisted.

"That's what I tried to tell her," Juror Number 10 explained. "But Jane–do any of you gentlemen happen to know Mrs. Snapp?"

"I'm sorry," the judge murmured, and the others indicated their regret.

"Well, in many ways," Juror Number 10 resumed, "she is one of the most admirable women in the world. She has qualities you will rarely find in other women——"

"Excuse me," His Honor interrupted, "but I'm afraid the district attorney has the floor ahead of you."

"Pardon me!"

"Not at all!" The district attorney nodded pleasantly. "All I wanted to say was I was very fond of this chair, though it may not have been much to look at; and then one day my wife went to an exhibition of modernist furniture——"

"My wife went to one of those too," said the judge. "For about two weeks——"

"Mrs. Gunther," the district attorney continued firmly, "fell for it. The next thing I knew, the living room was full of furniture made out of iron——"

"Iron!" exclaimed two of the jurors in unison.

"Yes, iron–plain iron!" repeated the district attorney, pleased with the effect of this startling statement. "Some of the old pieces that were gone I didn't mind; but in the place of my old easy chair——"

"On the right side of the fireplace," insisted His Honor.

"Yes—was an iron easy chair!"

"An iron easy chair!"

The entire court stared at him in consternation.

"Who could be comfortable in an iron easy chair?" demanded the judge. "I had just as soon sit in the electric chair and try to read a book."

"I'd rather," Uncle Alfred's lawyer said.

"Excuse me," said Juror Number 2—one of the two women in the box—"but what is this—a court or an experience meeting?"

Startled, everyone turned to her.

A grim-looking woman of middle age, she appeared to be holding her temper with some difficulty. She returned the stares boldly.

"Unless my hearing is bad," she continued, "we're here to try a man for an absolutely inexcusable attack on his wife. A poor, weak, frail woman, she was violently assaulted by this great hulk of a man now in the witness chair. As for all this gab-gab about his furniture, anyone with half an eye can see that he is of a particularly degenerate type and, unless placed behind the bars at once, is almost certain to return to his horrible and revolting practice of choking people."

"Madam," His Honor said with dignity, "that is almost contempt of court." He tried to fix her with a stern eye, but she proved to be a peculiarly unfixable type, and it was His Honor who finally looked away.

"Have you any more witnesses for the defense?" he asked Uncle Alfred's lawyer.

"No, your honor. The defense rests."

"Will there be any summing up?"

"With great heartiness," agreed Uncle Alfred's lawyer.

The door had scarcely closed on the ten men and two women before sounds of shouting and argument, shrill speeches and husky rebuttals, came from within. This lasted for fifteen minutes, and then His Honor was notified that the jury had deliberated and it was obvious that no agreement could ever be reached, no matter how long the jury as constituted was closeted.

"How does it stand?" His Honor asked.

"Ten for acquittal, two for conviction," was the reply.

"I see," His Honor nodded. "Discharge the jury with my thanks. It is a mistrial. Is the district attorney prepared to make any motions?"

"Yes, your honor. In view of the fact that the evidence for the prosecution as submitted can scarcely be increased, under the circumstances it seems highly improbable that a conviction could be obtained in another trial; in addition to which, the State is inclined, in the light of testimony produced in this court, to doubt the unquestionable justice of its case against the accused Parker. I move, your honor, that the charges be withdrawn."

"Granted gladly," said His Honor. "Mr. Parker, you are discharged."

Now, Margaret, I'd like to end this story on a happy note, and, fortunately, the circumstances permit me to. It was a victory for Uncle Alfred, of course, but he was not happy over it. He loved Victorine; he regretted his nasty impulse, and he regretted the cause of it; but deep in his heart he loved her, and he was lonesome in the apartment when, as soon as she could gather enough of her things, she left it for her mother's home in Brooklyn.

All his furniture was back where it had always been, and to that extent his mind was at rest, but it all seemed so empty, so worthless without her. So at the end of a week he choked down his pride and went to her for a reconciliation, and she welcomed him with open arms and tears of joy. She loved him, too, and had missed him; and, happier than they had ever been before for having passed through this ordeal and test, they returned to the love nest in Murray Hill.

Once, and once only, was mention ever made again of the cause of their trouble.

"Darling," Victorine whispered in his arms, "I'll never, never again shift the furniture."

"Sweetheart," he murmured.

Nor did she, though there was one interesting incident that took place shortly after her return, which showed how ingrained and deep-rooted such instincts may be. One night, late, Uncle Alfred was awakened by the sound of Victorine getting out of bed. Turning over quietly, he saw her sliding gently from between the covers, saw her, in the moonlight through the window, stand straight and white, like a ghost, with her arms outstretched before her, saw her move slowly, evenly toward the door. She was walking in her sleep.

As quietly, Uncle Alfred slipped out of bed and followed, to see that she came to no harm. She preceded him into the living room, where she stood for a moment in the center of the room, an eerie wraith, with arms still outstretched. Then, moving as slowly as sleepwalkers move, she went over to the divan, caught one of its arms and tried to pull it out from the wall. She pulled harder, and harder still; it never moved.

Uncle Alfred, a thoughtful expression on his face, tiptoed back to his bed, and a few seconds later Victorine returned, still unconscious, still feeling her way along, and as noiselessly as she had left, got back into bed and lay quiet.

But sleep eluded Uncle Alfred. The problem had risen again. He believed in a woman's promise, but he had gone to some effort to help Victorine keep hers. During her absence he had nailed all the larger pieces to the floor. He did not see what else he could do.

"And so, Margaret," I concluded, "you see where such a habit can lead one. I tell you the story purely as guidance for yourself. If you wish for happiness in our home—"

"That love seat," Margaret murmured absently, "is wrong."

IN THE INTRODUCTORY PART of this book I made mention of my early affection for the short stories of O. Henry. Some people might suppose that the emotional factor involved here is the same as that involved in a man's memories of his first sweetheart. The analogy doesn't fit. For all I know my first sweetheart is today a gin-soaked old bag wearing warts the size of cranberries. On the other hand, I read the stories of O. Henry today with all the enjoyment I got out of them twenty years ago.

Occasionally I come across a sharp criticism of these stories and the bleat is always the same: they are dated. The critics describe the O. Henry writings as transient, peppered with the slang of his own time, shot through with turn-of-the-century atmosphere and allusion. This, say the critics, is bad.

What on earth gets into such people! I venture to say that at this very moment there are several thousand authors and would-be authors engaged in serious research projects right here in our own land. They are prowling back into various periods of our past, digging for authentic atmosphere to be used in novels and biographies and other books. Right in the building where I work an author has been, for several months now, digging assiduously for the color and customs of the American Middle West during the early 1920s. He is after the songs and the slang and the habits and the mental processes of the people as they were at that time. He is going to incorporate all this into a novel and I have no doubt that it will be a great success, and much of its success will be attributable to the authenticity of its background.

What was I trying to start an argument about? Oh yes. O. Henry. The thing I wanted to say was that O. Henry's atmosphere, rather than being a fault of his work, constitutes one of its great attributes. I simply don't understand those critics. The back of my self to them!

I've picked one of O. Henry's studies in domesticity called *A Harlem Tragedy* and offer one small explanatory note to members of the dumber generation: Harlem in the time of O. Henry was not the Harlem of today.

A HARLEM TRAGEDY

By O. Henry

Harlem

Mrs. fink had dropped into Mrs. Cassidy's flat one flight below.

"Ain't it a beaut?" said Mrs. Cassidy.

She turned her face proudly for her friend Mrs. Fink to see. One eye was nearly closed, with a great, greenish-purple bruise around it. Her lip was cut and bleeding a little and there were red finger marks on each side of her neck.

"My husband wouldn't ever think of doing that to me," said Mrs. Fink, concealing her envy.

"I wouldn't have a man," declared Mrs. Cassidy, "that didn't beat me up at least once a week. Shows he thinks something of you. Say! But that last dose Jack gave me wasn't no homeopathic one. I can see stars yet. But he'll be the sweetest man in town for the rest of the week to make up for it. This eye is good for theater tickets and a silk shirt-waist at the very least."

"I should hope," said Mrs. Fink, assuming complacency, "that Mr. Fink is too much of a gentleman ever to raise his hand against me."

"Oh, go on, Maggie!" said Mrs. Cassidy, laughing and applying witch hazel. "You're only jealous. Your old man is too frappéed and slow to ever give you a punch. He just sits down and practices physical culture with a newspaper when he comes home—now ain't that the truth?"

"Mr. Fink certainly peruses of the papers when he comes home," acknowledged Mrs. Fink with a toss of her head; "but he certainly don't ever make no Steve O'Donnell out of me just to amuse himself—that's a sure thing."

Mrs. Cassidy laughed the contented laugh of the guarded and happy matron. With the air of Cornelia exhibiting her jewels, she drew down the collar of her kimono and revealed another treasured bruise, maroon-colored, edged with olive and orange—a bruise now nearly well, but still to memory dear.

Mrs. Fink capitulated. The formal light in her eyes softened to envious admiration. She and Mrs. Cassidy had been chums in the downtown paper-box factory before they had married, one year before. Now she and her man occupied the flat above Mame and her man. Therefore she could not put on airs with Mame.

"Don't it hurt when he soaks you?" asked Mrs. Fink curiously.

"Hurt!" Mrs. Cassidy gave a soprano scream of delight. "Well, say—did you ever have a brick house fall on you? Well, that's just the way it feels—just like when they're digging you out of the ruins. Jack's got a left that spells two matinées and a new pair of oxfords—and his right!—well, it takes a trip to Coney and six pairs of openwork silk lisle threads to make that good."

"But what does he beat you for?" inquired Mrs. Fink with wide-open eyes.

"Silly!" said Mrs. Cassidy indulgently. "Why, because he's full. It's generally on Saturday nights."

"But what cause do you give him?" persisted the seeker after knowledge.

"Why, didn't I marry him? Jack comes in tanked up; and I'm here, ain't I? Who else has he got the right to beat? I'd just like to catch him once beating anybody else! Sometimes it's because supper ain't ready; and sometimes it's because it is. Jack ain't particular about causes. He just lushes till he remembers he's married, and then he makes for home and does me up. Saturday nights I just move the furniture with sharp corners out of the way, so I won't cut my head when he gets his work in. He's got a left swing that jars you! Sometimes I take the count in the first round; but when I feel like having a good time during the week or want some new rags I come up again for more punishment. That's what I done last night. Jack knows I've been wanting a black silk waist for a month, and I didn't think just one black eye would bring it. Tell you what, Mag, I'll bet you the ice cream he brings it tonight."

Mrs. Fink was thinking deeply.

"My Mart," she said, "never hit me a lick in his life. It's just like you said, Mame; he comes in grouchy and ain't got a word to say. He never takes me out anywhere. He's a chair-warmer at home for fair. He buys me things, but he looks so glum about it that I never appreciate 'em."

Mrs. Cassidy slipped an arm around her chum.

"You poor thing!" she said. "But everybody can't have a husband like Jack. Marriage wouldn't be no failure if they was all like him. These discontented wives you hear about—what they need is a man to come home and kick their slats in once a week, and then make it up in kisses and chocolate creams. That'd give 'em some interest in life. What I want is a masterful man that slugs you when he's jagged and hugs you when he ain't jagged. Preserve me from the man that ain't got the sand to do neither!"

Mrs. Fink sighed.

The hallways were suddenly filled with sound. The door flew open at the kick of Mr. Cassidy. His arms were occupied with bundles. Mame flew and hung about his neck. Her sound eye sparkled with the love light that shines in the eye of the Maori maid when she recovers consciousness in the hut of the wooer who has stunned and dragged her there.

"Hello, old girl!" shouted Mr. Cassidy. He shed his bundles and lifted her off her feet in a mighty hug. "I got tickets for Barnum & Bailey's, and if you'll bust the string of one of them bundles I guess you'll find that silk waist—why, good evening, Mrs. Fink—I didn't see you at first. How's old Mart coming along?"

"He's very well, Mr. Cassidy—thanks," said Mrs. Fink. "I must be going along up now. Mart'll be home for supper soon. I'll bring you down the pattern you wanted tomorrow, Mame."

Mrs. Fink went up to her flat and had a little cry. It was a meaningless cry, the kind of cry that only a woman knows about, a cry from no particular cause, altogether an absurd cry; the most transient and the most hopeless cry in the repertory of grief. Why had Martin never thrashed her? He was as big and strong as Jack Cassidy. Did he not care for her at all? He never quarreled; he came home and lounged about, silent, glum, idle. He was a fairly good provider, but he ignored the spices of life.

Mrs. Fink's ship of dreams was becalmed. Her captain ranged between plum duff and his hammock. If only he would shiver his timbers or stamp his foot on the quarter-deck now and then! And she had thought to sail so merrily, touching at ports in the Delectable Isles! But now, to vary the figure, she was ready to throw up the sponge, tired out, without a scratch to show for all those tame rounds with her sparring partner. For one moment she almost hated Mame—Mame, with her cuts and bruises, her salve of presents and kisses; her stormy voyage with her fighting, brutal, loving mate.

Mr. Fink came home at seven. He was permeated with the curse of domesticity. Beyond the portals of his cozy home he cared not to roam, to roam. He was the man who had caught the street car, the anaconda that had swallowed its prey, the tree that lay as it had fallen.

"Like the supper, Mart?" asked Mrs. Fink, who had striven over it.

"M-m-m-yep," grunted Mr. Fink.

After supper he gathered his newspapers to read. He sat in his stocking feet.

Arise, some new Dante, and sing me the befitting corner of perdition for the man who sitteth in the house in his stockinged feet. Sisters in patience who by reason of ties or duty have endured it in silk, yarn, cotton, lisle thread or woolen—does not the new canto belong?

The next day was Labor Day. The occupations of Mr. Cassidy and Mr. Fink ceased for one passage of the sun. Labor, triumphant, would parade and otherwise disport itself.

Mrs. Fink took Mrs. Cassidy's pattern down early. Mame had on her new silk waist. Even her damaged eye managed to emit a holiday gleam. Jack was fruitfully penitent, and there was a hilarious scheme for the day afoot, with parks and picnics and Pilsener in it.

A rising, indignant jealousy seized Mrs. Fink as she returned to her flat above. Oh, happy Mame, with her bruises and her quick-following balm! But was Mame to have a monopoly of happiness? Surely Martin Fink was as good a man as Jack Cassidy. Was his wife to go always unbelabored and uncaressed? A sudden, brilliant, breathless idea came to Mrs. Fink. She would show Mame that there were husbands as able to use their fists and perhaps to be as tender afterward as Jack.

The holiday promised to be a nominal one with the Finks. Mrs. Fink had the stationary washtubs in the kitchen filled with a two-weeks' wash that had been soaking overnight. Mr. Fink sat in his stockinged feet reading a newspaper. Thus Labor Day presaged to speed.

Jealousy surged high in Mrs. Fink's heart and higher still surged an audacious resolve. If her man would not strike her—if he would not so far prove his manhood, his prerogative, and his interest in conjugal affairs, he must be prompted to do his duty.

Mr. Fink lit his pipe and peacefully rubbed an ankle with a stockinged toe. He reposed in the state of matrimony like a lump of unblended suet in a pudding. This was his level Elysium—to sit at ease vicariously girdling the world in print amid the wifely splashing of suds and the agreeable smells of breakfast dishes departed and dinner ones to come. Many ideas were far from his mind; but the furthest one was the thought of beating his wife.

Mrs. Fink turned on the hot water and set the washboards in the suds. Up from the flat below came the gay laugh of Mrs. Cassidy. It sounded like a taunt, a flaunting of her own happiness in the face of the unslugged bride above. Now was Mrs. Fink's time.

Suddenly she turned like a fury upon the man reading.

"You lazy loafer!" she cried. "Must I work my arms off washing and toiling for the ugly likes of you? Are you a man or are you a kitchen hound?"

Mr. Fink dropped his paper, motionless from surprise

She feared that he would not strike—that the provocation had been insufficient. She leaped at him and struck him fiercely in the face with her clenched hand. In that instant she felt a thrill of love for him such as she had not felt for many a day. Rise up, Martin Fink, and come into your kingdom! Oh, she must feel the weight of his hand now—just to show that he cared—just to show that he cared!

Mr. Fink sprang to his feet—Maggie caught him again on the jaw with a wide swing of her other hand. She closed her eyes in that fearful, blissful moment before his blow should come—she whispered his name to herself—she leaned to the expected shock, hungry for it.

In the flat below Mr. Cassidy, with a shamed and contrite face, was powdering Mame's eye in preparation for their junket. From the flat above came the sound of a woman's voice, high-raised, a bumping, a stumbling, and a shuffling, a chair overturned—unmistakable sounds of domestic conflict.

"Mart and Mag scrapping?" postulated Mr. Cassidy. "Didn't know they ever indulged. Shall I trot up and see if they need a sponge holder?"

One of Mrs. Cassidy's eyes sparkled like a diamond. The other twinkled at least like paste.

"Oh, oh," she said, softly and without apparent meaning, in the feminine ejaculatory manner. "I wonder if—wonder if . . . ! Wait, Jack, till I go up and see."

Up the stairs she sped. As her foot struck the hallway above out from the kitchen door of her flat wildly flounced Mrs. Fink.

"Oh, Maggie," cried Mrs. Cassidy in a delighted whisper, "did he? Oh, did he?"

Mrs. Fink ran and laid her face upon her chum's shoulder and sobbed hopelessly.

Mrs. Cassidy took Maggie's face between her hands and lifted it gently. Tear-stained it was, flushing and paling, but its velvety, pink and white, becomingly freckled surface was unscratched, unbruised, unmarred by the recreant fist of Mr. Fink.

"Tell me, Maggie," pleaded Mame, "or I'll go in there and find out. What was it? Did he hurt you—what did he do?"

Mrs. Fink's face went down again despairingly on the bosom of her friend.

"For God's sake don't open that door, Mame," she sobbed. "And don't ever tell nobody—keep it under your hat. He—he never touched me, and—he's—oh, Gawd—he's washin' the clothes—he's washin' the clothes!"

My friend Doc Rockwell is best known as a stage comedian though I prefer to regard him as a philosopher. One afternoon we were improving our minds in Lindy's when Doc got on the subject of dogs.

"There is only one fundamental difference between dogs and humans," observed Doc. "Humans can talk and dogs can't. If the day ever comes when dogs can talk they will conduct themselves just as humans conduct themselves, although I do not believe they will ever become expert with the knife and fork, or dice.

"Humans and dogs," he went on, "are, after all, engaged in the same basic pursuit: meat snatching. All that life amounts to, for humans, is refined meat snatching. Humans are capable of speech, so their meat snatching is polite. Two dogs, being speechless, will simply approach a chunk of meat and fang it. The dog with the greatest co-ordination, the greatest speed, and the strongest jaws will get the chunk of meat. If they were able to talk they would conduct the transaction human-style. They would argue about it and talk about sharing it and make promises and bargains and each dog would have it in his mind to get all of the meat. That's the way humans do it."

This is by way of introducing a small essay about dogs. Ring Lardner had courage to write it and have it published. I am not reprinting it because I agree with his point of view (which I do) but because I think it's a fine example of his style. When we had Mr. Lardner on-stage earlier he appeared as short-story writer. Here he is as essayist.

DOGS

By Ring Lardner

EVERY LITTLE WILE you hear people talking about a man that they don't nobody seem to have much use for him on acct. of him not paying his debts or beating his wife or something and everybody takes a rap at him about this and that until finely one of the party speaks up and says they must be some good in him because he likes animals.

"A man can't be all bad when he is so kind to dogs." That is what they generally always say and that is the reason you see so many men stop on the st. when they see a dog and pet it because they figure that may be somebody will be looking at them do it, and the next time they are getting panned, why whoever seen it will speak up and say:

"He can't be all bad because he likes dogs."

Well friends when you come right down to cases they's about as much sence to this as a good many other delusions that we got here in this country, like for inst. the one about nobody wanting to win the first pot and the one about the whole lot of authors not being able to do their best work unlest they are ½ pickled.

But if liking animals ain't a virtue in itself I don't see how that it proves that a man has got any virtues, and personly if I had a daughter and she wanted to get marred and I asked her what kind of a bird the guy was and she said she don't know nothing about him except that one day she seen him kiss a leopard, why I would hold up my blessing till a few of the missing precincts was heard from.

But as long as our best people has got it in their skull that a friendly feeling toward dumb brutes takes the curse off of a bad egg, why I or nobody else is going to be a sucker enough to come out and admit that all the horses, rams and oxen in the world could drop dead tomorrow morning without us batting an eye.

Pretty near everybody wants to be well thought of and if liking dogs or sheep is helping along these lines, why even if I don't like them, I wouldn't never loose a opportunity to be seen in their company and act as if I was haveing the time of my life.

But wile I was raised in a kennel, you might say, and some of my most intimate childhood friends was of the canine gender, still in all I believe dogs is better in some climates than others, the same as oysters, and I don't think it should ought to be held against a man if he don't feel the same towards N.Y. dogs as he felt towards Michigan dogs, and I am free to confess that the 4 dogs who I have grew to know personly here on Long Island has failed to arouse tender yearnings anyways near similar to those inspired by the flea bearers of my youth.

And in case they should be any tendency on the part of my readers to denounce me for failing to respond whole heartily to the wiles of the Long Island breed let me present a brief sketch of some so as true lovers of the canine tribe can judge for themselfs if the fault is all mine.

No. 1

This was the dainty boy that belonged to Gene Buck and it was a bull dog no bigger than a 2 car garage and it wouldn't harm a hair of nobody's head only other animals and people. Children were as safe with this pet as walking in the Pittsburgh freight yards and he wouldn't think of no more wronging a cat than scratching himself.

In fairness to Mr. Buck I'll state that a pal of his give him the dog as a present without no comment. Well they wasn't no trouble till Gene had the dog pretty near ½ hour when they let him out. He was gone 10 minutes during which Gene received a couple of phone calls announcing more in anger than in sorrow the sudden deaths of 2 adjacent cats of noble berth so when the dog come back Gene spanked him and after that he didn't kill no more cats except when he got outdoors.

But the next day De Wolf Hopper come over to call and brought his kid which the dog thought would look better with one leg and it took 5 people to get him not to operate, so after that Gene called up the supt. of a dogs reform school and the man said he would take him and cure him of the cat habit by tying one of his victims around his neck and leaving it there for a wk. but he didn't know how to cure the taste for young Hoppers unlest De Wolf could spare the kid the wk. after they was finished with the cat.

This proposition fell through but anyway Gene sent the dog to the reformatory and is still paying board for same.

No. 2

The people that lived 3 houses from the undersigned decided to move to England where it seems like you can't take dogs no more so they asked us did we want the dog as it was very nice around children and we took it and sure enough it was OK in regards to children but it shared this new owners feeling towards motorcycles and every time one went past the house the dog would run out and spill the contents, and on Sundays when the traffic was heavy they would sometimes be as many as 4 or 5 motorcycle jehus standing on their heads in the middle of the road.

One of them finely took offence and told on the dog and the justice of the peace called me up and said I would have to kill it within 24 hrs. and the only way I could think of to do same was drown it in the bath tub and if you done that, why the bath tub wouldn't be no good no more because it was a good sized dog and no matter how often you pulled the stopper it would still be there.

No. 3

The next-door neighbors has a pro-German police dog that win a blue ribbon once but now it acts as body guard for the lady of the house and one day we was over there and the host says to slap his Mrs. on the arm and see what happened so I slapped her on the arm and I can still show you what happened.

When you dance with mine hostess this sweet little pet dances right along with you and watches your step and if you tred on my ladys toe he fines you a mouth full and if you and her is partners in a bridge game he lays under the table and you either bid right and play right or you get nipped.

No. 4

This is our present incumbrance which we didn't ask for him and nobody give him to us but here he is and he has got the insomnia and he has picked a spot outside my window to enjoy it but not only that but he has learnt that if you jump at a screen often enough it will finely give way and the result is that they ain't a door or window on the first floor that you couldn't drive a rhinoceros through it and all the bugs that didn't already live in the house is moveing in and bringing their family.

That is a true record of the dogs who I have met since takeing up my abode in Nassau county so when people ask me do I like dogs I say I'm crazy about them and I think they are all right in their place but it ain't Long Island.

ONE BRIGHT SUMMER DAY back in the medieval era of 1925 a man was sitting at a small table outside his house in New Jersey. On the table was a typewriter and the man was trying to write a story on it. He was a small, serious man, and he was wearing nothing but sneakers and a pair of shorts. He enjoyed writing, or trying to write, in such a costume.

On this day a black depression was settling down on him, as it often did. The words weren't coming right and he was pretty well disgusted with himself and the notion that he could ever make a living as a writer outside an advertising agency.

Insofar as physical exertion was concerned, the little man was a colossal sluggard. Consequently the lawn that stretched in front of him was a mess. The grass was high and wild and nothing but a sharp scythe would have sufficed to get it down.

The little man sat staring out across this weedy jungle and

suddenly he saw a tail. The tail was a dog's tail but no dog was visible. It was a short tail and when the little man first spotted it, he recalled some years later, it was wagging. Then it stopped, moved a few feet, wiggled some more, moved again, and so on. The little man at the table was fascinated by it. He started thinking about a tail without a dog, and a dog without a tail. His imagination switched to human anatomy and he thought of legs without a body and a body without legs and various other weird manifestations.

He needed money, almost desperately, and he thought that now he had the germ of a short story that might sell. He went to work on it. The short story grew into a novel and the novel became the first of a series of fantastic tales that made Thorne Smith one of America's most popular humorists.

That first Thorne Smith fantasy, *Topper,* was having a moderate but steady sale when, in 1929, his second was published. It was called *The Stray Lamb.* I was a bug-eyed newcomer to Manhattan that year and I remember reading a note in O. O. McIntyre's column, a single sentence saying that the funniest book he had read in years was *The Stray Lamb.* I went out and bought it and from that moment forward I was among the most rabid of the Thorne Smith fans.

Since I was an interviewer there was a clear opportunity for me to meet him. It was arranged, and one afternoon I arrived at the Smith apartment in Greenwich Village. It was just such an apartment as is occupied by the Galts in the story that follows. It was a gloomy railroad flat in the basement of an old building and the furnishings were not only nondescript but shabby. As I came up in front of the house Thorne, who had never been interviewed before, popped out of the entrance and greeted me with an embarrassed sort of violence. He escorted me into his living room, introduced me to his wife, his two young daughters, and Lucy Goldthwaite, who was handling publicity for his publisher. There was a reason for Lucy's presence. They had decided to have a little whisky on hand and whenever whisky and Thorne Smith got into proximity there were likely to be explosions. Lucy Goldthwaite was there to see that Thorne didn't get his hands on that bottle, even though it was only a pint. He was working on another book and someone explained to me later that if he took one drink he would be drunk for six months.

After that first meeting we got to be quite friendly and visited back and forth. Much of the time he was off traveling in Europe, or sitting out a contract in Hollywood, but whenever he was in New York we managed to get together. He was a caution with the bottle. He told me once that he didn't mind the penalty he had to pay after his long benders, except for one thing. He said that everyone would let him alone, let the thing run its course, until it was time for him to square away and write another book. Then they'd haul him off to a sanitarium in the country.

"They'd take me out and stand me up against a brick wall, mother naked," he said, "and they'd turn a fire hose on me. That was a thing I resented, bitterly."

Once he decided he would go to France to write a new book. He resolved, at the same time, to show everybody that he possessed will power. He got on one of the big liners and took squatter's rights on a table directly in front of the ship's bar. He put his portable typewriter on the table and every morning he sat down, facing the bar, and worked on his book. He got it more than halfway finished during the crossing and didn't take a drink and he was so pleased with himself that the first day ashore he got orry-eyed.

In many respects he was a character right out of his own books. He was unpredictable and in time his publishers were beyond the stage of being surprised at anything he did.

One morning he arrived at the publishers' offices, then on Madison Avenue. He could be dapper when he chose and he was dapper this day. He was carrying a cane and wearing a fairly loud sports jacket with a cornflower at the lapel. He was bright and shining and full of enthusiasm for a new project he was planning. Somebody noticed a bulge on his hip but so far as his deportment was concerned he hadn't had a drink. After a while he took his merry departure.

Half an hour later a girl in the publishers' office glanced out an open window overlooking Madison Avenue. She saw Thorne, just as he stepped off the curb across the street. She leaned out and yelled a greeting at him. He halted in the middle of the pavement, looked up at her, took off his hat, and executed a sort of curtsy. A few feet from where he was standing was an open manhole with a portable iron railing, a red flag, and a "Men Working" sign. Thorne put his hat back on, blew a kiss to the girl in the window, and stepped over to the manhole. He removed his gaudy jacket and hung it on the railing. He blew another kiss toward the girl. Then he disappeared into the manhole.

Thirty minutes or so after that two of the company's editors arrived on the sidewalk, headed for lunch. One of them glanced at the manhole.

"Hey!" he said. "Isn't that Thorne's coat hanging out there?"

They drew back against the building and decided to wait around for a while and see what happened. They didn't have to wait long. They saw a workman come out of the hole. Then another, and another, until half a dozen grimy laborers had emerged. Last to come up was their best-selling author. He followed the workmen as they trudged across to the curb. Each man had his lunch bucket and they sat down in a line on the curbstone. Thorne solemnly took his place at one end of the line. There was little conversation. The workmen seemed to accept him without either suspicion or amusement. One workman handed Thorne half a sandwich and another passed a banana down the line to him. Thorne in turn pulled his half-filled bottle from his hip and each workman solemnly took a swig from it before returning it to its owner. Lunch was finished and the bottle killed. Then they sat on the curb staring at traffic and finally one of the workmen got up, stretched, and headed for the manhole. The others followed him, Thorne again bringing up the rear. He went into the hole without so much as a glance around the street.

The two editors couldn't wait all afternoon so nobody up above ever knew just when Thorne came up, got his coat, and left. When I asked him about it he said he couldn't remember any of the details.

The story of Thorne's which follows is a sort of scoop because it has never, so far as I can determine, appeared in a book. Moreover, few members of the vast Thorne Smith cult are aware of its existence. Thorne wrote but three short pieces that were ever published, but this is the only one of the three that has the unmistakable Thorne Smith flavor and zip. It appeared in *Redbook* magazine back in 1934, the year Thorne died in Sarasota at the age of forty-two. It seems to me that I should have heard about it, but I didn't. I didn't hear about it until I started putting this book together.

"Birthday Present," to be truthful about it, is not Thorne Smith at his best. I think he's at his best in *Turnabout,* and *Topper Takes a Trip,* and maybe *The Night Life of the Gods, The Stray Lamb,* and *The Bishop's Jaegers.* It is next to impossible to lift a section out of one of his novels and let it stand alone.

I don't know how long people will continue to read Thorne Smith. I do know that today, more than ten years after his death, booksellers say there is a steady demand for his works. Thorne himself had no conception of the lasting quality of his books. He considered himself little more than a hack writer. He regarded himself as a passing fad. The income from his work didn't reach large proportions until it was too late for him to enjoy it. He got out of that basement apartment but the last place he lived in New York differed from it only in that it was upstairs. He had so little faith in the future earnings of his books that he neglected to write a will, with the usual consequence that his estate has been in somewhat of a snarl ever since.

If, in this brief attempt to give you a picture of Thorne Smith, I have made him out to be a depraved sort of person, I haven't intended it. He was the kindliest of men. He loved dogs and cats and children. His conversation was brilliant, for he was a man of excellent education and, of course, imagination. When he talked, whether in casual chitchat or in telling a story, his conversation carried much of the sharp flavor that went into his writing.

I imagine the editors of *Redbook* had to tidy up this story a bit. For all the ribald quality of his novels, it may be said that they did not appear precisely as he wrote them. He told me once that the editors trimmed about twenty per cent out of every manuscript he delivered to them, the publishers having no desire to see both the author and themselves in prison.

This, then, is the story as it appeared in the magazine.

BIRTHDAY PRESENT

By Thorne Smith

The Galts as a family are emotional about the doorbell. It seems to appeal to their lowest instincts. Whenever it rings hey revert, losing all poise and frequently some clothing. Dropping whatever they are doing, forgetting whatever they are saying—and the Galts are forever saying something—they ush to the front door, impelled thither by the two fundamental impulses of curiosity and fear. In every stage of dress or undress save the final one in either direction, they converge from their various rooms in the narrow reaches of the hall. There, forming themselves into a sort of flying edge of Galts, they advance to discover who on earth could have conceived the astonishing idea of ringing their bell. From heir actions one would be led to believe that no one ever rang their bell; whereas, in truth, the Galts' bell is always being rung for some irritating reason or other.

Inevitably there is much fumbling and fussing with the door latch. It is doubtful if the Galts' front door has ever been opened in one swift and decisive motion. The deed is usually accompanied by a certain amount of rattling and muttering, caused by a characteristic lack of teamwork. Too many nervous hands.

Rarely does the caller have a chance to grow impatient. He becomes far too absorbed in what is going on behind the Galts' door.

"You look a sight," he hears someone whisper. "Drag your tocking up."

"You're not so hot yourself," the criticized one snaps back.

"Either pull your wrapper together or turn your back to the door."

In between these exchanges, as well as during them, the other Galts ask questions such as, "Who is it?" "Is somebody there?" "Who rang our bell?"

These questions take on the monotonous rhythm of a chant.

"Why doesn't the person speak?" a Galt demands the moment the door is opened.

"He just stands there looking," another one complains.

One Galt alone has refused to become a party to these unseemly exhibitions of undisciplined curiosity. This one is Galt himself. He has remained decently above the battle and contemplated his flesh and blood with repugnance made endurable only by the philosophy of despair. With a mixture of pain and unwilling admiration he has time and again noted that the woman who has so casually presented him with all these unsatisfactory children is always well up in the lead in these impassioned stampedes to the door. As harassed and exhausted as she vigorously proclaims herself to be, she nevertheless seems to possess a sufficient reserve of energy to make herself a serious contestant for first-place honors whenever the doorbell rings. . . .

On a certain day not completely buried in the past Red Galt was seated dispiritedly before his drawing board, brooding over the vast futility of all creative effort. He was doing this in the privacy of a small back room which he was allowed to use as a studio whenever no one else had need of it. At his right was the back door, which gave uninviting access to the gloom of the outer hall. In front of him a series of equally gloomy rooms telescoped into a sort of dim obscurity. Those rooms alone were sufficient to make any sensitive spirit break out into violent protest; but being an eminently unsuccessful artist, Red Galt was the only member of the household who was given no opportunity to express his temperament in public. Little good would it have done him had he attempted to do so. In that family he could seldom make himself heard and but rarely understood. For the simple reason that his wife and his children shared the same sort of unacy, they considered themselves entirely normal, while to heir way of thinking he—the only sane member of the famly—was as mad as a hatter. They rather liked and pitied him or it.

From the front of the flat came the clamorous voices of his contentious brood. In loud, exacting voices his sons were denanding coffee, his daughters passionately accusing each other of both grand and petty larceny, while the twins—the youngest of the lot—were being implored by everybody not only to get out of the way but also to remain always and orever out of the way. Exactly where such a place could be vas somewhat obscure to the twins, because wherever they vent they seemed to encounter a seething mass of Galts. Consequently they stayed where they were and contributed heir share to the general confusion.

From time to time the distracted voice of the artist's wife could be heard assuring the entire family that the good God n the press of business had seen fit to give her only one pair of hands, that everyone very well knew how nervous and shaky she was, and that someday in the almost immediate future the whole confounded lot of them was going to be mmeasurably sorry for the way they had treated her and his prediction also held for that disgusting lump of a father of theirs, who did nothing all day but sit comfortably in his chair pretending to be an artist, while others slaved and died at his great ugly feet.

Galt was desperate, because on the morrow his wife would come into another birthday. Even though she had passed an unpleasant remark about his feet, he still felt the desire to give her a present. Every member of the family save himself vould be giving her a little something. To this end, his children one after another had levied heavily on his small supply of cash. He was now completely deflated. The money hus wheedled from him he had planned to expend in the purchase of a pair of shoes for those same great ugly feet. Now there would be no shoes, and his feet would continue on in their unlovely condition. Looking at them, Galt found t difficult to bear with them himself. What chance would hey have with the office boys and reception clerks who guarded the sacrosanct corridor of the better advertising agencies?

The small amount of money remaining in the house was in the possession of his wife Sue. Only too keenly did he realize how impossible it would be to pry any of this loose from that one. So long as he had enough tobacco for his pipe Sue considered the man well fixed. After all, he was little better than a semidomestic animal with red hair at one end and big feet at the other. Money would do him no good. It might give him delusions of grandeur.

Impatiently Galt unfolded himself from his chair and began prowling about the small room. His slipping on a short length of lead pipe almost put an end to this mild emotional outlet. Cursing the pipe bitterly, he stooped and picked it up. Idly he tapped it against the palm of his left hand; and as he did so a desperate enterprise sprang full-armed into his mind.

Was not this an era of violence and direct action? It was. All over the country, all over the world, individuals no less than nations were taking by force what they wanted. Why should he alone of all the human race remain at peace with his fellow men? No, he should not. At this moment he needed money, needed it desperately. Not for himself did he need this money, but for the mother of his children. What simpler way to get it than through the medium of a lead pipe?

In this dangerously exalted frame of mind he recommenced his prowling. He was plotting evil against mankind for the first time in his life. He was quite impersonal about it. Little did it matter to him whom he hit upon the head with that lead pipe, as long as it was an expensive head with lots of cash on hand.

While engaged in these dark meditations Galt became vaguely aware of the sound of refined tapping on the door of the outer hall. He stopped in his tracks and looked at the door. He even scowled at the door as if it were a living adversary. Who could be standing on the other side of it? No one ever used that door. Had Providence provided him with a victim?

Without further hesitation Galt crossed the room and opened the door. A surprisingly well-preserved face, for the amount of russet beard that adorned it, presented itself to the momentarily unhinged artist. A pair of mild but myopic eyes peered into Galt's. The artist with his keen perception noted that the face looked like an expensive face, and that the body to which it belonged appeared to be expensively garbed. Then the mouth of the face opened, and words came from it.

"I beg your pardon," began the face in a cultured voice, "I was wondering if——"

At that moment the face ceased to wonder about anything. With the precision of one who had been slugging heads with lead pipes since early adolescence, the desperate artist now slugged this one. Automatically he reached out with his left hand and snatched a wallet from the gentleman's breast pocket. Then, completely losing his nerve, he slammed the door on his victim's expressionless face, idiotically muttering as he did so the single word "Beaver."

For a moment Galt leaned weakly against the door while on the other side of it the assaulted gentleman did likewise, but with more justification. Then, pulling himself together in all his trembling parts, the criminal artist, now thoroughly cowed, thrust the wallet from his sight as if it were already accusing him of murder. He hid the wallet behind a picture —not behind one of his own pictures, but behind a large photograph of a family group which he especially disliked. He had no desire to have either himself or anything he had ever created associated with the mute witness of his one criminal act.

In the meantime the assaulted gentleman, accompanied by his beard, rolled rather than staggered along the wall of the outer hall, eventually bringing up with a thud against the front door of the Galts' flat. With his rapidly failing strength he pressed a limp finger to the bell push, then abandoned himself to a vacuous twilight which at last grew dark. . . .

At the sound of the bell the strident voices of the Galts were hushed as if all tongues had suddenly been gagged.

Then came the rush for the door, the sound of piercing whispers, and the fumbling of many hands. Finally the door was opened, and all the Galts looked. Then they blinked and looked again. Here was something indeed worth looking at, something to break the monotony of the daily routine—of which there was scarcely any in the Galts' establishment.

"Ooo!" breathed a thin girl of seventeen. "He's all bluggy."

"It's a murder," pronounced Mrs. Galt in the voice of one who had been long suspecting just such a contingency. "A corpse, no less."

"Then shut the door," some callous soul suggested.

"Oh, look at the murdered gentleman's beard," the twins chanted in unison. "Isn't there a lot of it?"

"Altogether too much of it," someone said fastidiously. "I loathe such facial adornments."

"It would be just our luck," Tom, the eldest son, was heard to mutter. "A murdered body would have to call on us! Let's have a cup of Java."

"He's in our flat," objected Mrs. Galt's spinster sister in a slightly outraged voice. "Somebody push him out."

"It's against the law to disturb a dead body," proclaimed Tom, who knew his detective stories and very little else.

"Well, this dead body started in disturbing us first," argued seventeen-year-old Fanny. "Does the law expect private families to keep open house for any old corpse that feels like dropping in?"

"Maybe he's just drunk," suggested the spinster sister. "Most men are, you know."

"His beard is doubled up," one of the twins morbidly observed.

"It continues to grow after death," contributed Dora, a plump child of fifteen. "I forget how long it grows, either in time or space."

In spite of having associated with her family for so many demoralizing years, Mrs. Galt still managed to retain a small shred of decency. She knelt and examined the crumpled results of her husband's enterprising act.

"He doesn't smell drunk," she announced, looking up at the others with her large, slightly wild eyes.

"What does he smell like?" Dora wanted to know.

"Why, I don't know," she replied innocently. "He smells like a man, I suppose."

"How horrid!" murmured the spinster sister.

"He's still breathing," Sue Galt suddenly announced. "Quick, everybody! Help me to get him into bed."

"Into whose bed?" several voices aggressively demanded.

"Into my bed, then," Sue replied wearily, not wishing to start a family brawl.

Motivated more by a desire to close the front door than out of any consideration for the potential corpse, the Galts dragged the body into the room, and after nearly dismembering it in their general carelessness and lack of co-ordinated action, finally succeeded in dumping the unconscious man on the bed jointly shared by Galt and his wife.

"Dear me!" panted Mrs. Galt. "That was a battle royal. If he wasn't dead already he should be now."

"I'm strained for life," declared Dora. "I had practically all of his left leg."

"I had what it grew out of," said Fanny.

"Why, I had his feet—one foot, anyway," replied Tom.

"I wasn't referring to his feet," the girl told him with quiet dignity.

Eventually Mrs. Galt succeeded in gathering her family round her in the front room.

"What are we going to do next?" she asked helplessly. "We should get a cheap doctor—don't you think so?"

While this conference was in progress in the front room the cause of it was growing increasingly terrified in the back one. He was afraid to be alone with himself. For the first time in years he preferred the company of his family to his own. On passing through his room he saw in the dim light the form of a perfect stranger seemingly sleeping comfortably in his bed. Not noticing the stranger's beard, Galt rushed to the front room and confronted his wife.

"What do you mean by letting a stranger go to sleep in my bed?" he demanded. "Haven't I any place left in this house? Why, I'll tear the beggar limb from limb. I'll——"

Galt stopped suddenly and swung round to face Fanny.

"What the devil are you laughing at?" he demanded.

"I don't know," declared Fanny, struggling to throttle her mirth. "It just struck me funny, that's all. You see, that man in there is dying, and when you mentioned tearing him limb from limb—well, I don't know—we've just had a go at that."

"What does she mean?" asked the mystified artist, turning once more to his wife.

"She means," said Mrs. Galt coldly, "that some homicidal maniac has hit that man on the head with a blunt instrument. And I hope you give me credit for having better taste than to prefer a man with a couple of yards of beard—although I shouldn't expect much, seeing that I married you."

Galt was too stunned to take up the insult. When he reached the bed he roughly turned the body over. Then with shrinking eyes he looked down on the bearded face of the ruin he had created.

"Quick!" he called out. "Somebody run for a doctor. If this chap dies your father is a murderer."

Immediately the room was jammed with Galts, all talking at the same time.

"How do you mean, you're the murderer?" his wife wanted to know.

"I did it," said Galt hoarsely. "I nipped him over the head with the twins' lead pipe."

Mrs. Galt's furious eyes sought for and found the twins. "What did I tell you about that pipe?" she cried. "Now see what you have done! You've made your father a murderer, that's what you've done; and God knows he was bad enough as he was. I've thrown that pipe away, and what happens? Back it comes. Back comes the pipe. Right into the house." Pausing for a much-needed breath, she turned on her husband: "Why did you nip him over the head?" she inquired in a perfectly matter-of-fact voice.

"Well, you see, my dear," Galt began in a weak voice, "tomorrow is your birthday, you know, and quite naturally I wanted to give you a bit of a present, and I didn't have any money at all; so when this chap——"

"Don't go on," interrupted Mrs. Galt. "Don't reconstruct the crime. Save it for the judge." Helplessly she looked at the assembled faces. "Isn't this terrible?" she demanded. "Isn't it? Think of it, children! Your father has given your mother a bearded cadaver for a birthday present! Nice of him, wasn't it? Jolly. Many happy returns of the day." She laughed hysterically.

"But, Susie," protested the artist, "I didn't have any money, and——"

"Don't call me Susie at a time like this," his wife cut in. "Don't call me Susie at any time unless you want to start a riot; I won't be called Susie by a man with blood on his hands. And he gives me a corpse for a birthday present! I can't get over that. A corpse with a flaming beard. And I'm just fool enough to tuck it into our bed, beard and all. What a birthday present!"

With a pained expression Galt gazed back at his wife.

"A nice family," he muttered. "Just a lot of pals. There you stand, the lot of you, callously laughing your father into the electric chair, when you should be getting a doctor."

Sue Galt doubled up and pointed to the still figure in the bed.

"My present!" she gasped. "All mine." She straightened herself again, and with brimming eyes regarded the demoralized face of her husband.

"Had I known you enjoyed murders so much," he remarked, "I'd have taken up the practice earlier."

To the infinite surprise of everyone present Sue Galt suddenly flung her arms around her husband's neck and hugged him ruthlessly.

"What a man!" she said to his neck. "What a man! To give his wife a birthday present he'd actually commit murder! I must have at least one kiss."

She had it, while Galt remained stupefied. Such endearments had become rare.

"We haven't any time for all these goings on," he said rather feebly. "Must get a doctor."

"You go," replied his wife. "Look for a cheap one."

"I can't be seen on the streets in these shoes," he protested, looking at his feet.

Sue's eyes followed his gaze, then fairly snapped to the feet of the man in bed.

"Borrow his," she said. "They're dandy. Might just as well make some use of him."

"Do you mean," said Galt, "that you actually suggest I step into a dead man's shoes?"

"Easier to step into a dead man's shoes than a live one's," his wife logically replied. "And anyway, he's not dead yet—not entirely."

Fearfully the artist allowed his gaze to rest on the feet of his victim; and as he did so he experienced a pang of envy. Those turned-up feet were shod in exquisite boots. And they looked to be about the right size. As if fascinated, he moved to the bed and began to unlace the shoes.

"I'll just try them on," he muttered. "Just to prove to you they won't fit."

While Galt was straining at the injured man's feet the stranger suddenly opened his eyes and gazed at the artist with an expression of dying reproach. Breaking out into a cold sweat, Galt sprang from the bed.

"He opened his eyes," he quavered, "and he rolled them at me."

"Nonsense," said Sue briskly. "The way you go on, one would think he flung them in your face. Here, let me at those feet."

In a businesslike manner she began to tug at the man's shoes. A hollow groan escaped his lips.

"Oh, God!" exclaimed the artist, clapping a hand to his forehead. "I can't stand here watching this. The poor chap is groaning in anguish."

"He's got nothing on me," complained Mrs. Galt. "I'm actually grunting. Ah! Off they come! Did you ever see snappier shoes?"

In the privacy of his studio Galt put on the shoes of the wounded man. They fitted his feet perfectly; and in spite of his self-repugnance, his spirits rose a little. When he returned to the bedroom they fell with a decided thud. It seemed to him that all the hands in the Galt family, includng those of the twins, were on some part of the man's person, the majority being in his pockets.

"He's practically penniless," complained Sue. "So far we've been able to find only three dollars and seventeen cents. A man who wears such expensive shoes should carry a fat wallet. We must have money, you know."

At the mention of the missing wallet Galt turned even paler than he had been before. He had not the heart to tell his wife that in addition to brutally assaulting the man he had also stolen his wallet. It seemed to him that there was a little more dignity in being a murderer than a common thief.

"I'd leave him to his own devices," he said, "until the doctor gets here. If you keep on tossing his body about we won't need a doctor."

A quarter hour later, when Galt returned with a doctor, the artist was both gratified and surprised to find his victim still alive and intact. The first thing the doctor wanted to know was the name of the patient.

"It doesn't matter who he is so much as *how* he is," Mrs. Galt answered.

"Madam," said the doctor sharply, "I'm not going to argue with you."

"Thank God for that!" said Mrs. Galt.

The little doctor made no reply. Instead he devoted a vast amount of nervous irritation to the man in the bed. When he had finished examining the wound and dressing it he turned and faced the standing army of Galts.

"What," he demanded in an exasperated voice, "are all these strange-looking people doing in here? It looks like a mob scene. Those small, soiled children should be removed at once."

"It's affection," said Mrs. Galt promptly. "Pure affection. How is he, Doctor?"

"The patient is a very sick man," replied the doctor. "Must have absolute quiet. Can't be moved or disturbed in any way. A slight concussion, but it can be dangerous. Very."

"How long will he be in my bed?" Red Galt wanted to know.

"Our bed," corrected his wife.

"Maybe two weeks. At the least, ten days," said the doctor. "That is, if he lives."

Galt drew a quick breath.

"Who is he?" asked the doctor.

"He's our uncle," was Mrs. Galt's unexpected reply, while the rest of the Galts stared at her in astonishment.

"Whose uncle?" snapped the doctor. "There are all sizes and ages present."

"Oh," replied Sue vaguely, "you know. He's everybody's uncle. It's like that."

"He isn't *my* uncle," retorted the doctor. "What's his name?"

"Uncle Galt," said the artist's wife.

"It isn't enough," replied the doctor with rapidly rising impatience. "Hasn't he any more to his name than that?"

"No," said Mrs. Galt. "He might have had once, but we just call him Uncle Galt. You know how it is."

"I do not," retorted the doctor. "And I can't bring myself to write out prescriptions just for Uncle Galt. It would look silly. Can't you remember the rest of it?"

"George Washington," said Mrs. Galt explosively. "That's it, George Washington Galt."

"That's something," replied the doctor as if talking to himself, which was a much wiser thing to do when one was dealing with Galts. "George Washington Galt," he went on. "Sounds a lot like Harlem. It doesn't matter." Here he ceased muttering, to scribble off several prescriptions, which he handed to Mrs. Galt. "Get these filled at once," he told her, "and follow instructions closely. Take his clothes off and put him to bed. No noise at all. How did it happen?"

"He ran into a door," said Mrs. Galt.

"They all do," replied the doctor cynically. "I'll be back this evening."

"Must you come back?" asked the lady in tones of deep anguish.

"Certainly," snapped the doctor. "Unless you want George to die."

"That would never do at all," hastily put in the artist. "We want George to live. You don't know how much we do, Doctor."

"Well, he may pop off anyway," the little man heartlessly observed. "I know I would, with all these faces around me. Chuck 'em out of the room. That will be five dollars."

"If everybody will stay here," said Sue Galt, "I'll go get it." At the door she paused and looked archly back at the doctor. "I have to keep the money hidden," she explained. "There are so many thieves about."

The little doctor started slightly, then surveyed the assembled thieves with professional interest. The thieves in turn calmly surveyed the doctor.

That evening the stranger unexpectedly regained consciousness. The circumstances attending his return to reason were not auspicious. It so happened that the twins had selected that moment for a minute examination of this new and altogether fascinating face. The room was quite dark when the patient came to and found himself being unwinkingly stared at by two pairs of large round eyes. In his fevered imagination the man concluded that these eyes, so close to the ground, could belong to nothing less than a couple of wild animals. Uttering a shriek of mortal terror, he fell back into bed in another dead faint. The Galts, always willing to run in any direction, ran madly in the direction of the shriek and began to chatter round the bed with all the sparkle and animation of a French picnic.

"Has he passed beyond?" asked the spinster sister in a hollow voice.

"I hope so," replied Mrs. Galt, "if he's going to kick up a racket like that."

"He's passed beyond the limits of good taste," observed Fanny. "I hate shrieks in the night."

Galt laughed mirthlessly.

"That's one of the few things this house is ever full of," he said. "Shrieks by day, and shrieks by night."

"You'd better go shrieking for that doctor," Mrs. Galt told him.

This time the little doctor was even more disgusted than on his first visit.

"Why don't you ask in the neighbors," he inquired in a nasty voice, "and make a real party of it?"

Not a Galt answered. They were impervious to any form of sarcasm or insult. Then a voice spoke weakly from the bed, and all eyes turned in that direction.

"Doctor," complained the voice, "is this place a railroad station or a skating rink? More people come dashing back and forth through this room than in the Grand Central Terminal. A moment ago I caught a couple of animals trying to crawl into bed with me. I never saw such people. Don't they ever sit down?"

"Don't you call my children animals," Sue Galt cried, angrily confronting the sick man. "I'll have you to know they're my twins. Look at them, Doctor."

"Why?" demanded the doctor. "Why should I look at your twins?"

"I don't know," replied Sue. "I'm rather tired of looking at them myself; but just the same, they're not animals."

"Madam," said the doctor severely, "I have neither the time nor the inclination to discuss your twins. My duty in this house is to protect this patient. I must have a nurse."

Had the doctor deliberately striven to drive the Galts into an emotional frenzy he could not have set about it more expeditiously. He was almost mobbed.

"A nurse!" cried Mrs. Galt. "That's just great, isn't it? And what are we going to use for food—the nurse? And who is going to pay her wages? The NRA, I suppose."

"By rights," said the doctor calmly, "you should have two nurses."

"Did you hear that?" Mrs. Galt whispered. "If that man keeps it up I'll need a couple of nurses myself. What does he think this is—a death watch?"

While this was going on Red Galt was trying to avoid the eyes of the stranger. At any moment now the artist expected to be discovered and denounced. Once he caught the man gazing intently at his feet. Galt broke into a cold sweat.

"Doctor," said the stranger, "I don't seem able to remember a thing. I don't even know who I am."

"That's easily settled," the doctor told him. "Your name

is George Washington Galt, and, according to this lady, you're all these people's uncle. Does that make you feel any better?"

"My God, no!" said the man. "It makes me feel worse. Can't I go home?"

"You are home," continued the doctor soothingly. "You live right here with your family."

For a full minute the stranger savored the honor of this shocking information, then turned his eyes to the doctor.

"I must have led a terrible life," he observed. "Perhaps it's just as well I've forgotten most of it. It's better to be among one's own, I dare say. I'd not like to be obligated to strangers."

"What's that he said about not being obligated to strangers?" Sue Galt broke in. "Why, that man owes me five dollars already, not including the prescriptions; and now with the expense of the nurse——"

"Madam," interrupted the doctor, "your own flesh and blood, remember."

"I won't have any of his flesh and blood," Mrs. Galt answered furiously. "He's my husband's brother. He's not mine."

"And he's not our uncle," put in one of the twins—only to have his mouth covered by half a dozen hands.

"How did this happen?" asked the stranger. "Was I in an accident?"

"We won't worry about that now!" said the doctor.

"No," agreed the artist quickly. "Don't worry your head about how you got hurt. It's important to all of us that you get well."

"You might as well tell him," said Mrs. Galt in a malicious voice. "He's your brother, and he should be told." She turned to the man in the bed. "If you must know, George," she continued, "you came home that way again, and after falling all over the place you ran into a door."

"Do I get drunk?" asked the stranger, his eyes bright with alarm.

"Do you get drunk?" Sue Galt repeated, and answered her own question with a harsh laugh.

This was too much for Fanny. She covered her face with her hands and leaned weakly against her father.

"Is that girl one of my nieces?" asked the stranger.

"She is," replied the doctor.

"Then I have very little to live for," murmured the man.

As a result of the presence of a nurse in the house, the spinster sister was forced to sleep on the sofa, while the artist and his wife occupied chairs. Whenever Sue awoke during the course of the nights that followed she made a point of thanking her husband for his lovely birthday present. The children with their customary generosity remained comfortably in bed.

In compensation for the discomfort she was forced to endure Mrs. Galt succeeded in borrowing every penny the nurse possessed, so that the poor woman was forced to become a part of the family, whether she liked it or not.

At the end of his first week in bed the stranger was eating his head off. As a consequence the Galts became more deeply indebted to the local provision dealers. The doctor insisted that George Washington Galt should be given only the best and most nourishing of food.

Red Galt was by this time wearing his victim's suit as well as his shoes. Sue wanted him to make use of the man's socks and underwear, but this the artist refused to do. Attired in this borrowed outfit, he had made the rounds of the advertising agencies and had landed a few cash jobs. In spite of this slight relief, however, the problem of maintaining the recently acquired uncle was daily becoming more serious.

As soon as the man had regained his strength Galt made a daily practice of taking him out for long walks and trying to lose him. Frequently it was the stranger who found his way home first.

"You can't tell me there's anything wrong with that chap's memory," Galt complained to his wife after one of these unsuccessful expeditions. "I've left him in every out-of-the-way corner of this city, and damned if he doesn't get back like a homing pigeon. He must have been a postman once."

Mrs. Galt grinned at her husband.

"Next year," she said sweetly, "I'll be satisfied with just a couple of elephants for my birthday. Nothing elaborate, you know."

Then the arrival of a long letter from their eldest daughter Bonnie, who was studying music in Rochester, momentarily created a diversion—not that diversion was necessary in the crowded days of the Galts. The young lady wrote to inform her mother that she would be almost immediately among them. Something had happened which was worrying her greatly, and she felt sure that her mother would be helpful.

Sue put down the letter and looked thoughtfully at her family, including Uncle George.

"I hope," she said quite distinctly, "I'm not about to become an illegitimate grandmother."

On the day of Bonnie's arrival Red Galt played his last card. He took the stranger to one of the busiest places he knew. It was a railway terminal where trains, subways, taxicabs, and humanity struggled for survival. Here he excused himself for a moment, and never came back. When the artist got back to the flat he was jubilant over his success. The stranger had not preceded him. But as the hours passed he found himself strangely missing the man he had both assaulted and abandoned. His feelings seemed to be shared by the other members of the family.

The nurse, who by this time had been taken almost too fully into the confidence of the family, sat rocking placidly.

"It leaves me in a difficult position," she observed. "Here I am a nurse without a patient."

"We're all patients," declared Mrs. Galt. "This family should live under observation, especially its criminal head."

"Mr. George, or whatever his real name is," went on the nurse, "admitted to me that he didn't dislike you all too much. I don't myself. Do you think there's ever going to be any money?"

Mrs. Galt thought not, but a sudden ringing of the front doorbell put an end to the conversation. Everyone save the artist hurried nervously from the room. He rose and stood listening anxiously.

"Dear, dear me!" he heard his wife exclaim in the hall.

"My birthday present is back again. Where have you been, George?"

Before George could say where he had been Red Galt heard the voice of his eldest daughter.

"He's been wandering around the station dressed like a tramp," she said. "That's where I found him."

"Why, Bonnie," said Mrs. Galt reproachfully, "he's wearing your father's best and only suit. You shouldn't say such things, even though they're true."

"Well, I'd like to know," the artist heard his daughter say, "why on earth my fiancé is wearing my father's suit?"

"He's been doing more than that," came Sue's reply. "He's been sleeping in your father's bed. Tell me, dear, just who is this gentleman?"

"His name is Worthing Wright Taylor, and——"

"You don't mean the famous art critic and collector?" broke in Mrs. Galt in an appalled voice.

"None less," replied her daughter. "And he is going to become a member of your family."

"He already has," said Mrs. Galt.

"On the day he so strangely disappeared," Bonnie continued, "he was coming to call on you. He doesn't know what happened to him."

"Now I do," came the familiar voice of the erstwhile George. "The pleasant shock of so unexpectedly encountering you, Bonnie, has completely restored my memory of things past and present."

Upon the reception of this news a low groan escaped the artist's lips. Retreating to the next room, he hastily divested himself of his borrowed clothing and placed it on the bed. It was quite a blow to his feet to be separated from the shoes. Then he stood listening fearfully as the family trailed into the front room. Mrs. Galt was laughing softly.

"Do you remember everything?" she asked the restored mind.

"Too much," replied the great man.

"That's just wonderful," said Mrs. Galt. "Then you can appreciate how funny it all is."

"Oh, fully," replied Mr. Taylor. "In all its phases. But it's hard to figure out who the joke is on."

"My husband will be so happy when he hears about all this," added Mrs. Galt. "He has a remarkable sense of humor."

"Why does she torture me?" Galt miserably asked himself.

He was stricken by the enormity of his crime. He had assaulted his future son-in-law, one of the wealthiest and most influential art collectors in the country. Not content with that, he had stolen the man's wallet, bereft him of his clothing, and repeatedly tried to lose him. One man could hardly do more to another fellow creature.

It was at this low tide in the life of Red Galt that his twins came staggering in from the outer hall with their arms laden with toys and their mouths filled with candy. With a suppressed exclamation Mrs. Galt collared them.

"Where did you get all those things?" she demanded.

"A nice man gave them to us," mouthed one of the twins without the slightest hope of having his invention accepted.

As he spoke a fat wallet slipped from his blouse and fell with a dull plop to the floor.

"At last!" exclaimed Mr. Taylor, stooping to pick it up. "I remember this too. It's mine."

When he opened the wallet Mrs. Galt turned pale at the sight of so much money.

"God will never forgive you," she said in a choked voice to the twins, "for keeping all that money from your mother."

Unable to look on the scene longer, Galt removed his eye from the slit in the portieres and fled in his underwear to the studio, where he stood looking about like a trapped animal. A voice from the doorway made him whirl about.

"My brother!" said Mr. Taylor, smiling at him enigmatically from the doorway. "Don't you recognize your brother George? I drink, you know."

Without attempting to reply to this playful greeting, Galt picked up the lead pipe and handed it to the man.

"Go on," he said. "It's your turn now. You will find your clothing neatly folded on the bed."

With the lead pipe nicely balanced in his hand, Mr. Taylor followed the artist across the room.

"You perhaps are not aware of it," he said, raising the pipe to a striking position as Red Galt flinched, "but that oil thing over there is a little masterpiece. Splendid, really. What price?"

"Absolute silence," answered Red Galt in a low voice. "Is it a deal?"

"Done!" cried Mr. Taylor. "And I'll throw in my shoes to boot."

THE COCKTAIL HOUR

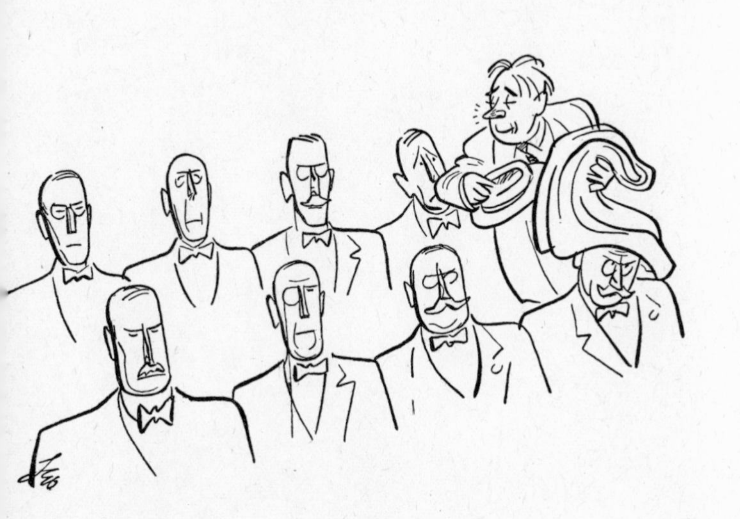

VII. THE COCKTAIL HOUR

As THIS BOOK is being hammered together there appears to be some sort of a moral renaissance going on in our country. One aspect of it that commands attention is the rise of the organization called Alcoholics Anonymous. Through this group a sort of evangelical fervor is seizing many of our nation's most depraved souses. The organization's membership has grown so prodigiously and its propaganda has been so effective that it is becoming downright unfashionable to get cockeyed. It doesn't seem impossible that in the end AA will abolish drunks. When that day comes I suppose the world will be much better off, but I, for one, will be a little sad about it.

Using pure logic, there is no gainsaying the enormous amount of good AA has done, but who the hell wants to go around using pure logic? These people have salvaged tens of thousands of Lost Weekenders and I hear reports that they have God on their side. Among my friends are a great many no-good bums, and AA has shorn them of bumhood and made respectable citizens out of them. From the point of view of the ex-bum this has been a good thing. From my point of view, it hasn't. My own position is stated clearly and beautifully in the Wolcott Gibbs story which you will find in this section.

Conscience demands that I wish continued and overwhelming success to Alcoholics Anonymous. I would, however, ask that they refrain from making it a clean sweep, that they leave me just a few wild and unpredictable drunks.

A few years back I wrote briefly on the subject of drinking, with emphasis on the horror of hangovers. I got a lot of mail from people who had hangover cures to offer. Some of them were, of course, fantastic and none of them, to my knowledge, would work. In the latter part of 1944 even the austere *British Medical Journal* tried its hand at the problem. The best method of curing a hangover, according to tha periodical, is:

> Take a bottle of Vichy before retiring. Take a teaspoon of sodium bicarbonate on arising. Then take a cold bath. After that eat breakfast, no matter how revolting it may appear. And then—a small dose of the hair of the dog.

The cables didn't say what the *British Medical Journal* considers a "small dose."

I well remember Jim Burchard's prescription for curing a hangover. Jim was a sports writer on the newspaper where I worked and I encountered him, one noontime, sitting at the bar in a neighborhood tavern. He confessed that he was hung over and he remarked that he was going out shortly and get it cured. I asked him how.

"There's only one way," said Jim. "I go to Artie McGovern's gym. First thing I do is take a hot shower. Then I put on a heavy rubber shirt and get in the ring and box three fast rounds. After that I go to the steam room and sweat like a pig for twenty minutes. Then I do a few laps around the track and come back and let the rubber pound on me until I ache all over. Soon as he is through, another session in the steam room. Then I stand up naked against a wall and a guy comes up with two high-pressure hoses. One of them shoots boiling-hot water and the other shoots ice-cold water. He plays those hoses up and down my back like mad. Cures any hangover in the world."

I'd rather die.

Some of the stuff in this section of the book deals with hangovers. Some of it deals with the getting of them. I recall that a few years ago a New York author got up a sort of anthology about drinking. He sent out a questionnaire to a lot of prominent people, asking them to set down their drinking habits. One of the questions was: "Why did you ever take that first drink?"

The most refreshing answer to this question was turned in by William Saroyan. He replied:

"Because I was thirsty."

Mr. Saroyan also wrote, in one paragraph, one of the most sensible things I ever read about marathon drinking.

In Act II of Mr. Saroyan's play, *The Time of Your Life,* the girl called Mary L. is cross-questioning Joe on the general subject of his drinking. He tells her that he doesn't drink all the time, only when he is awake; that he likes to drink as much as he likes to breathe. And Mary L. at last asks him why. His response:

JOE (dramatically): Why do I like to drink? (Pause.) Because I don't like to be gypped. Because I don't like to be dead most of the time and just a little alive every once in a long while. (Pause.) If I don't drink, I become fascinated by unimportant things–like everybody else. I get busy. Do things. All kinds of little stupid things, for all kinds of little stupid reasons. Proud, selfish, *ordinary* things. I've done them. Now I don't do anything. *I live all the time.* Then I go to sleep.

The three pieces which follow have been selected because their authors, quite obviously, know what they're writing about. You will get little pleasure out of them if you have never been plastered. If you have been, then you'll probably like this part of the book best of all. Let us begin with a beautiful piece of prose.

A MAN MAY BE DOWN

By Wolcott Gibbs

IN JUNE, after a series of small mishaps of no conceivable interest to anybody, my friend Munson gave up all alcohol except for beer, which of course may be drunk by the bucket without inducing either gaiety or grace, but only a sort of gassy stupefaction, very dismal to behold. In the succeeding three months I have followed his uninteresting experiment with the greatest care, and can only say that it all seems to have been a very tiresome mistake.

In the first place the advantages have been negligible. His health, he says, is a lot better. A well man gets out of his bed in the morning, shaves with a firm hand, and eats a hearty breakfast—several eggs, I believe, and some ingenious form of patented bran. He goes to work whistling and spends the day in a fine executive lather, making instantaneous decisions regarding the disposition of small pieces of paper with a vigor and clarity that his old dissolute self would have viewed with amazement and derision. At four o'clock in the afternoon he feels about the way he did at ten in the morning; there is no sensation of being about to fall over backward, like a tree, or of listening miserably to the slow ticking of an inward bomb.

Where once he roared dangerously through the streets, pursued by all the yelping imps in hell, or in the daylight crept along nervously, obsessed with calamity, he drives now surely and evenly, contemptuous of traffic. On Saturdays and Sundays he scampers vivaciously around a tennis court, or plunges carelessly into the most uproarious surf. His epidermis is brown, his eye clear and candid, his hand steady. If the occasion arose, probably he could thread a needle.

Financially, too, Munson is fine. His salary lasts from Friday to Friday, and there is a small but growing balance in the bank. In the old days the first sight to greet Munson's coppery Sunday-morning eye was a miserable litter on the table beside his bed, consisting of his watch, his keys, several incomprehensible memoranda scrawled on the covers of match folders and about four one-dollar bills, torn halfway across. These would be the sole residuum of his rather comfortable salary; the rest he had spread generously across Fifty-second Street, like the clues in some disreputable paper chase. Munson has bought a new car, with hundreds of cylinders, and a great many clothes which enhance the new glories of his physique.

Sobriety has also brought an unfamiliar simplicity and order into Munson's relations with women. Formerly he was what might be described as "the marrying kind," although I use the term in a rather special sense. He never actually achieved the altar, but after midnight Munson was in the habit of asking almost anybody to marry him. It was quite automatic with him, a sort of tic, but it always led to embarrassment and frequently to bitterness, there being ladies unworldly enough to imagine that marriage with Munson might be feasible and even mildly agreeable. I think it was only the superlative nature of Munson's hangovers that kept him from having more wives than Solomon. As it was, though, they could never get at him to pin him down. He'd sit with them at lunch the next day, white and far away, while the subject was tentatively approached.

"Of course"—humorously—"I don't suppose you remember what we were talking about in Tullio's last night?"

"No," Munson would say, intent on his private desperation. "Look, I wonder if you'd mind very much if we got the hell out of here? I'm sick as a dog, and I better get some air."

They never got anywhere with him, but as I've said, it complicated his life. Now his whole attitude is brisk and fraternal. "He keeps thumping his stomach at you and talking about his serve," one lady said, wrinkling her pretty nose.

In that there is a clue to the whole tragedy of Munson's sobriety. He has turned, I fear, into an extremely dull man. The old Munson was outrageous at times—a liar and a bankrupt and the enemy of order—but I liked him. He was a man living on a volcano who had no confidence in any tomorrow, and gave you and the moment all he had. The new Munson, this sepia changeling with the hard stomach, leaves me cold. There is something nastily calculating in his eye, and I don't approve of his new interest in time and money. The old Munson never looked at a clock or a check; at eleven o'clock the spirit of the new Munson almost visibly gets up and leaves the room, although his body remains for a reluctant half hour, yawning and squirming; and he has developed a certified accountant's eye for a ten-cent error in addition.

None of these things, however, are as bad as the dismal change temperance has effected in his conversation. The old Munson never told a story the same way twice. On

Monday he would tell you that he had been arrested for driving seventy-four miles an hour down Fifth Avenue and had spent the night in jail. On Tuesday it had become ninety miles, and he had climbed out of his car and magnificently destroyed the policeman. Munson used to say that nothing ever happened to anybody that would make a good anecdote without at least a little embroidery. The new Munson is scrupulously truthful, and nothing he says is worth a moment of your attention. This dreary punctiliousness hasn't affected only his own conversation; it has become an almost intolerable nuisance to his friends.

"The first time Theodore Roosevelt was elected President," I began the other night, when Munson raised a protesting hand.

"As a matter of fact," he said distinctly, "Roosevelt was only *elected* once. He first *became* President in 1901, upon the death of McKinley."

With it all—with his money and his health and the peace that must come from being able to recall his entire day from breakfast to bed—I don't think Munson is a happy man. The nature of life in New York makes it impossible to avoid people who vehemently are not on the water wagon, and it seems that they pick on him.

"I hear you're supposed to be funny," they shout. "Say something funny."

He's hounded, too, by friends who bring up his wayward past.

"Do you remember the time you brought that *very* odd girl to Mother's party?" someone will ask. It leaves him cold with distaste and embarrassment, and the worst of it is he's quite helpless. The gift of repartee left Munson the day he drank his last martini. He can only sit there, smiling uneasily and wishing they were all in hell. It is strange to me that a man of Munson's background should persist in trying to make sense out of drunken talk, but he does. He leans forward, full of anxious politeness, listening to their tangled nonsense, and making dreadful sensible little comments from time to time.

"I really think you ought to wait and see how you feel

about it in the morning," I have heard him say earnestly to a dreary bore who was threatening to jump in the bay. The old Munson would have given him carfare and his benediction.

Lately, though, there has been a troubled light in his eye, and the other night he made really quite an encouraging remark just before he left me.

"You know," he said, "I've been living the life of a hunted animal."

I think perhaps Baby is coming home.

THE HANGOVER has been handled and mishandled in literature. Mr. Jackson in *The Lost Weekend* produced a perfect picture of it, from a cold analytical point of view. There was nothing comical about a hangover in his book. I refuse to be realistic, however, and I've picked two morning-after stories which, peculiarly enough, were written by women. The first is—

YOU WERE PERFECTLY FINE

By Dorothy Parker

THE PALE YOUNG MAN eased himself carefully into the low chair and rolled his head to the side, so that the cool chintz comforted his cheek and temple.

"Oh dear," he said. "Oh dear, oh dear, oh dear. Oh."

The clear-eyed girl, sitting light and erect on the couch, smiled brightly at him.

"Not feeling so well today?" she said.

"Oh, I'm great," he said. "Corking, I am. Know what time I got up? Four o'clock this afternoon, sharp. I kept trying to make it, and every time I took my head off the pillow it would roll under the bed. This isn't my head I've got on now. I think this is something that used to belong to Walt Whitman. Oh dear, oh dear, oh dear."

"Do you think maybe a drink would make you feel better?" she said.

"The hair of the mastiff that bit me?" he said. "Oh no, thank you. Please never speak of anything like that again. I'm through. I'm all, all through. Look at that hand; steady as a hummingbird. Tell me, was I very terrible last night?"

"Oh goodness," she said, "everybody was feeling pretty high. You were all right."

"Yeah," he said. "I must have been dandy. Is everybody sore at me?"

"Good heavens, no," she said. "Everyone thought you were terribly funny. Of course Jim Pierson was a little stuffy, there, for a minute at dinner. But people sort of held him back in his chair and got him calmed down. I don't think anybody at the other tables noticed it at all. Hardly anybody."

"He was going to sock me?" he said. "Oh, Lord. What did I do to him?"

"Why, you didn't do a thing," she said. "You were perfectly fine. But you know how silly Jim gets when he thinks anybody is making too much fuss over Elinor."

"Was I making a pass at Elinor?" he said. "Did I do that?"

"Of course you didn't," she said. "You were only fooling, that's all. She thought you were awfully amusing. She was having a marvelous time. She only got a little tiny bit annoyed just once, when you poured the clam juice down her back."

"My God," he said. "Clam juice down that back! And every vertebra a little Cabot. Dear God. What'll I ever do?"

"Oh, she'll be all right," she said. "Just send her some flowers or something. Don't worry about it. It isn't anything."

"No, I won't worry," he said. "I haven't got a care in the world. I'm sitting pretty. Oh dear, oh dear. Did I do any other fascinating tricks at dinner?"

"You were fine," she said. "Don't be so foolish about it. Everybody was crazy about you. The maître d'hôtel was a little worried because you wouldn't stop singing, but he eally didn't mind. All he said was, he was afraid they'd close he place again, if there was so much noise. But he didn't are a bit, himself. I think he loved seeing you have such a ood time. Oh, you were just singing away, there, for about n hour. It wasn't so terribly loud, at all."

"So I sang," he said. "That must have been a treat. I sang."

"Don't you remember?" she said. "You just sang one song fter another. Everybody in the place was listening. They oved it. Only you kept insisting that you wanted to sing ome song about some kind of fusiliers or other, and every-ody kept shushing you, and you'd keep trying to start it gain. You were wonderful. We were all trying to make you top singing for a minute, and eat something, but you vouldn't hear of it. My, you were funny."

"Didn't I eat any dinner?" he said.

"Oh, not a thing," she said. "Every time the waiter would ffer you something you'd give it right back to him, because ou said that he was your long-lost brother, changed in the radle by a gypsy band, and that anything you had was iis. You had him simply roaring at you."

"I bet I did," he said. "I bet I was comical. Society's pet, must have been. And what happened then, after my over-vhelming success with the waiter?"

"Why, nothing much," she said. "You took a sort of dis-ike to some old man with white hair, sitting across the room, ecause you didn't like his necktie and you wanted to tell iim about it. But we got you out before he got really mad."

"Oh, we got out," he said. "Did I walk?"

"Walk! Of course you did," she said. "You were absolutely ll right. There was that nasty stretch of ice on the sidewalk, nd you did sit down awfully hard, you poor dear. But ood heavens, that might have happened to anybody."

"Oh sure," he said. "Louisa Alcott or anybody. So I fell lown on the sidewalk. That would explain what's the natter with my—— Yes. I see. And then what, if you don't nind?"

"Ah, now, Peter!" she said. "You can't sit there and say ou don't remember what happened after that! I did think hat maybe you were just a little tight at dinner—oh, you

were perfectly all right, and all that, but I did know yo
were feeling pretty gay. But you were so serious, from th
time you fell down—I never knew you to be that way. Don'
you know, how you told me I had never seen your real sel
before? Oh, Peter, I just couldn't bear it if you didn't re
member that lovely long ride we took together in the taxi
Please, you do remember that, don't you? I think it woul
simply kill me if you didn't."

"Oh yes," he said. "Riding in the taxi. Oh yes, sure
Pretty long ride, hmmm?"

"Round and round and round the park," she said. "Oh
and the trees were shining so in the moonlight. And you sai
you never knew before that you really had a soul."

"Yes," he said. "I said that. That was me."

"You said such lovely, lovely things," she said. "And I'
never known, all this time, how you had been feeling abou
me, and I'd never dared to let you see how I felt about you
And then last night—oh, Peter dear, I think that taxi ride wa
the most important thing that ever happened to us in ou
lives."

"Yes," he said. "I guess it must have been."

"And we're going to be so happy," she said. "Oh, I jus
want to tell everybody! But I don't know—I think maybe i
would be sweeter to keep it all to ourselves."

"I think it would be," he said.

"Isn't it lovely?" she said.

"Yes," he said. "Great."

"Lovely!" she said.

"Look here," he said, "do you mind if I have a drink?
mean, just medicinally, you know. I'm off the stuff fo
life, so help me. But I think I feel a collapse coming on."

"Oh, I think it would do you good," she said. "You poo
boy, it's a shame you feel so awful. I'll go make you a whisk
and soda."

"Honestly," he said, "I don't see how you could ever wan
to speak to me again, after I made such a fool of myself las
night. I think I'd better go join a monastery in Tibet."

"You crazy idiot!" she said. "As if I could ever let you g
away now! Stop talking like that. You were perfectly fine."

She jumped up from the couch, kissed him quickly on the ›rehead, and ran out of the room.

The pale young man looked after her and shook his head ›ng and slowly, then dropped it in his damp and trembling ands.

"Oh dear," he said. "Oh dear, oh dear, oh dear."

Jow COMES the piece I wrote about back in the introductory :ction—the story Mr. Lank was so stubborn about. It is—

GOD REST YOU MERRY

By Cornelia Otis Skinner

IRS. JONES was awakened at an untoward hour and with sensation of oppression and pain. The hour was seven-fteen, the oppression was caused by Adrian, her six-year-ld son, who was sitting for the most part on her chest, and ıe pain arose from the rhythmic pounding of Adrian's fist n the side of her head.

"Time to get up, Mummy," Adrian was calling in a tone ıat implied she must be very far away. It would have been ice to have been far away. Mrs. Jones had stepped out ıe previous night with Mr. Jones and some friends from :hicago (or were they friends?) and she found it difficult › share her child's early morning exuberance. In fact had ıe been an introspective person she might have been horri-ed to recognize in herself a sudden tendency toward in-ınticide . . . an abnormality apparently shared by Mr. ›nes, who, from the other side of the bed, raised a some-·hat ghastly head, muttered, "Why don't you kill that boy?" nd sank back into the state of someone just emerging from brain operation. Mrs. Jones, collecting what she could nd of herself, asked Adrian what his idea was in waking er.

"You're coming to the play!" Adrian apparently though his mother had suddenly gone deaf.

"What play?" It seemed an odd hour for the theater.

"The Christmas play at school, of course."

Then it all came back to her. Adrian had appeared som days ago with a mineographed handbill that looked as if hi entire class had walked on it, and that bore the announce ment of a Christmas play to be presented by the primar class and the fond hope that at least one parent would atten . . . a veiled command to all mothers. At the time Mrs Jones had thought it would be very nice. Even last nigh before going out, as she was tucking Adrian into bed, sh thought it would be very sweet. Now she knew it was goin to be terrible.

"What time is the play?" she croaked weakly.

"Eight-thirty. But I've got to be there at eight to get m halo on. I'm an angel." At which Mr. Jones mumbled, "O yeah?" and Mrs. Jones struggled out of bed. She hadn't bee in it long. In fact their home-coming taxi had pulled up a the apartment door alongside of Borden's wagon. That, sh told herself, was why she felt so awful. It had nothing t do with any final nightcap at the Stork Club.

Mrs. Jones, of course, was a perfect lady. She dispatche Adrian to his room, put a couple of Alka-Seltzers in a glas to dissolve, and set about the laborious business of dressing Mr. Jones remained comatose except for an occasiona grunt and a moment when he reared up on one elbow glared at the bubbling Alka-Seltzer, and complained tha "it made too damn much noise." Mrs. Jones managed t stagger first into her clothes, then into the dining room where she found that while she had no appetite she had a overwhelming capacity for drinking ice water. Adrian di mayed her by talking incessantly and scattering puffed ric about and she was further unnerved to behold through th glass of the pantry door the baleful eye of the cook, who wa a fanatical teetotaler. She choked down some black coffe sent Adrian back to his room three times to collect forgotte articles of clothing, and gathered her own hat and coat. Sh had even the saintlike forbearance to gaze upon the recun bent form of Mr. Jones and refrain from yelling, "Sissy!" in his somewhat inflamed ear. In a daze she descended in the elevator and in a daze and a taxi rode with Adrian to school.

She felt a little shy on entering the building. Mrs. Jones was a good mother but she wasn't fanatic about it. By that I mean she didn't put in much time at Parent-Teachers' meetings, nor was she one to pay frequent calls on the headmaster for the sake of discussing Adrian's sense of group consciousness. In fact, except for the opening day, she hadn't set foot in the place. She was determined, however, to make a gracious impression. An elderly gentleman standing just inside the door exchanged greetings with Adrian. Mrs. Jones, thinking he looked distinguished, extended her hand and in a voice that she forced to be bright said: "How do you do? I'm Adrian's mother."

The gentleman hesitated, then silently took her hand while Adrian collapsed with mortification against a statue of Zeus.

"Mother!" he hissed (he never called her Mother unless he was particularly ashamed of her). "That's Bill, the janitor!" Mrs. Jones repressed the impulse to say, "Then what the hell's he doing here?" and with what dignity she could muster followed the rapidly retreating figure of her son.

"Where do I go, Adrian?" she panted, feeling as she did her first day of freshman year. Adrian waved his schoolbag in a wild gesture that might have meant anything and vanished through a door. At the end of the corridor a number of women were being ushered into a room by a young master who looked awfully pure and unjaded. Still smarting from the janitor episode, she was hesitant to inform him about being Adrian's mother. Judging by the way she must look, it would be giving Adrian a break to keep her identity secret. So she merely smiled and the young man smiled back and told her to go in and just take any seat. A classroom had been converted into a theater with rows of chairs facing an improvised stage. Mrs. Jones selected a position toward the back and near a door. It being an affair of the primary class, the chairs were those designed for little tots. Mrs.

Jones was a tall gal and when she sat down her knees came up somewhere in the vicinity of her chin.

She looked at her watch and sighed. Twenty minutes to wait. Perhaps she should have gone with Adrian to help him with his halo. But who was she to deal with halos this bleak morning? She must try to get herself into the spirit of Yule-tide and little children, however hard. Snatches of music she'd heard at the Stork Club kept running through her head, and her head was in no condition to have anything run through it except a few cool mountain streams. She had a very awful pain at the back of her neck and her eyes felt like freshly dipped Easter eggs. Moreover, her heart was thumping in an alarming way. She told herself this was stage fright for Adrian.

In misery she gazed at the stage. The curtain, which sagged badly in the middle, gave indications of violent activity on the Thespian side. It fluttered and bulged and kept coming apart until an adult hand reached out and secured it with a safety pin. The room began to fill with mothers, governesses, and a few protesting fathers. A young woman in a tweed suit plopped herself down in the adjacent seat. She looked annoyingly clear-eyed and healthy . . . obviously one of those splendid mothers who take courses in vital subjects and go in for exercise as if it were a Cause. She smiled energetically at Mrs. Jones and said, "Your boy in this?" in the cheery voice of a girl scout captain.

Mrs. Jones nodded wanly and at the same time edged slightly away. It hadn't been so long since she'd had that last nightcap and (degrading thought!) she hadn't thought to chew any coffee beans.

"Both my sons are taking part." The woman talked like a Roman matron. "I have twins."

She would have, Mrs. Jones reflected, and thought how fearful it would have been to have been aroused by two Adrians this morning. She managed to cheep, "How lovely," and the woman asked what was her little boy's name. On being informed she said, "Oh," in a tone that hinted darkly that she knew him all right. "He's Primary 1 B, isn't he?" she continued. Mrs. Jones considered it pretty nosy of this woman to know more about Adrian than she herself did but she said she guessed he was and were her twins in the same division? "Oh dear, no, they're a whole class ahead." Then as an afterthought, "They're a year younger than Adrian." Mrs. Jones started to bridle but it hurt to bridle so she sank back into her state of moral apathy, reflecting moodily that, considering his heritage, it was only just retribution that her child should be a mental defective. A new arrival took the chair on the other side. Influenced by the community spirit of the mother of the twins, Mrs. Jones essayed a feeble grin and said, "How do you do?" The woman returned a stiff salutation in the unmistakable accents of an English governess . . . the superior variety to whom misguided Americans pay a hundred a month to turn their domestic household into living hell. The situation was eased by the entrance of the piano teacher, followed by a line of little boys bearing cymbals, tambourines, triangles, and other instruments of torture. The entrance of the orchestra coincided with that of a group that looked to be a bevy of green and red elves but turned out to be a portion of the primary glee club clad as choristers.

The footlights went on and the rest of the room was in darkness. A murmur of fatuous anticipation arose from the rows of beaming mothers but nothing else happened. The piano teacher rose and in a loud hiss told some unknown behind the scenes that they'd put out his light, too, whereat all the lights went on again and the mothers laughed good-naturedly. After considerable snapping of buttons and some playful going on and off of side brackets, the desired effect was obtained and an impressive chord struck on the piano.

The opening selection was "God Rest You Merry, Gentlemen" sung in sweet treble by the glee club and punctuated by the orchestra, who, on words like "*dismay*" and "Christmas *Day*" came forth with a goodly wallop of tympany. The mother of the twins looked happy and said wasn't it darling and Mrs. Jones concurred, although in her private opinion it was more like gems from *Hellzapoppin*. After the carol there was a pause and then the curtains were yanked as far as they'd go with the safety pin still holding them. They were then yanked back and the fastening removed, all of which convulsed the choristers. Finally the curtains opened on a bare stage and a pause that turned into an awkward stage wait. There were sounds of scrambling and a juvenile voice distinctly said, "Cut it out, will ya?" At length there entered from the left three rather diminutive Magi, orientally splendid in glazed muslin, bearing their respective gifts on sofa cushions. The scene was in pantomime, the glee club furnishing the narrative with a rendering of "We Three Kings of Orien-*Tar*." There seemed to be some difference of opinion in regard to the locality of the star. One looked before him, one searched the audience like a veteran actor counting the house, and one looked directly overhead until his crown started to slip off, whereat he lowered his gaze to the ground. The Roman matron nudged her and pointed out one of her Gracchi. He was, of course, the only one acting correctly. The scene closed with the finish of the carol. At the curtain one or two of the spectators ventured gentle applause but were shushed by the rest who regarded it somewhat in the nature of a performance of *Parsifal*. During the entr'acte the English governess leaned over and asked if she'd had her boy bring his own costume. She replied why no, that she understood the school furnished them. The governess made a face like Beatrice Lillie making a face like a governess, and said yes, but *she* never let *her* charge wear something that had gone the rounds goodness knew *how* long, and Mrs. Jones wondered morbidly if she'd better start watching Adrian for symptoms of bubonic plague.

The second scene was reminiscent of the first, it being in this instance a case of shepherds instead of kings and the theme song being "While Shepherds Watched Their Flocks." On a table disguised as a celestial promontory there appeared a small angel who made beckoning gestures and the finale was considerable enlivened by the angel's little sister, who from the audience emitted a joyful, "Why, there's Brud!" The second intermission was very long. From backstage came sounds of shuffling feet and of heavy things being dragged forth . . . possibly bodies. The curtains vould seem about to part, then would ease up, amid muffled ries of, "No, wait!" The choristers threw in a carol or two s a filler. Adrian's big moment was approaching and Mrs. ones's hands became clammy. Finally all was ready and here was presented a really very charming Nativity tableau. The manger with its participants was at one side, while in he background on and around the same table as that of Act I a close-ranked host of angels gave an impression that eaven was at the moment slightly overcrowded.

"That's my other twin playing Joseph," her neighbor vhispered. Mrs. Jones nodded and noted with satisfaction hat one side of his beard was noticeably unstuck. For a ime she looked vainly for Adrian. After a bit in the back ow she spotted a cherub whose diabolical behavior made ner recognize her son. Half hidden from view, he had a vantage place over his sanctified buddies whom, judging by heir wriggling and squirming, he was pinching in their all oo mortal rears. She could only hope the All-American nother hadn't noticed but she had, for she said, "Why, here's Adrian." Then added, "Restless type, isn't he?" Adrian's pastimes were cut short by some unseen authority in the wings and for one carol he remained comparatively tranquil. He looked very sweet, Mrs. Jones thought, except for the fact that his halo was cocked at the angle of a gob's hat. It was apparently loose and he eventually discovered that he could do all sorts of fascinating things with it. As it was about to slide off one ear a violent jerk would bring it back, while a few vigorous nods would throw it into a sort of spin. To Mrs. Jones it seemed as if all eyes were fixed on her appalling child. Beside him the principals in the drama paled into insignificance. She prayed fervently for some cataclysm that would wipe out both herself and Adrian at once. It looked as if her prayers were about to be granted, at least in part, for after a few minutes of fiendish head waggling the angel quite suddenly and unexpectedly fell from view in the tradition of Lucifer.

Mrs. Jones waited to hear those all too familiar bellows but there followed so complete a silence she began to think that perhaps it was a case of concussion. However, in a second that same adult arm was stretched forth and she could make out the huddled-up form of her son being dragged ignominiously from the boards. This was her cue to make an exit also. The play was nearing its finish and she thought it best to make a quick getaway. As she stumbled out the choir was again singing "God Rest You Merry, Gentlemen," the audience being asked to join in. She heard herself singing her own version, which began, "God Help You, Weary Gentlemen."

In the corridor she was met by Adrian. Far from looking contrite, he was all smiles.

"Hi, Mum," he called serenely, "how did you like it?" The words of vituperation died on her lips. She said she liked it very much. Adrian beamed.

"Did you see me?" he asked.

"Yes, dear," she said. "Where do we go to get a cab?"

DONALD HOUGH, who wrote the concluding article in our Liquid Department, deserves an award of some sort—perhaps a bronze shot glass (double) suitably engraved. I, for one, admire him, agree with him, and salute him for—

I DRINK AMERICAN

By Donald Hough

I DO NOT LIKE to sit down and drink like a gentleman, neither do I like to stop drinking because I can feel my liquor, as gentlemen do in England, or anyway in English books.

I am an American and I drink American.

I do not understand this constant bickering about drinks and gentlemen. A man who drinks like a gentleman is, it is popularly supposed, one who sips his liquor sitting down,

ooks straight ahead with dignity, drinks with all the gusto
ınd expression of an Indian taking his balsam tea against
he evil spirits, and ends by rising slowly to his feet and say-
ng, "Well, old fellow, I'll toddle up to bed."

And then he really does toddle up to bed.

This is a waste of time, a waste of liquor, and a waste of
;entlemen.

It makes it difficult for the layman to discover why Eng-
ishmen and others who drink like gentlemen drink at all.
)rinking, throughout America excepting the Harvard Club,
ınd among non-gentlemen the world over, is an adventure,
ıot a heathen ritual. It springs from an understandable and,
o far as I am concerned, a laudable curiosity as to what will
ıappen if, just about the time the gentlemanly drinker is
oddling up to bed, you shake your head vigorously and
tart walking in a northeasterly direction.

It is at this point that the spirit of the pioneers in the
American bloodstream comes bounding to the surface, and
he American steps forth. He is unafraid. The impenetrable
ıight lies just ahead, holding dangers that are exceeded in
nagnitude only by the rewards that are possible. Where the
Englishman knows he's going to end up in bed, the Ameri-
an likes to think he may end up in Bali. Frequently he
nds up in jail, but, incredible as it may seem, he often does
;et to Bali. It's worth trying for.

There is a basic difference, it seems to me, between a
nan who drinks like a gentleman and a really and truly
;entleman. A genuine gentleman often takes to drink be-
ause he is infernally tired of being a gentleman and wishes,
or the time being, to get away from it all.

It is important to remember that gentlemen sometimes
;et drunk. It's all right to carry on the tradition among the
ads in prep school that gentlemen never get drunk—espe-
ially English gentlemen, from whom all gentlemen the
vorld over are said to stem—but the real truth is that a large
ercentage of the gentlemen who drink, drink like gentle-
nanly fish. I have seen some splendid gentlemen get very
tiff. Not only very stiff but very ungentlemanly and often
n everybody's hair and on everybody's hands.

Looking at the other side of it, I have seen many people strictly non-gentlemen, become wonderful gentlemen the minute they reach the proper solution. They are polite, con siderate, and polished. They take their hats off constantly bow every few minutes, murmur the most charming phrases help ladies in distress and even ladies who are not in dis tress. They are democratic and magnanimous, equally a home in the lodgings of the poor and beneath the tables of the very rich.

They are no bargain in any language. Examined closely they usually are cads escaping from the boredom of being cads by going out and drinking like gentlemen.

Personally, I do not know whether I am a gentleman or not, but the reports that keep coming in to my wife all the next day following a little drinking on my part indicate vividly that I do not drink like one. This is all right with me. It is the only indication I have that I may be a gentle man after all. The reports vary as to detail, but on one poin they are unanimous: when out drinking, I'm a cad. I'm no weakly, part-time cad, either. I'm the real article. I'm a cad you may hate, but whose steadfast purpose and workmanlike job you can't help but respect.

All right. If I can't be a cad I won't play. I care nothing whatever about sitting down and sipping a drink, and I do not like the kind of parties where some nice person with an imitation Oxford accent keeps looking me firmly in the eye and saying, "Don't you think you've had enough, old man?

The answer is no.

I am out to drink enough to make it pay. Lots of people think this is not well bred. I think it is very genteel. I am out to get rid of a lot of inhibitions, including myself, with which I am bored, and the idea that I am a gentleman which gets in my hair. I also want to get rid of the hauntin fear that someday I may take a few drinks and begin to ge real polished, Oxford style.

Once I saw a concrete example of the difference, both i approach and results, between American- and English-styl drinking. I was invited to hear Bruce Lockhart, author c *British Agent,* give his first lecture in the United States, a the Harvard Club of New York. Of course the idea of anybody entering this country by way of the Harvard Club is slightly confusing. The Harvard Club is American soil only through courtesy and inescapable geographical considerations.

With my host I had the usual two whiskies and soda before dinner, and brandy at the end. I then thought it would be fine if we had quite a few more drinks. I never had heard Mr. Lockhart, but during my days as a newspaper reporter I had heard quite a few lectures and I felt I was on firm ground when I suggested that we hurry to the bar and get ready for the evening.

I thought the lecture was more or less an excuse, a kind of rallying point, to be used next morning as circumstances might require. I had looked forward to the evening for a couple of days, but the thought that we would have to take time out to listen to the lecture never had entered my thick skull. I had reckoned without the Harvard Club. At the Harvard Club you listen to the lectures.

So we sat in the game room and discussed English literature until it was time for the lecture, at which time we went into the auditorium as cold as a couple of herring.

We went into a large and impressive hall. It rose in smoky, black walnut grandeur some three or four stories, so that the upper timbers were lost in aristocratic gloom. Portraits in oil—representing, I was told, past presidents of the club—hung at well-bred intervals on the walls, each with its individual electric light. These august gents, each sitting in one of the three poses permitted Harvard Club presidents, dominated the scene: looking at it, for some reason I could not fathom at first, in extreme disapproval.

Our seats were along the wall, up front, flanking the speaker's rostrum, giving us a side view of Mr. Lockhart, when he should appear, but affording us a splendid front view of the entire assemblage. The entry of the guests into the hall was all but imperceptible. They came singly and in pairs, sat down quietly and unobtrusively by bending the hip and knee joints, and froze solid in place.

The committee, in tails, anticipated the entrance of Mr.

Lockhart when they paraded into the hall and filed into their seats, which were separated from the hoi polloi by pieces of string and a sign which said, "For the Committee." This section used up one quarter of the entire seating capacity. The committee was a wow.

The committee got seated and arranged their beards across their beautiful shirt fronts, Mr. Lockhart and all the chairmen arrived, and we were ready to proceed, or rather, to listen to Mr. Lockhart proceed. Mr. Lockhart stepped to the rostrum as soon as the various chairmen had introduced him, and commenced his address.

To get to the point quickly and impolitely, Mr. Lockhart, at the time of his first American, or Harvard, appearance, was not a blood-stirring elocutionist. He seemed distinctly impressed by the past presidents on the wall, and spoke with a great deal of deference and in a genteel monotone. He occasionally interrupted himself to mop his brow with his pocket handkerchief, and gave me, at least, the impression that he wished to heaven this really was London, instead of the Harvard Club version thereof, so he could toss the whole evening into the laps of his audience and tell them what to do with it.

He was three quarters through, and well into the intricacies of the financial situation in the Balkans, when the entire occasion suddenly went straight American on him.

The door in the rear of the hall opened and a drunk walked unsteadily down the broad center aisle.

He was a plain drunk, American style. He had his hat and overcoat on, and he kept them on. His overcoat was unbuttoned and it flopped around like the wings of a cockeyed bat. He wanted to sit down and hear the lecture, or anyway he wanted to sit down, and he searched for an empty place. His system was simplicity itself. He would stop at each row, spread his legs apart for support, and ask the person on the aisle if there was a seat vacant. Nobody answered him.

Slowly, inexorably, he came to the committee.

Here, he thought, was something classy. This was his style. He nudged the first member of the committee he came to. The member, in common with everybody else in the place, gazed stonily ahead. Maybe, thought the drunk, he's deaf. He looks deaf. He nudged harder, and repeated his request in a voice he evidently had been saving for the committee.

No soap. The drunk looked hurt. He tried a few other rows but met only chagrin and defeat.

All right, if everybody wanted to be so damned impolite, he could be impolite too. He stepped back, took good aim, and rushed the nearest member on the aisle. But he had overlooked the string. The string tossed him into the member's lap.

Our friend recovered himself, got out of the beard that was enveloping him, and regained the aisle. He looked around in horrible uncertainty. Not a face, not an eye, was turned in his direction, save only the faces and eyes of the past presidents on the wall, which were turned in everybody's direction with what, as I have mentioned, was an expression of permanent disapproval.

The poor fellow felt this. A hopeless look came over his face. Maybe, he thought, this is all just a terrible dream. He looked as though he were about to flee, and Mr. Thomas Lamont, the head chairman, took a deep breath; I mean, I suppose he took a deep breath. You couldn't tell.

But the drunk did not flee. He wanted to find out about the financial situation in the Balkans. He steered himself carefully down the front of the aisle, some fifteen feet in front of Mr. Lockhart, and, after turning around a few times to trample down the long grass as his ancestors had done, sat down on the floor and crossed his legs Indian fashion. He did not bother to remove his hat.

But our drunk was not entirely without manners. Having lit a cigarette, he looked around and noticed nobody else was smoking. His better nature rose to the surface. He tossed the cigarette to the carpet directly in front of him. He now proposed to step on it.

Had he been a student of the human body he would have realized in the first place that from his position it is impossible to step on anything without breaking the ankle. He tried one foot, then the other, laboriously untangling them before each trial. It seemed to him, from where he sat, that he was stepping on the cigarette, but each time he withdrew his foot the cigarette still was burning. Despair plainly was written on his face.

Finally, after a period spent in deep thought, sitting there looking at the wisp of smoke curling up between him and Mr. Lockhart, he got to his feet after much trouble and fuss, and stepped squarely on the damned thing, ground it beneath his heel, resumed his seat, and heard the lecture through to the end.

During all this time not an eye in the place was turned toward this common American drunk. The feeling seemed to be that if nobody looked at him Mr. Lockhart would not see him either. Or, if he saw him, he would think it was just somebody from the Balkans.

What is even more remarkable, while we were walking out of the hall, while we were moving around the club afterward, I never heard the presence of the drunk so much as hinted at by anybody. He had not existed. He was a ghost.

We went up to Hugh Leonard's house and discussed the lecture at some length. I guess Hugh noticed that I looked rather glum. Perhaps he felt I had the drunk on my mind and was disappointed with the whole evening. He said, "Well, I'm sorry about that—interruption down at the club."

The subject having thus been brought up and thoroughly aired, it was dropped—forever.

Hugh had been right about my thoughts. I did have the drunk on my mind. I was regretting that I had not thought of it first. Our man evidently had started his evening on the American plan—take a few drinks, shake your head, and follow all hunches. As hunches go, he had come up with a superepic. Since that night I have had a Goal. I never have attained it. I have tried. But in the circles in which I move I am not appreciated. They have bouncers. It never ends in the way I had planned.

The lone drunk, of course, is an American institution. This type of sport seldom is practiced in foreign lands.

In fact a fine British stigma has come to be associated with the individual who takes his spirits without benefit of companions. There is no sense to this, but there is a great deal to be said for the American point of view. If a person is tired of his routine, tired of himself, tired of being a gentleman, why should he not be equally—or more—tired of his friends? In many cases this is easily the number 1 reason for the bender.

A person on a tear with his usual companions is progressing vertically, but he is standing still horizontally. Only when he has broken away from all things familiar does his binge begin to pay dividends.

New scenes, new people, new policemen fill his life—into and out of bars, into and out of the lives of innumerable people, into and out of love, into and out of magnificent business deals, great adventures, dazzling projects.

He drinks, not sitting down, but standing gloriously at the bar, facing half toward the door, poised for the leap into the Unknown, on and ever on, to greater and ever greater things.

That is the American way, and it is mine.

So let my companion finish his gentlemanly drink and toddle up to bed or toddle over to the lake and jump into it. Let him, and be damned. I get up from the table with him, but I do no toddling.

I walk with brisk, elastic step to the main entrance and look eagerly into the black night.

I am ready to plow a white furrow through the darkness, leaving in my turbulent wake a growing accumulation of insults, lost friends, dropped acquaintances, indignant waiters, discouraged cops, people named Marie, disregarded phone calls, promissory notes, and a lot of miscellaneous seaweed, all churned up into a phosphorescent glow.

I now am on the threshold of high adventure, and I take my first step firmly, realizing that someplace, far off on the horizon, is the only certainty that awaits me—the dawn.

NOPALERA

VIII. NOPALERA

THE COCHINEAL BUG, once used extensively in the production of dyestuffs, feeds on a species of cactus called nopal. In southern California a long time ago the slopes to the south of Cahuenga Pass were covered with this nopal and the Spaniards called the region Nopalera. It is now called Hollywood and there are many individuals who believe the world would be much better off if that land were still inhabited by nothing but cochineal bugs. I am not among them, disliking bugs much more than I dislike four-toned shoes and stilettos.

In the 1880s a lady named Daeida Wilcox, out of Hicksville, Ohio, came to Nopalera with her husband and they bought up a lot of property. A few years later Mrs. Wilcox went back to Hicksville for a visit and on the train met a lady who had a summer home near Chicago. The name of this summer home was "Hollywood." Mrs. Wilcox thought that a mighty pretty name and when she got back to the Pacific Coast she appropriated it and gave it to the Wilcox ranch. She set out some English holly on her property but it wouldn't grow. Maybe the cochineal bugs ate it up. At any rate she stuck to the name "Hollywood" and before long the whole town came under that designation.

I don't know why I'm telling you all this, except that neither Mrs. Wilcox nor the cochineal bugs could ever have dreamed of the things that were fated to happen in their old stamping grounds. I would enjoy, I think, getting up an entire book of literature about Hollywood because some wonderful things have been written about the town. Boulder Dam couldn't hold back the ocean of slop that has been turned out on the subject, yet there's good stuff to be found if you know how to find it.

I've limited myself to a pair of stories for this section. One is by an Englishman. John Collier might be described as the British Thorne Smith, though in some respects they are fourteen and a half parsecs apart. Mr. Collier, incidentally, is now living in Hollywood and a number of his stories have the town for their locale.

The story of Gavin O'Leary had not been published anywhere when I first set eyes on it. It's another tale that I wish I had thought up and then been able to write. If you want more in a related vein I recommend that you dig up a copy of Mr. Collier's book of short pieces called *Presenting Moonshine.*

GAVIN O'LEARY

By John Collier

THERE WAS a young, bold, active, and singularly handsome flea who existed in a state of rustic innocence on the divine body of Rosie O'Leary, nursemaid in the comfortable home of a doctor in Vermont. No flea has ever been better pastured since the beginning of the world: he was as well off as a landowner in a country flowing with milk and honey, and he delighted in every undulation of the landscape. Rosie was the merriest, most ardent, laughing, bounding, innocent, high-spirited creature that ever trod on earth: these qualities are a very alphabet of vitamins to a flea; besides which, she was appetizing. Lucullus himself would gladly have taken a knife and fork to her.

This particular flea bounded higher than most, and ceaselessly extolled his good fortune. All his nourishment came fresh and ruby from her untroubled heart: there was never such a gay, silly, glossy, high-jumping, well-developed flea as Gavin O'Leary. Gavin was his given name; the other he took from Rosie, as a nobleman takes the title of his domain.

There came a time when Gavin found something a little heady in his drink, and his heart was filled with delicious dreams. On Thursday evening this sensation rose to a positive delirium. Rosie was being taken to the pictures.

Our flea at that time had no great interest in the screen: he sat through the first half of the performance in a nook that offered no view of what was going on. At ten o'clock he began to feel ready for his supper, and, as Rosie showed no signs of going home to bed, he resolved to picnic, as it were, on the spot. He was a little surprised to find his light and sparkling sustenance changed to a warm and drowsy syrup, with a fire smoldering under its sweetness, which robbed him of all his bounding enterprise. A tremor ran through his body, his eyes half closed, and when his shy retreat was suddenly and inexplicably invaded he was neither amazed nor hopping mad, but crawled half reluctantly away, with a languid simper, for all the world as if he were a mere bug.

Gavin took refuge in a cranny of the plush seat, and surrendered himself to the throbbing intoxication that filled his veins. He awoke from his drunken sleep several hours later, with a slight sense of shame. It was early morning, the picture house was empty, no food was in sight. Gavin waited eagerly for the beginning of the matinee, for his appetite was of the best. At the proper hour people began to file in. Rosie's seat was taken by a pale youth who fidgeted impatiently till the performance began, and when the performance began he sighed. Gavin, brushing his forefoot over his proboscis, entered between a pair of waistcoat buttons, and, without any affectation of saying grace, tapped his new host in the region of the heart, in order that he might drink as fresh and pure as it came.

I think it is Dante who describes a lover's blood as running pale and fiery like old wine: by this comparison Gavin's lunch was vodka or absinthe at the very least. No sooner had he drunk his fill than he began to sigh like the sound effects of Sam Goldwyn's South Sea idyll, and he could not clamber up fast enough out of the top of the young man's waistcoat to feast his eyes on Miss Blynda Blythe, who at that moment occupied the screen.

This flea was now consumed with a passion too ardent to

be described. He was in the condition of one who has made a whole meal of a love potion. He was devoured, wrought up, hysterical, mad; he began to rhyme like a demon, for his host was a poet as well as a lover: in short, no flea has ever throbbed, burned, tingled, longed, and hungered as Gavin did at his very first sight of Miss Blynda Blythe.

Very soon he rode home to a hall bedroom, where he spent the night studying fan magazines, and now and then sipping the burning potion that was the cause of his furious passion. A number of lesser fleas, and other creatures of a baser sort, shared this dangerous dinner with him. The young man was too besotted with love even to scratch. The crazy drinkers were free to take their perilous fill, and the scene was worse than that in any opium den. Some wept and moaned their lives away in corners; some, dirty, unkempt, lost to the world, lay abandoned in feverish reverie: others sprang from the window, drowned themselves, or took Keatings. Many, mad with desire, blunted their proboscises on one or other of the glossy photographs of Blynda Blythe which adorned the mantelpiece and the screen.

Gavin, though he sipped and sipped till the potent liquor entered into the very tissues of his being, was made of sterner stuff. It was not for nothing that he had spent his youth on the finest flower of the indomitable immigrant stock. With the dawn his bold plan was made. His host rose from his uneasy slumbers, dashed off a few lines, and went out to seek his breakfast at a drugstore. Gavin rode boldly on his coat collar, calculating like mad from the position of the sun.

No sooner did the poet turn from a westerly direction than Gavin was down on the sidewalk and hopping furiously on the first stage of his three-thousand-mile trek to the coast. He hitchhiked when he could, but as he left the town behind him these opportunities grew fewer. The dust choked him, the hard surface of the highway proved lacerating to those sensitive feet, accustomed to nothing coarser than the silken skin of Rosie O'Leary. Nevertheless, when the red sunset beaconed where the long trail crossed the distant hills, a keen eye might have discerned the specklike figure of Gavin, jigging lamely but gamely on.

It was long afterward, and after heaven knows what adventures by prairie, desert, and mountains, that a travel-worn, older, and gaunter Gavin entered Hollywood. He was gaunt not merely by reason of his incredible exertions but because of the knight-errant asceticism which he had practiced through all the hungry miles of the way. Fearing lest any full meal should fill him with some baser, alien mood, he had disciplined himself to take the merest semisip, except where he was well assured that his entertainer was also an adoring fan of Blynda Blythe.

He now hastened along Sunset Boulevard, paid his pilgrimage to her footprint on the threshold of the Chinese Theater, and considered what his next step should be.

He thought at first of striking up an acquaintance with some of the lounging, idle, disappointed fleas of the town, to find out which laundry she employed, but his wholesome pride rejected this backstairs approach. He dismissed, with equal contempt, the idea of perching on the cuff of an autograph hunter and leaping upon her when she signed the book. He might, had he money and voice enough, have commissioned one of those cars which take tourists to spy at the film stars' homes, but he longed above all for a dignified and wholesome approach to her: he wanted to be recognized as a fellow being, possibly even as a fellow artist.

It was this last thought that drew him to the portals of her studio, where he mingled, for everyone must begin somewhere, with the ranks of shabby extras who hung about in the hopes of being called in on some emergency. Fortune favors the brave: he had not been waiting there many weeks when an assistant director dashed out, crying in an urgent voice: "Say! Any of you guys got a performing flea? Anybody know where I can hire one?"

The word was spread. The extras on the sidewalk began to search themselves hastily. Genuine professional flea masters patrolled the boulevards whistling and yodeling up their troupes, who had been long sunk in idleness and despair.

Gavin boldly entered the studio and took up a point of vantage on the producer's desk. "At least," thought he, "I am first in the queue."

Some flea masters soon entered, carrying their unenterprising artistes in matchboxes, pillboxes, and phials. Gavin could hardly suppress a sneer.

When all were assembled: "We got a part here for the right kind of flea," said the producer. "It's not big, but it's snappy. There's a close-up in it. Listen, this flea's gonna have the chance to play opposite Blynda Blythe. He's gonna bite her on the shoulder in a lodging-house scene. Say, where's your fleas from, feller?"

"Dey're Mex, boss," replied the impresario he had addressed. "Mexican flea, him lively, him jumpa, jumpa . . ."

"Cut it out," replied the producer. "This scene's laid in the East. Listen, you can't fool the public these days. Come on, boys, I want a New England flea."

As he spoke he spread the contract out before him. A babble rose from the flea masters, all of whom swore their fleas had been imported from Boston, Vermont, New York itself, by plane. While they still argued Gavin dipped his proboscis in the ink bottle and scrawled his minute signature on the dotted line.

Everyone was amazed. Union rules were invoked but contemptuously dismissed by the producer. Gavin was hurried onto the set. "You wouldn't like your stand-in to do this scene, Miss Blythe?" said an overobsequious assistant. Gavin's heart sank.

"No," said Miss Blythe. "It is for my art."

"Get that into the *Reporter*," said the producer to another hanger-on. "Okay, Jack," to the director. "I'll watch you shoot."

"Better get it rehearsed up a bit," said the director. "Somebody stand by with a glass of brandy for Miss Blythe when she gets bit."

"You're not to go on if you feel faint, Blynda," said the producer.

"All right, Benny," said Blynda. "It's for my art."

"Look how it is, Blynda," said the director. "This is where you've walked out on Carew, just because you're nuts about him. Want to see if he'll follow you down to the depths. You're yearning for him. And you're lying on the lodging-house bed—get Miss Blythe's tears, Alfie—and you feel something, just where he kissed you in the scene we're gonna shoot when that God-damn art department gets the country-club-revel set done. See?"

"I see, Jacky. It's just the flea."

"That's right, Blynda. And you look round——"

"I got it."

"Okay. Quiet."

"*Quiet* for Miss Blynda Blythe and Mr. Gavin O'Leary rehearsing!"

Gavin's heart swelled. To become at one stroke a successful film actor and a happy lover is enough to turn a larger head than a flea's.

Miss Blythe flung herself on the bed. She wept. "Mr. O'Leary." Gavin leaped forward. He wished only he had a delicate scrap of cambric, to wipe his proboscis, and to toss into the hands of a bystander. It would show a nice feeling.

"I'm afraid you moved, Blynda."

"Look, Jack. I'm going through this for my art."

"Okay. We'll try again."

The rehearsals went on all afternoon. Gavin nearly burst with rapture. Toward the end, however, a peculiar mood overcame him. "This is extaordinary," said he to himself. "I love her. I adore her. Besides, I'm a he man. Didn't I cross the prairie on foot?"

It was agreed that the scene should be shot on the morrow. After some discussion the principal writer was told to put Gavin up for the night. "See? You got the whole feeling of the thing. He'll get something from you, Georgie."

"Yeah?" muttered the writer. "He'll get an underdone steak at the Trocadero."

At the Trocadero, however, Gavin had no appetite. He glanced uneasily right and left, straining his eyes to see a face he did not know, alert to catch a voice he had never heard. "If this is 'going Hollywood,'" said he to himself, "I wish I had stayed in Vermont. To think I have crossed the prairies on foot! I hate myself! I loathe myself! I wonder if he is here?"

Fleas sleep little at night in any case, and Gavin was

unable to close his eyes. A bundle of nerves, he allowed himself to be carried to the studio in the morning. He no longer had the least inclination to act with Blynda Blythe. "She talks about what she goes through for her art!" said he with a sneer. "A mere fleabite! The price I am paying for mine!"

It is well known, however, that the show must go on. Today, after the briefest rehearsal, the camera began to roll in good earnest. Blynda, an actress to her finger tips, scarcely needed glycerine tears. She flung herself on the bed, dissolved in an ecstasy of longing. "Carew! Carew!"

"Now then, Mr. O'Leary!"

Gavin glanced right and left as if for deliverance. "Dorian Gray," he muttered with a mirthless laugh. He sprang, and drank deep.

"Boy! Did you see that bite?" said the director to the producer. "This little guy gives it all he's got."

"Looks like stealing my scene," said a handsome burly male star who at that moment appeared on the set.

At the sound of his voice Gavin turned and, with one record-breaking leap, flung himself upon his new idol's breast, sobbing in mingled ecstasy and shame.

"Boy! Did you see that jump?" cried the director enthusiastically.

"Get out a long-term contract," said the producer to his secretary.

"The little feller seems to take to me," said the actor good-humoredly. "Goin' to be buddies, huh? Might be worth mentioning to the *Reporter*."

The biographer prefers to draw a veil over the next stage of Gavin's career. To know all is to excuse all, but to know less is to have less to excuse. It was not Gavin's fault that the actor was less emotionally wrought up by his part than Blynda was by hers.

It cannot be said that he was happy, and his unhappiness should at least turn derision into sympathy. The stories of his fantastic costumes, his violet evening suits, his jewelry, his scent-spray shower bath, and of strange parties at his bijou house in Beverly Hills are mainly the concoctions of coarse malice or unscrupulous publicity. Moments of bliss he

ndoubtedly had, moments when his New England upbring-
ng was forgotten, his principles betrayed, and when the
vorld seemed well lost for the blind enjoyment of the pass-
ng hour. Other and more frequent spells were passed in
gonies of remorse and self-abhorrence. He could not bear
o think that it was he who had crossed the prairies on foot.

Time passes, however, and the day dawned when the actor
vas no longer suited to play the lover. He must take up
haracter parts or go in for production. Character was never
is strong point; he therefore felt himself admirably suited
o produce. Producers are Godlike creatures; they must either
reate a new star or get no public.

Splendid parts, full of nimble wit and biting satire, were
vritten for Gavin, but the ex-actor could nowhere find a new
eauty. His talent scouts spread far and wide; their eulogies
arried little conviction. At last, however, a short list was
nade. The ex-actor read it over and, thoroughly dissatisfied
vith the world and himself, retired to bed. Gavin naturally
hared his dissatisfaction. His thoughts turned on the happy
lays of his youth and innocence, and the hour of his salva-
ion was upon him.

He rose, cast off the flimsy night attire that he had re-
ently affected, and sought, with an already less mincing
eap, the list upon the writing table. The inkwell stood open:
o him its sable depths were a positive Jordan, in which,
f he dipped seven times, he might yet cease to be a social
eper. He immersed himself with a shudder, and, clamber-
ng painfully out, he stood for a moment upon the dark rim
of the inkwell, nude, shivering, gasping, yet tensing his
nuscles for a leap to a certain spot at the head of the list.
He made it, and made it without splash or blot. With the
accuracy of a figure skater, but with all the slow difficulty
of a tar-clogged victim of the Ku Klux Klan, he described
the word "Rosie" in a perfect imitation of the sprawling
hand of the chief talent scout.

Another painful leap, and he was back, sobbing and choking in the bitter, glutinous ink. The hot weather had thick-
ened it. This time he completed the word "O'Leary." Five
times more, and her address was written. Gavin, utterly

worn out, black as your hat, half poisoned by ink, sank exhausted on the blotting pad. But a great gladness had dawned in his heart.

The ruse was successful. Rosie was brought to the coast for a screen test. Needless to say, she passed it triumphantly. Gavin, with a thankful sigh, nestled once more upon her heart and drank deep of its cleansing, life-giving vintage. At once his aberration fell away from him like a shoddy outworn garment. He was a new flea. The past was dead. The ex-actor was revealed to him as a mere steppingstone, privileged to be a fleeting incident in the glorious career of the most beautiful Irish colleen, and the greatest little actress, and the most important human being, in the world. And, as Miss O'Leary never faltered in that opinion during all the rest of her days, our good Gavin was happy ever after.

To finish off our Hollywood Department, let us turn to Ben Hecht. Mr. Hecht is conclusive proof that Hollywood doesn't give a damn what is written about it. Year after year he has assaulted the town and year after year the Hollywood producers coax him out to California and sweeten his existence with bulging casks of gold.

This Hecht story is from *A Book of Miracles* and is easily the longest single piece in our collection. The reason it is so long, I think, is that Mr. Hecht has a tendency to write for posterity in spots. Nonetheless, this story of Robert Gary and God is my notion of a minor American classic. Get to work on it—there's a lot of it.

THE MISSING IDOL

By Ben Hecht

It is generally said by thinkers, old and new, that the people of the world own hardly anything in it. Their religions, like their governments, seem to have provided only perpetual policemen for the protection of goods not their own. And the only diversions designed exclusively for them and not for their immemorial handful of betters are those which are said to exist in heaven.

At least this was true until the advent of the movies. Someday historians writing about the ups and downs of the people will stumble upon the fact that, in a struggle beginning among the glaciers and seemingly getting the people no nearer any of the enchantments of existence, the movies were their first unchallenged possession.

It is strange that the people's first inheritance should be wrested out of the kingdom of art, a kingdom in which they had less of a foothold than in any of the other mirages of empire and power.

You get a very sad picture of the people when you study the history of art. It was always something the people didn't like. Particularly in modern times, beginning with the Renaissance, art became more and more of a nuisance to the people.

Not only had they to toil and watch a little handful of their betters loll in idleness, not only to starve and watch this handful feed, and to stagger about in rags and see this handful glittering in satins, but they must also observe this immemorial handful most mysteriously swooning and applauding and rolling their eyes in bliss over the arts.

Approaching the sources of all this ecstasy, the people found nothing in them. This is perhaps because beauty is the product of a superior kind of life which the people, who have so much difficulty keeping alive, have no time to develop in themselves.

When you think of all the books, statues, paintings, oratorios, symphonies, cantos, et cetera, that the people have never been able to enjoy, you can begin to understand their excitement over the movies. Suddenly and inexplicably a diversion appeared in the world that belonged to nobody but themselves.

A kingdom had blossomed, not in its usual place—the sky—but under their feet; and staring at it warily at first, for there is always a catch to the kingdoms offered the people they invaded it and took possession with whoops of triumph

Today the people, so long the limbo dwellers, rule thei kingdom mightily. The movies are their Cellinis and Angelos their Shakespeares and Shelleys. They control all the plot and elect their own geniuses. And, like some internationa Lorenzo the Magnificent, they distribute rewards undreamed of by their ancient enemies—the artists.

I write these few obvious generalities about the movie not that you may understand them—for who doesn't know all there is to be known about the movies?—but as an intro duction to one of the heroes of my tale, Mr. Leo Kolisher who is the reigning producing genius of Hollywood. There are two other heroes in my story—Robert Gary and God—bu I shall explain about them later.

Unless you knew that Mr. Kolisher had been rather mys tically enthroned as a genius by the people, you would, am sure, wonder how he happened to exist at all—and earn a living. Mr. Kolisher neither wrote nor directed his produc tions, nor acted in them, nor did he even produce them. (A for financing them—well, Mr. Kolisher was not entirely fool.)

During the writing, acting, and producing of one of hi movies by scores of other people, Mr. Kolisher charged about like one of the headless horsemen of the Apocalypse and committed almost as much damage. But not enough, how ever, to prevent the movie from finally appearing and being hailed as far as the hill passes of Tibet as another evidence of his genius.

But how, you will ask, did all this happen; how could such great fame come so undeservedly to anyone? Th answer to such a query must be that Mr. Kolisher's fam was not undeserved. It was not merely that he placed hi name—with a staggering frequency—on the product sent ou from his studio, or that when the work was done he con trolled the channels of publicity that celebrated its and—who can blame him?—his own wonders.

This helped a little. But self-acclaim, however tireles does not alone make for triumph, even in the movies. I would be a small and captious diagnosis of Mr. Kolisher's genius that stopped there.

The real truth was that of all the artists and artisans (there is a sprinkling of the latter in Hollywood) who toiled in the creation of a Kolisher movie, Mr. Kolisher alone understood the historical and spiritual significance of his product. Mr. Kolisher knew, and knew passionately, that it belonged to the people; that every foot and phrase of it, every tear and grimace of it, was theirs. Mr. Kolisher knew that he was a Man with a Mandate. It was his duty (and in the evasion or abuse of it he perished almost instantly) to keep the kingdom of the movies free from the ancient enemy of the people—art.

And how did Mr. Kolisher know, so mysteriously, what would delight the people? By knowing nothing, is the only answer I can give. By being as devoid of all subtleties, refinements, dreams, cultural equipment, and talent as any of the lowliest whom he served. He was the Man in the Street with bay leaves in his hair.

It may seem a simple thing to be merely dumb, and to remain so in the midst of the many voices of life. But I assure you it is not. It is as difficult as remaining young. And in Hollywood this accomplishment is rewarded above all others. It enabled Mr. Kolisher to sit enthroned, not as an ego full of creative birth pangs and garbled messages, but as a peevish and incorruptible representative of some two hundred million folk to whom art for some hundred centuries had been a closed book.

Considering all this, you can see how fair it was for Mr. Kolisher to be a genius. It was a title the people gave him (just as they called other men, much more foolishly, their kings and presidents) because they knew instinctively what was what. They knew that he, and not the never-to-be-trusted artists whom he employed, was their servant; that it was he who saw to it that the kingdom of the movies, unlike all the other kingdoms they had created, remained their own.

In the twenty-fifth year of his reign as genius Mr. Kolisher was engaged in producing (or rather, in having produced) a movie which he considered the greatest child, yet, of his world-famed talents. This movie was called, tentatively, *The Redeemer,* and for its plot concerned itself with the teachings and tribulations of Christ.

The way this had come about is that some nine months before the beginning of the events I have to relate Mr. Kolisher had discovered religion. I do not mean that he had taken to praying and throwing himself wantonly at the feet of God. What Mr. Kolisher discovered was that for a long time religion had been something in which the people had been remarkably interested. Or, as he put it himself, everybody is religious or knows somebody who is. Wherefore, religion, my hero had concluded, would make a wonderful movie; more than that even, a tremendous piece of entertainment.

Having called around him a half dozen of his superior intellects, he had laid his inspiration before them. They had demurred and offered as their general opinion that people were tired of religion.

"You are all wrong," said Mr. Kolisher; "I like religion." And he rumpled the bay leaves in his hair.

Accordingly Mr. Kolisher's artists fell to work devising a plot and characters that would best express their chieftain's inspiration.

I shall spare you the details of the preliminary work that preceded the filming of *The Redeemer.* At least I shall merely summarize them. Some eight different scripts were prepared by a dozen different authors, all of them of considerable renown (for it was Mr. Kolisher's principle to discard only the best). Hundreds of drawings were made by scores of artists who might once have labored on the ceiling of the Sistine Chapel. World-famed musicians and costumers crossed seas and continents to sink exhausted at Mr. Kolisher's feet. Biblical savants and university scholars and a whole bevy of German playwrights were put to work on a "breakdown" of the New Testament.

Throughout the preliminary hours of darkness and creation Mr. Kolisher, as confused as any rabbit at the peak of the hunting season, scurried and backfired, rampaged and combinated. Observing Mr. Kolisher during these months, you would have thought, most certainly, that his only ambition lay in seeing that no movie of any sort ever came to light again under his aegis. You would have marveled at how Mr. Kolisher, with no ideas at all about anything, without even the vaguest knowledge of history, biblical or secular, and without any conception whatsoever of drama, poetry, philosophy, music, painting, or even carpentry, sat as arbiter supreme on all these matters and regulated their creation by the simple process of running amuck some fifteen hours a day.

But it would be captious and shortsighted to look on the Kolisher antics of this period as the product of a deep-rooted mania for sabotage. There was behind all Mr. Kolisher's gyrations an almost mystic pattern. Without being aware, from any point of view, of what he was doing, Mr. Kolisher was doing something profound. He was keeping the movie of *The Redeemer* from becoming art. He was reducing it, day by day, to that type of kindergarten saga he could understand and feel, as he said, without getting a headache. (In the kingdom of the movies it is the artists who must have the headaches.)

After nine months of gestation Mr. Kolisher sat back with the sunny feeling that he himself, despite the blundering efforts of some fifty overpaid creative intellects, had produced a marvelous script.

The casting of the central character of *The Redeemer* was in itself a period of special travail. It was Mr. Kolisher's contention that Christ would have to be played by someone who meant something at the box office.

The Kolisher staff argued to the contrary. They thought the part of Christ sufficiently important as a dramatic role to warrant trying a newcomer in it. It might, they argued, make a star out of some unknown thespian, but it hardly needed one to begin with. They begged Mr. Kolisher further to remember that the original character had Himself been a man of no consequence, recruited from the simpler folk of Palestine, and that His appeal had been to equally unfashionable people. Mr. Kolisher was somewhat surprised to hear this, but in no way unhorsed.

The real Christ, countered Mr. Kolisher noisily, may have been a nobody, but there would be no nobodies in any production of his. He believed firmly in the star system. Times had changed since Bible days. It would be an affront to the public to offer it some fifty-dollar-a-week actor as its Savior.

"I don't know how much the people love Christ," said Mr. Kolisher honestly, "but I know they love Robert Gary. Get me Robert Gary. We don't want to take any chances on a movie that's going to cost two million, and possibly three million before we're through."

Nearly all Mr. Kolisher's talented underlings paled at this command. The idea of Robert Gary's playing Christ struck them as a fantastic mixture of insanity and sacrilege. Mr. Gary was, at the moment, the outstanding great lover and matinee idol of the movie public.

It is of course unnecessary to tell you who read today about Mr. Gary. But if these pages survive a few years there will be readers, amazingly enough, who may never have heard of our Robert. And though his every movement, breath, and dimple is as familiar to you as your own face in a shaving mirror, I shall nonetheless describe and discuss him with an eye to his fickle posterity.

But before doing so, one more moment of Mr. Kolisher's final tantrum on the subject of *The Redeemer's* casting, for he was being violently opposed in the matter.

"How long," demanded Mr. Kolisher, who had been reading up on the subject overnight, "how long did it take Christ, who you say was a nobody, to become popular? It took years. He went along with a few crazy people following Him down the street—for years. And even when He was crucified there was hardly anybody in attendance. Following which," Mr. Kolisher pursued, "what happened? More years of unpopularity. More years of nobody knowing Him and people even killing off anybody who claimed to know Him.

"I wish to observe," continued Mr. Kolisher, "that Christ became popular when fine people took Him up. And I wish you to consider further that He was supposed to be God's

Son. He was only *acting* a nobody. Whereas, as a matter of fact, He was actually all the while, incognito, so to speak, the most important man in the world. Which exactly fits the case of Robert Gary.

"Now the problem is, do we want somebody as unknown and as unpopular as Christ used to be? Or do we want someone as well known and respected as He has become in modern times? It seems to me, gentlemen, there is only one answer. Gentlemen, when we crucify Robert Gary we are crucifying somebody the public loves and will feel sorry for, and the whole picture will have some meaning. I am not going to wait two thousand years—or even one thousand years—to have *The Redeemer* a hit."

Mr. Gary was engaged for the part.

And now, before recounting the historic conference that resulted in Mr. Gary's playing Christ at a ten per cent cut in his salary, I shall finish his description and discussion for Posterity—to whom I address the following few paragraphs.

In the days, O Posterity, of which I write, the people, just as they nominated their geniuses, elected their idols.

What it was that turned a vacuous and unknown actor into a movie idol I am unable to say (at least without a great deal of thought). And I doubt whether your own historians, with more perspective and data at their disposal than I have, will be able to determine it any more positively.

It may be a sort of Lady Bountiful wantonness on the part of the people that leads them to confer the largess of their worship on the least expectant or deserving of their servants.

Or it may be that the people prefer to make idols out of dummies because in doing so they remain conscious more of their own power than of the divinity of the thing to which they make offerings.

Besides, when you make an idol out of such very ordinary clay as Mr. Gary you are taking no chance that it will become one of those Frankenstein images which the people have so often created for their own destruction.

All this, and its connotations, may be what is in the

collective soul of the people who scream the glories and wonders of such as Robert Gary.

For Mr. Gary, outside of being an idol, was nothing. His very beauty, worshiped by millions of women, lay not so much in his face and body as in their need to worship something beautiful, and, at the same time, not too beautiful. (For that would have made them idealists rather than idolators.)

And on the day when these millions of ladies ceased worshiping Mr. Gary, as they did long before you idly opened these pages, that bewildered young gentleman, like an altar suddenly ungarlanded, lapsed promptly into the limbo of the commonplace, and even the repugnant.

For me, even in his little hour as an idol, Mr. Gary never emerged from this limbo. But the people, at least the female contingent, contradicted me most amazingly.

This contingent, combining into one collective coquette whose fancy is inflamed by a mole, an ear lobe, or an eyelash, had suddenly nodded to the little man who was Robert Gary, and by this nod turned him into a reigning beauty.

And having turned him, willy-nilly, into Apollo, they had given themselves ecstatically to his courtship, knowing that, however wantonly they adored him, he was their victim—a creature to be cast aside in a few years for another favorite.

Poor Mr. Gary's helplessness, like that of some tender lamb being fattened for oblivion, only made him all the more appealing. It is always pleasant to love someone whose heart, and not yours, is to be broken.

Thus for several years more millions of ladies than I care to imagine in such an intimate relationship kept the image of Robert Gary bright in their libidos, and shrieked their rapture over his presence as if he were some shadow Pan.

What they actually worshiped was a bovine-eyed, long-faced, fat-chinned youth (the lower part of whose phiz looked like a dimpled buttock) with a repulsively thick thatch of curly black hair which gave him the look of a wigmaker's dummy. And, as are so many of the idols acclaimed by the ladies, he was sexually as harmless-seeming as some tender-mannered and well-behaved nephew.

Whereas men, a little bolder about their secret longings than women are, will admire a flagrant and pneumatic-looking strumpet and set her up as their collective mistress, the ladies usually choose for a shadow lover someone whose appearance will not betray too much the lewd delight it inspires. They can then gurgle their admiration over him and seem to themselves, each other, and their parsons more aunties than nymphomaniacs.

I may be all wrong about this and it may be quite the opposite of what I have said.

It may be that our ladies, suffering from crippled libidos due to the fire-engine tempo of modern life, simply elect as their heroes non-sexual-looking types and that the whole thing is on a platonic basis. I have heard psychiatrists say that sex has become a very spiritual thing and is driving people crazy instead of into beds. Perhaps it is not infidelity they practiced in their dreams of Robert Gary so much as relief from it.

Then again, it may be that, loving shadows as much as our ladies do, this empty doting is what has turned them into female eunuchs.

The whole thing is extremely complicated and will bear more scrutiny than I have place to give it.

As for Mr. Gary's talents, which made him the highest-paid and most-adored actor of his day, these were even more nonexistent than his beauty. The dullness of his face was no mask for hidden fires.

In the movies in which he played he was usually to be seen standing around a little awkwardly and speaking up rather bravely, as if making any sort of public statement were a difficulty which he was barely able to overcome.

Also, in revealing to his worshipers the various emotions, such as pain, longing, heartbreak, or merriment, Mr. Gary's natural modesty and also his natural lack of these emotions were the despair of his directors.

Foolishly, these latter worthies demanded of Robert that he disturb the lineaments of his face, that he flash his bovine eyes and stop shifting from leg to leg like a frozen pigeon. But all that poor Robert could do was just that—

shift from leg to leg, as if waiting for change in a candy store, and say his lines like any high school boy lost in the fogs of graduation day.

What the directors didn't understand and Mr. Kolisher perhaps did was that these very shortcomings were enchanting to his worshipers. Although they were willing to acclaim a bit of talent here and there provided it didn't disturb, depress, irritate, or confuse them, as a true idol they still preferred a symbol as impotent as any golden calf.

Mr. Gary—whose beauty they could forget without regret and whose talents in no way commanded the homage which they bestowed—was just that. He was a symbol of the people's wantonness, an answer to the artists and critics who had so long selected for them idols to admire that gave them only headaches.

And what happens to a little man, harmless and well meaning, and working modestly for a living, who abruptly finds himself the adored of the world; who suddenly hears his name breathed soulfully or lecherously by millions of fevered maidens and matrons; who encounters wherever he goes, hosannas, worshipful throngs, and police escorts? Various things happen to various idols so precipitously garlanded. But none in the history of movieland reacted quite so astonishingly as Robert Gary.

For Mr. Gary failed to react at all. In the midst of acclaims greater than befell the Caesars, nothing happened to Mr. Gary. No sense of greatness disturbed the pleasant, bovine smile of his eyes. No vanities bloomed, junglelike, in his soul. No horizons opened for his boy's mind.

Mr. Gary knew he was an idol, knew that now he was receiving a salary of fifteen thousand dollars a week instead of the seventy-five dollars a week he had been glad to receive two short years ago, and knew, finally, that someday the people would tire of him and he would be able to eat a meal in a restaurant without having his socks snatched off him by admirers.

But though he knew these things, Robert had no feeling about them. He was content to sit glittering with the ruby eyes that were not his own and shining in the gold paint he knew would soon wear off.

He had at times some thoughts on the subject of "it all ending." These thoughts, which took the form of stares more often than of words, had to do with the people.

Robert felt they had made a willful mistake in adoring him, just as if some millionaire had left him a fortune under the false impression that he was a son. He felt that the lawyers would find out about his true lineage and take the fortune away.

This in no way saddened Robert, for there was nothing very much in him to sadden or elate. But it made him look on all the hullabaloo, which he had so unexpectedly inspired, with a true idol's eyes, in which is always the soul of indifference.

Mr. Kolisher, unlike all his lesser colleagues who knew Robert, felt an awe in the young star's presence. On their first casting get-together for *The Redeemer* he spoke to Robert quietly, and in such a manner that, had any of the people who adored Robert been eavesdropping, they would have overheard nothing to offend them. And Mr. Gary was awed, too, because he knew that the greatest genius in Hollywood was speaking to him.

Mr. Gary did not know why Mr. Kolisher was a genius any more than the latter knew why Robert was an idol. These things were mysteries into which true servants of the people never pried. So they faced each other with a certain heady comradeliness which exists among altars as well as gods.

Mr. Kolisher outlined in full all the troubles he had had in preparing the story of *The Redeemer,* the heroic expenses already incurred, and added, as calmly as if he were the most aloof of critics, that this same movie which was costing him his shirt (and, of course, all his stockholders' shirts) was going to be the greatest he or anyone else had ever produced.

In confirmation of this Mr. Kolisher said that he had already bought five hundred camels, one hundred dromedaries, three hundred cages filled with vultures, roped off a hundred square miles of desert, and that he was at the moment building Jerusalem.

Robert nodded.

Furthermore, Mr. Kolisher added, he had thirty men on the pay roll doing nothing but research and Mr. Gary could feel assured that every button on every priest, soldier, and early Christian would be exactly right.

Again Robert nodded.

Continued Mr. Kolisher, the part he had in mind for Robert to play was the title part of the picture—in short, the Redeemer himself.

Again Robert nodded.

Further, Mr. Kolisher pointed out that Mr. Gary would not play this part in black and white, but that for the first time in history Christ would be revealed to the world in technicolor.

"And now," said Mr. Kolisher, "I will be frank. You are the only man in the world fit to play Christ. I have told that quite openly to everybody. I want you to take into consideration, however, (a) the importance of the role, (b) the tremendous costs of the production, (c) what it will mean to your future to appear in a part so full of audience sympathy, and, finally, (d) I want you to bear in mind that this whole picture, from the first scene to the last, is about Robert Gary—nobody else."

Robert nodded again.

"And finally," said Mr. Kolisher, who in conference was always like an army with inexhaustible reserves, "the director in chief of the entire production—working immediately under me—is going to be Gustave Lingbaum."

"Mr. Lingbaum," said Robert softly.

Movie actors look on great directors as a combination of magician and midwife. Aware in their hearts of their own lack of talent—their non-pregnancy, so to speak—they are inspired by the hosannas of the critics over their magnificent performances with the notion that the director somehow delivered them of a child not in them. And, since the director thinks so too, this completes his status as magician.

It is a moot question whether the director rides to fame on the idol or pushes it there at his own expense.

Leaving this problem unsolved, I return to Robert. Having said softly: "Mr. Lingbaum," he had exhausted his side of the debate.

It was thus it befell that Robert Gary signed up to play the character of Christ for ten per cent less than he had received for playing, three months before, the character of Bert Haskell, all-American quarterback and hero of the intercollegiate Rose Bowl game.

And now all that Mr. Kolisher prophesied of the greatness of his production came to pass. Somehow, despite his most furious eleventh-hour outbursts of sabotage, Jerusalem arose pillar on pillar in the desert a hundred miles from Hollywood.

The temple of the Jews, bewailed through centuries, reared its glories again and round it lay once more the land of Bible days.

All was as it should be, and Mr. Kolisher, riding in his town car through the streets and byways of his Jerusalem, felt as great a pride, if for different reasons, as any patriarch who had ever trod the original.

It is with cameras turning, troops of soldiery, citizens, and chariots moving and the streets of this facsimile Holy Land alive with rabbis, Romans, electricians, pigeons, dromedaries, money-changers, harlots, dreamers, and prop men, that I leave not only Mr. Kolisher but all terrestrial matters, and turn to the third hero of my story, sitting benign and omniscient beyond the vaults of space.

It was much easier to describe and discuss God in the days when so little was known of Him that any monk with an attack of dementia praecox became a revered authority.

Until the end of our last century visualizing the Deity required no particular effort, even for the sane. Our immediate forebears (of all denominations) beheld Him as a sort of talented mind reader who knew everything that was going on and occupied Himself busily with a system of rewards and punishments for man.

Whatever differences there were concerning the sort of

prayer, music, genuflexion, or costume He preferred, on one point all the schismmongers were agreed. He had created the soul of man and was mightily preoccupied in striving to improve and purify it.

The considerable evidence to the contrary was majestically ignored. The arresting fact that in the whole of history atheists had been about the only harmless, well-behaved people, whereas every firm believer in God had devoted most of his energies to murder, torture, arson, and calumny, is of course more of a reflection on piety than on omnipotence. But there is a corollary and one which scratched away early at the doors of reason.

It is more than a little difficult to understand why a Deity mightily preoccupied with our purification should inflame us with all the seven lusts the moment we took to paying definite attention to Him.

It is only in the past few decades that the true and even stranger reality of God has come into the world. Human egomania, which had for so long kept God in heaven like a critic in an opera box surveying excitedly our Wagnerian antics, was badly jolted by the first laboratory reports of His new meanings.

With every fresh discovery of molecules, atoms, electrons, and all the other minute and enterprising paraphernalia of nature, it became more and more obvious that God had other things on His mind than the purifying of our souls. Heaven, it appeared, was no suburb awaiting our retirement, but a most amazingly busy superlaboratory.

And if there were angels, it was obvious they had little time to blow trumpets or strum harps, what with the inconceivable business of keeping all the molecules dancing, all the atoms bombarding space, and every particle of dust obeying the labyrinthian laws of existence.

As for God, however omniscient His mind, how much time proportionately could He devote to our words and philosophies in the midst of the eternal cataclysm of space with whose governing He eternally grappled? Very little indeed; and it is this new understanding of God and His preoccupation with superior forces that has depressed the soul of man, these recent years, and turned it into dark ways.

We have taken to behaving like children whose teacher is too busy to note our conduct, and to the ancient accusations of Godlessness that once brought us to heel we reply—very scientifically—that it is not we but God who is Godless.

We have only to go to heaven to see the truth of the new findings. And thither we shall go, if for no other reason than to be near the third hero of my tale. And since, according to all theologies, even those of the laboratories, He is all shapes and all things, we find Him in that partly human guise He assumes when He desires surcease from Himself.

On this day of our visit God had turned over His forces to His innumerable assistants, who, though they are not so learned as He, are able nonetheless to supervise, after a fashion, the incalculable labors of the universe.

With God idling in human guise, His mind for the moment free of all the chores of creation, His angels sat in trancelike silences and carried on the work. Smilingly the Deity looked about Him and saw His racing caldrons glowing in infinity; saw, too, the mighty alchemy of His largest stars repeated in the soul of the tiniest grain of matter.

This orderliness pleased Him, for it had taken many aeons to achieve. He was proud of His laws and of the rhythm that had transmuted the pure nothingness of His pioneer days into the obedient wheel of life.

"Observe," He spoke to the Archangel Michael, whom He had called to His side for company and a little disputation, "observe the precision in which all is confined. My universe is a clock inside which other clocks are ticking.

"The great gases rearing like serpents of flame in My most distant seas of space," said God, "feel this ticking and the law of form within them. My system of weights and counterweights imprisons chaos itself. And in all this traffic which sweeps headlong down the arches of infinity, observe there are no collisions."

"Or at least none worth mentioning," said the Angel Michael.

"Yes," said God, without meaning to change the subject,

"I am fascinated by My clocks and pleased by them. Observe that within each form I have hidden a brother to guide it; and within each brother I have inserted yet another brother to watch over it.

"I have been so careful in the creation of this brotherhood that there is no brother but has a guide within him, so that the most invisible speck of My universe wears the full mantle of My infinity.

"Were this all around us to disappear," said God, "as the result of some hypothetical miscalculation, one speck of My work remaining would contain in it all the secrets and powers of My laws and be sufficient for the reconstruction of infinity. It is pleasing to Me that chaos should hum like a housewife at her tasks and that all My geometrics should lie in My palm like a coin well earned."

These last words, so reminiscent of our own world, apparently reminded God of something, for He opened His eyes and asked softly:

"Where is it?"

"Forgive me," said the Angel Michael sleepily, "what are You looking for?"

"Earth," said God, "that bit of moon dust in the minor group."

"I know the name," said the Angel Michael and, after a look around while God rested, pointed out the planet asked for.

God smiled approvingly.

"I am pleased to note," He spoke, "that its speed, size, and shape are exactly as they should be. It looks quite perfect, does it not?"

Michael nodded.

God spoke again.

"This is the one," He said softly, "that has developed thought. It is inhabited by creatures who call themselves men."

"Men?" said Michael with an inquiring look.

"Man," said God, "is a highly developed particle who operates under a rather large multiplicity of My laws. In fact, in some ways, he is the final mutation of dust, although I have had other experiments in mind at times.

"They have minds," said God, looking down, "that move like gnats along the walls of infinity, seeking its measurements and its meanings. They wrestle with the secrets of themselves and look for the light within light."

"Why do they do this?" asked the Angel Michael.

"They dream of detaching themselves from the laws that operate them," said God, "and emerging into divine supremacy over matter."

The Angel Michael was shocked.

"In fact," God continued, "they already have achieved a belief that on changing their atomic arrangements, which they call dying, they pursue a triumph over nature in the guise of souls."

The Angel Michael was puzzled.

"They fancy that their souls," said God, "rise like some refined sort of smoke and come straight to Me to partake of My omniscience. As far as I can make out, that is their belief."

Michael wondered at God's calm.

"It is nothing to frown upon," God answered him, "since We are in no way inconvenienced by it."

"They sound very troubled," said the Angel Michael.

"Yes," said God. "It is that fact which filled Me with compassion a little while ago, as you may recall. I listened to them harassing each other and floundering at death grips with each other in the shallow surfs of reason and I sought to lift them a step toward the deep in which We reside."

"I do not recall," said the Angel Michael.

"You were probably busy elsewhere," said God and fell silent, as if remembering something. Removing the distances from His eyes, He looked casually at the earth. A curious expression came upon Him.

"I am amazed," He said.

"What is it?" asked Angel Michael.

"Look, observe what is happening," God said, and brought the earth close to Michael's vision. "I am truly amazed."

The Angel Michael looked for a while and then spoke.

"They are nailing someone to a cross," he said.

"My Son," said God, frowning. "I am extremely confused."

The Angel Michael regarded the Deity with surprise.

"Confused?" he said, and looked very awed.

"Either this is the Devil's work or I have had a sort of lapse," said God. "What you see there is something I could swear has already happened."

"It is difficult," said the Angel Michael, "to determine which events have happened and which are going to happen. I have often found Time a very confusing witness."

"I have never made that mistake before," said God, still frowning. Then He continued, as if putting the problem of the error from His mind.

"I was telling you of My compassion," He said. "It was out of that compassion that I sent My Son to instruct the thought of the world. Knowing its crude talent for remembering only what is too obvious, I decreed that My Son should be crucified."

"I do not understand," said the Angel Michael. "It seems very cruel."

"I wished to create sympathy for Him," said God, "and through sympathy, belief. And through belief, understanding."

God stopped and sighed.

"At least," He said, "it was My impression I had done all this, and that My Son Jesus was living in happy retirement. But apparently . . ."

Again He paused.

"I have been doing them a great injustice," said God, indicating the men on the earth. "I have thought for some time that these human particles whom I sent My Son to instruct had not only abjured but wretchedly misinterpreted all His hints."

"You have been very busy with the new nebula," said the Angel Michael thoughtfully.

"I have," said God, "but that is no excuse for such wool-gathering. At any rate, there He is and My decree is being put into operation."

"What is the name of that desert city?" asked Michael.

who continued to be deeply surprised by the Deity's abstraction. Perhaps he even recalled things that his banished brother, Lucifer, had once spoken of.

"Jerusalem," said God. "It is a little field I have been working in for some time. Those bearded men are Jews and those others with the clean-shaven faces are Romans. And that glittering little house was built for Me. It is My favorite temple. Or was."

"You mean is, I think," said the Angel Michael softly.

God scowled.

"I can't have been that busy," He spoke. "Yes, is. I am very fond of it. But the whole thing amazes me. I could have said that this little house had been destroyed and this whole field long ago uprooted and given over to error and desolation."

"It looks very busy," said the Angel Michael.

"Poor little man on the cross," said God, "He will cry out soon, inquiring why I have forsaken Him."

"Does He know He is Your Son?" asked the Angel Michael.

"Yes," said God.

"Then why does He not say so to everyone?" asked the angel.

"He has," said God. "We will talk of that later."

He sighed.

"The whole thing is very confusing," said God. "It is my first aberration in a long time. It proves the folly of peering at Time too casually.

"However," He continued, "there is some profit in the incident. It was My original intent—in fact I thought I had carried it out—to allow My Son to die and be buried and then restored to Me in secret."

"Why in secret," asked the Angel Michael, "if You wished to impress humanity with His true meaning?"

"I had a theory about reaching into their wisdom by gentle and unmagical pressure," said God. "It is degrading to Reason to educate it unreasonably. I was averse to hypnotizing them with a bit of legerdemain. In fact," He added after a pause, "I was afraid of frightening them into some sort of hysteria instead of leaving behind a calm divine seed of Reason.

"I am pleased that I have had this chance to reconsider My plan," said God, "for in a dream I had, which in My moment of confusion I considered an actual part of My past, it was revealed to Me by My intelligence that My first plan was dangerous."

Michael pondered on how God could dream of that which had never happened, nor was to happen, but kept his silence.

"My lack of boldness in asserting Myself," said God, still on the subject of this odd dream, "was greatly responsible for the mishaps that followed—or rather, I mean, that would have followed—My Son's sojourn there. Had He been there.

"The point is," continued God, extricating Himself from these remarks with a smile that blinded Michael almost completely, "the point is, I am very pleased to have this opportunity for changing My mind about the spiritual redemption of man."

"Then You are not going to redeem Him?" Michael asked.

God smiled again.

"You don't understand, Michael," he said. "The point is I am going to redeem Him but in a much simpler way than I had originally intended. I realize now that in addressing Myself to the soul of man I must take into consideration the monkey mind through which My message is filtered. And I think it will be best if I perform some tricks."

"You will perform a miracle?" Michael widened his eyes eagerly, for he had heard tales of such matters.

God nodded.

"It is in many ways degrading," He said, "to perform like a charlatan for these half-beasts for whom I am seeking a finer mold. But a miracle will simplify their impression of Me.

"It will do away with sects," began God and then looked at Michael kindly. "You must take for granted, Michael," He went on, "that I know more about the thought of man than you do. And that if I have decided to dominate that thought by a few miracles there is wisdom in what I do.

My Son shall not cry out in vain to Me. When He calls to Me from the cross I shall be there to take Him in My arms. And He shall not go down in history as a myth or a phantom. Nor shall those who write of Him be identified later as liars and bigots.

"You will," said God, beaming fully on His angel, "proceed at once to earth and remove Him from the cross in the presence of all who have gathered in Gethsemane."

"Gethsemane?" inquired Michael.

"That is the name of the little spot where all this is happening," said God. "You will find it easily. It is to the east of the planet as it now lies, near the bottom of one of its continents called Asia."

The Angel Michael arose. He stretched his pinions and regarded the earth.

"I will bring Him back," he said softly.

Saying this, the Angel Michael leaped forward and was gone.

Some moments of confusion ensued, for, arriving in Asia and seeking out the spot named by God, Michael found no sign of a temple, no activity around a cross, and no glimpse of any Son.

Apprised of this, God said nothing for a long instant and then, in words that seemed to the Angel Michael strangely faint, bade him go westward to another continent. Obeying this uncertain divine guidance, Michael finally—by merest good luck, it seemed to him—arrived on the scene he had watched from God's side.

"Investigate fully," God sent a message, "and tell Me the name of the city."

The Angel Michael inquired quickly and replied.

"It is called Jerusalem," he said.

"Is there a man named Pilate present?" God sent another query into the angel's mind.

"He is here," Michael answered after a moment, impressed by the Deity's social knowledge of this remote bit of dust.

"Are there Jews?" came a query from heaven.

"Innumerable ones," the Angel Michael answered.

"Tell Me of them," God queried softly.

His angel paused.

"They have false beards," Michael finally answered.

There was yet a longer pause from the Infinite.

"Am sending another angel to assist you," God spoke at length. "Do nothing till he comes."

A few moments elapsed and Michael beheld his brother, the Angel Azriel, at his side.

"What of My Son?" God asked of His two messengers.

The Angel Michael hesitated.

"You reply," he said to his brother. Azriel answered God.

"No sign of Him yet, but we have found Lingbaum," said the Angel Azriel.

"Lingbaum?" The name was a question from on high.

The two angels looked at each other, astonished.

"It is strange," said Michael quietly, "that He should know of a man named Pilate, who is of no consequence here, and not know Lingbaum, who is the master of the city."

"Lingbaum," Azriel answered the Infinite's question, "is master of the city and director of its destiny. It is he who is putting Your Son to death. He is giving many orders."

There was a long pause.

"Where is My Son?" God spoke again.

The two messengers conferred. Michael was for keeping silent, but Azriel feared the divine impatience.

"Which one?" the Angel Azriel asked, keeping his thoughts as calm as he could. "For there are two of them."

By the length of the silence that followed Azriel's reply and by the darkening of their spirits, both messengers knew that God was wroth.

"I am sending Malliol," the Deity finally answered.

The arrival of the Angel Malliol cheered the two messengers, for he was one of the wisest of the Host. They related to him what had passed and acquainted him with the facts around them. The Angel Malliol turned his thought confidently to heaven.

"Which one, O Lord, shall we bring back to You?" he spoke. "For there are two of them."

This time God answered loudly out of the infinite.

"Impossible!" He thundered. "One of them is an impostor!"

Luckily for the angels, Mr. Lingbaum, directing the filming of *The Redeemer,* at this moment ordered the stand-in for Robert Gary, who resembled him in make-up, lineaments, and size, removed from the cross.

"We will use Mr. Gary himself for the medium shots as well as the close-ups," said Mr. Lingbaum. "We don't want any wiseacres spotting a stand-in on the cross. It would kill all the illusion."

Accordingly this stand-in, whose name was Joe, jumped to the ground, to the amazement of the three angels closely watching the strange events. Robert Gary climbed a small ladder leisurely and was adjusted into place by the prop men.

"Now, Mr. Gary"—Mr. Lingbaum stood on the ladder beside him with final directorial instructions—"put everything out of your mind. Just hang there. Remember those are nails through your hands and feet. But don't overdo it. The Savior was no coward. He didn't scream and mug. He just hung there and took it. Keep the drama inside you."

"Yes sire," said Robert.

"All right—shoot!" cried Mr. Lingbaum, and a great silence fell on Gethsemane.

The Angel Michael addressed his thought to God.

"They are shooting Him now," he said.

"Shooting whom?" God demanded.

"Your Son, I think," said Michael.

There was a pause from on high.

"Azriel," God's voice spoke, "is there or is there not a cross on which My Son is being crucified?"

"There is," said Azriel.

"Is My Son in agony?" God continued in a softer voice.

"It is difficult to tell," said Azriel, "for He is making no sound nor yet expression."

"Look close," said God.

"Yes," said Azriel, "it seems to me He is suffering. He is complaining to Mr. Lingbaum about his eyes smarting."

"The time has come for My miracle," God's voice whispered within the three angels.

It was then that the heavens suddenly darkened and the

bright desert day was transformed into eerie night. Fires flashed from the sky and ominous sounds rolled over the desert. A strong wind smote the sands. The city of Jerusalem shook under these manifestations. Several of its towers toppled. Scores of Mr. Kolisher's booster lights and arc lamps were smashed to bits and altogether some hundred thousand dollars' worth of scenery and equipment was destroyed. To add to Mr. Lingbaum's troubles, panic seized the herd of one hundred dromedaries and they bolted, screaming and snorting, into the hills.

"It's a simoom!" Mr. Lingbaum bellowed through his megaphone. "Bury the film cans!"

The storm, unprecedented for violence and peculiarities even in California, lasted less than three minutes. Hardly had the wind struck, the fire flashed, the thunder rolled, and the darkness engulfed the scene, when it was day again, serene and bright. So quickly had the storm come and gone that its witnesses could barely credit their memories. But there was evidence in the wreckage left.

Mr. Lingbaum, emerging from a sound wagon where he had sought refuge, surveyed the set and then issued a number of commands. He ordered the debris cleared at once and his crews to erect new lights.

"Lucky it didn't knock the cross down," said Mr. Lingbaum. "We've got three more good hours of light to shoot in if that God-damn simoom don't come back. Get Mr. Gary. And tell him we're going on with the scene. Hurry it up."

Mr. Lingbaum's assistants scurried off to dig Mr. Gary out of whatever refuge he had sought during the storm. For he was not on the cross.

Of course Mr. Lingbaum's assistants were not looking in the right place.

When Robert Gary opened his eyes he knew something amazing had happened. But Robert, though he might recognize the need for amazement, was not the one to feel it.

He surveyed the scene, into which it was obvious he had been transported by some supernatural agency, with a well-ordered and undemonstrative interest. God, aware of the human content of the mind before Him—for He had clothed His Son within and without as a man—had welcomed His Child home with a display of lesser magic. He had descended to aesthetics and produced for His home-coming shapes and colors and ensembles of great beauty.

A hall of such proportions as to have filled any earthly mind other than one from Hollywood with blank awe lay before Robert. Down the sides of this vast hall stretched a forest of pillars made of incandescent matter that resembled the precious stones of the world. They rose like varicolored flames and their ruby, sapphire, and diamond light made a symmetrical bonfire whose beauty was almost too devastating for critical evaluation. Among these pillars was a host of figures with golden wings outstretched in an architectural hosanna.

The beauty of these figures, for they were the chosen ones of the Host, was also of that superior kind which no eye of earth could fully encompass or tongue appraise. The far vanishing floor of the hall was made of a single pearl that gave forth a light of dreams.

Overhead Robert observed that there were more angels, for he had already identified the lovely troops about him. They hovered in deliciously arranged groups, some with trumpets to their mouths, others in attitudes of celestial languor; some with wings arched in flight, others in postures of adoration. They formed a continuous domelike frieze as far as the eye could see.

Robert's senses felt faint with the impact of so much color, sound, and glory. But God had calculated carefully the frail human capacities for beauty. He had curbed His displays to a gentle exhibition, fearful of overwhelming His Son, in the first moments of His return, with those blasts of loveliness which Robert would not have been able to endure nor I to describe.

At the end of the hall Robert perceived God. He knew His identity instinctively, for, though the Deity had reduced Himself, with some effort, to approximately human proportions, He had retained a single particle of divinity in His eyes. These blazed like a pair of continuous cannon flashes and Robert, realizing that, whatever the occasion, he was a sort of guest of honor, advanced slowly toward their light.

It may have been that Robert's own eyes, used to the intensity of the movie lights, and his mind, used also to the ambition and caprice of the movie sets, were not as overwhelmed as they should have been. There was also Robert's incapacity for reaction, which had infuriated some of the more sensitive Hollywood directors.

In fact miracles to Robert were not entirely without precedent. Having been raised, for no reason he had ever been able to understand, from a nobody to an idol, finding himself now raised into heaven, he was hardly more astonished. It was inexplicable, of course, but to one who had already tasted the incomprehensible it had lost somewhat of its flavor with repetition.

The angels, watching Robert's progress down the hall, attributed his calm demeanor to the fact that he was of divine origin. For the tale of God's compassion and His experiment in a planet's education had been swiftly told by Michael, Azriel, and Malliol.

God waited happily for His Son and, as He approached, felt inclined to admire the grace of His movement. Considering the agony His Son had recently been through, His bearing, thought God, was extremely commendable.

But as He watched, a misgiving came into the Deity's wisdom. There was that about His Son which confused Him and in an odd, unpaternal way irritated Him.

"It is possible," thought God, "that He has been spoiled a little by the world."

Robert was now before the throne. He stood in silence, a bit frightened as always during mob scenes. He had also begun to think that it might be God was about to punish him for some sort of sacrilege.

It occurred to Robert that despite Mr. Kolisher's rhapsodic statements, which had made him cut his salary ten per cent, the role of *The Redeemer* was not without its unhappy side. Robert felt worried about this and was about to explain rather lamely that he had been talked into the whole thing by Mr. Kolisher, when he heard the Deity's voice and shivered and held his tongue.

"Advance to My feet, My Son," God began. "You whom they called Christ and whose poor body, racked with agony, sought to reveal to them the greatness of My compassion and Your own services, advance and——"

God failed to finish His speech. For one thing, He did not like its content and, for another, He realized with a sudden divine clarity that the young man standing attentively before Him was no Son of His. God cast a quick look down the hall of angels and decided it would be better to dismiss all the witnesses to this most extraordinary situation.

"My error will only confuse them," He thought inwardly, "and take their minds off their duties." Even more inwardly He brooded: "A little thing such as this might start them talking about Lucifer."

Turning His thought on the Host, he bade them all leave and take the home-coming hall with them.

Robert watched the multitude of angels, pillars, colors, and the pearl floor vanish even more quickly than any movie set he had ever worked in. He realized that in the handling of scenery God had a natural advantage over any of the Hollywood producers, not excluding Mr. Kolisher. God interrupted his meditations.

"What are you doing here?" God spoke.

"I don't know," said Robert. "I suppose it has something to do with my being on the cross."

"What were you doing on the cross?" demanded God.

"They're shooting the final scene," said Robert, "and I had to be there as—as the central figure."

"What final scene?" God asked.

Robert hesitated and then answered desperately.

"I had nothing to do with it," he said, "except obey the script."

"Scriptures," said God sternly.

"No," said Robert, and then added quickly: "I beg Your pardon. We work from a script and the script called for me to be crucified. I think Mr. Kolisher himself decided on that ending."

"Mr. Kolisher," God repeated the name.

"Yes," said Robert.

"Who are you?" God asked.

For an instant the novelty of the question startled Robert Gary, for he realized quickly that fame must be a terrestrial product and answered with the modesty of greatness in a strange land.

"I am Bob Gary," he said. "I work in the movies as an actor."

"The movies?" said God, and thought an instant. "They are something recent?"

"Yes," Robert answered eagerly, "we are in our infancy."

"I have been busy elsewhere with other matters," said God, and fell silent again. Taxing His mind a bit, He understood what the movies were. His silence continued for several moments while His thought mastered the industry.

"Then what I witnessed was not actually happening," said God. "You were just posing for photographs."

"It's a little more than that," said Robert. "It's more like acting."

"To be sure," said God kindly, "I know all about acting."

Robert nodded humbly. "I would like to hear what You have to say about acting," he faltered, for he thought these were matters that might interest the erudite Mr. Lingbaum.

"Acting," said God, "is the art of making real for others that which is real only for oneself. Man has many nets with which to fish for truth. Of these, acting is the largest and strongest. In it he can retain truth for a vivid hour so that all may look and see its secrets."

Robert was silent.

"I perceive," added God, "that the movies are somewhat different."

"Yes, in a way," said Robert cautiously.

"Tell me," said God.

"Well," said Robert, who felt more at home in interviews on the movies than in any other type of discourse, "it's like this. You see, there's so much truth in the world that the movies try to show the other side."

"The other side of truth?" said God. "What would that be?"

"Oh," said Robert, smiling, "pleasant things. You see, the movies are sort of a dream life for the masses."

Robert had read this curious statement in a scurrilous criticism of one of his pictures when someone, by mistake, had left a radical magazine in his dressing room. Feeling, however, there might be some mental relation between God and a left-wing movie critic, Robert offered the explanation hopefully.

"Why were you re-enacting the story of My Son's agony?" He asked.

"It was Mr. Kolisher's idea," Robert answered, rather caddishly. "He engaged me for the part."

"Who is Mr. Kolisher?" demanded God.

Robert widened his eyes.

"He is the leading genius of Hollywood," said Robert, thus extending the reach of Mr. Kolisher's publicity department beyond its happiest dreams. "I mean, there is no doubt but that he produces the best pictures. This one is his greatest work so far. It's called *The Redeemer.*"

God nodded.

"Is Mr. Kolisher producing *The Redeemer* for religious reasons?" he asked.

"What do You mean?" Robert murmured.

"I mean," said God firmly, "has Mr. Kolisher any interest in the redemption of humanity?"

"I don't think so," said Robert honestly.

"Then why," said God, "is he producing *The Redeemer* instead of something else?"

"Well," said Robert nervously, "first, it's a great subject and appeals to everybody. And, as he told me himself, he's taking the greatest care not to offend anybody—particularly the Jewish people. So that the picture will have a universal appeal. It's bound to gross several million dollars. Religion, if properly handled, always gets big grosses."

"I know that," said God, and with some effort continued to smile at Robert Gary, who He saw was too simplehearted either for divine wrath or for disputation.

"What makes Mr. Kolisher," God continued, "imagine that My Son's life and death are a pleasant lie?"

"I'm afraid," said Robert, "that I have not made myself clear. *The Redeemer* is what we call an escapist picture. It's about things that happened so long ago that they don't matter any more and one can look at them sort of aloofly, so to speak."

"I see," said God.

"People like history that has already happened," went on Robert, "and they enjoy looking at it in the movies no matter how many people were killed. I read in a magazine once that the masses like watching blood-and-thunder movies because they take their minds off their own troubles."

God nodded.

"That's the secret of why costume pictures are coming back," went on Robert; "the world is pretty badly off right now and likes to forget what's going on for an hour or two, and just sort of enjoy the past and all its superstitions."

God felt a stir of anger at this speech but, looking into Robert Gary's heart, He saw that it was simple and that the young man was doing his best to be agreeable.

"So My Son makes them forget their troubles," He repeated.

"Oh yes," Robert agreed quickly.

"I wish I had heard of this movie earlier," said God. "I might have been of some help."

"I can assure You," said Robert eagerly, "that it's been beautifully done. Some of the lines I have to speak are almost like poetry. Mr. Kolisher has spared no expense or effort."

"Still," God mused, "there are some things . . ."

"He's built a whole city," pursued Robert, "Jerusalem, and filled it with all its original inhabitants and animals and everything."

"I saw it," said God.

"The Garden of Gethsemane is really a gorgeous shot," said Robert.

There was a long pause and God appeared to be thinking.

"What sort of music are they using?" He inquired at ength.

"The very best," Robert answered. "Both modern and ncient."

"What about the Hill of Skulls?" asked God.

"You mean Golgotha," said Robert.

"Yes," said God.

"Mr. Kolisher built it from replicas," said Robert. "That's vhere I carried the cross on my back."

"I know," said God.

"It's one of the best shots in the picture," Robert offered.

"The temple of the Jews looks a little skimpy," said ɔod, who seemed still to be brooding.

"It doesn't photograph that way," said Robert. "I'm sure ʻou will be pleased. That is, if You see the picture."

"I am going to look at it," said God, and again He sat in ilence, thinking.

"I wonder," God thought, "if this Mr. Kolisher is wiser han I am, at least in the eyes of the little planet on which ɪe lives?

"I have always tried to educate its inhabitants through uffering," thought God. "For it seemed to Me that people nust take seriously and study deeply that which was reɾealed to them through pain.

"I have always reasoned," thought God, "that the ultimate ɡoal for thought was the understanding of My mysteries. Might it not be the forgetting of them?"

God studied the history of the world for a moment.

"There seems to have been a great deal of suffering," He esumed inwardly, "and all this suffering appears to have mproved the race of man very little."

He recalled now, without any confusion, the sending of His Son to the eyes of man.

"It was folly of a sort," He went on within Himself, "to think that the agony of one figure, even though He was My Son, could influence to any degree the mind of a people to whom slaughter and torture are a daily diet. Indeed, it was like"—and God searched for a phrase—"like sending coals to Newcastle." He smiled.

"I wonder," God thought, "if these movies, which turn event into dream, which rob existence of its sting, and which remove all vestiges of troublesome intelligence from the tales they reveal—I wonder if they are not more sensible than My Redeemer, as an influence? And more desirable than all my floods, locusts, famines, and other manifestations as an educational source?

"Yes," said God, "I wish I had thought of them and sent them into the world as My messengers. But, alas, I was thinking in another direction."

Casting His thought over His universe, He sighed and added: "There are many things to do.

"I begin to feel now," thought God, "that My efforts to increase the intellectual talent of man were a well-meaning error. It is better that he grow less, rather than more, intelligent. It is better that he see himself less and understand less the meanings of his existence as well as of Mine. It is better that he learn to look on life as a pleasant and even pointless dream; that he turn from the abortive cries of artists, saints, and sages and go to the movies. It is better, I am sure, that he know nothing happily than know a little, most unhappily.

"These movies," God continued inwardly, "with My assistance, might, in a while, take the place of all man's present troublesome investigations into beauty, nature, and truth. They might become an ephemeris of images among which the mind of man could wander without pain or mishap for eternity.

"A sort of millennium of anti-thought," God mused, "that would fill the world, and all of life would become a shadow to be enjoyed as a child enjoys the dancing of a sunbeam across its cradle."

God looked at Robert Gary, who had been standing for a long time in His silence. Robert, for his part, was reminded of the days when, as an extra, he had waited hour upon hour for a nod from some head in the casting department.

"I am in favor of the movies," God said aloud, and smiled. "And despite your assurances that Mr. Kolisher's production is perfect, I should like to be of some help."

"I don't know what You could do, exactly," said Robert, unless there are some retakes."

"You said," God answered, "the final scene was still to be hot."

"I don't think Mr. Kolisher would care for any changes n that," said Robert.

"Nor should I," said God, and looked sternly at the young nan. "I am not trying to interfere with Mr. Kolisher," He dded; "I am sure he knows what he is doing."

(At the moment—I should like to interject—Mr. Kolisher vas out of his head, bellowing for his missing star. But I hall come to that scene soon.)

"But there must be something," God said thoughtfully.

Robert had never known anybody who had not thought hat way about a movie—that there was something, some-ow, which, if thought of, would improve it. He recalled hat such afterthoughts had often spoiled some of the best ictures he had been in. He doubted, too, that God, who eemed just to have learned about the movies, would be able o offer anything constructive for *The Redeemer*. But he ept silent, for Robert had learned long ago not to argue vith critics.

"You," said God, "I can improve you."

Robert glanced around him quickly, forgetting that the ngels had been dismissed.

"My performance," said Robert, "looked all right in the rojection room. That's where the rushes are shown every lay," he added informatively, "I mean, the showing of the revious day's work. Of course you can't always tell from he rushes. But Mr. Kolisher was more than satisfied. And o was Mr. Lingbaum."

"Lingbaum," God repeated. "I heard that name before!"

"He's my director," said Robert. "He thinks I've done a ery good job."

"I am sure you have," said God kindly. The simplicity nd courage of this little human appealed deeply to Him. I was not referring to your acting but to your soul," He vent on. "I could improve that."

"In what way?" asked Robert, interested.

"I could make you a little more true to character whe
you perform on the cross," said God.

"How?" asked Robert stubbornly.

"By making you divine," said God.

Robert stared.

"You will be truly My Son," said God. "I shall place
particle of My light within you. There will be a glow o
beauty in your face. And through all the hours of you
agony there will shine the glory and simplicity of My truth
as evidenced in you. The world will weep when it sees you
and the soul of man will see into heaven."

Robert flushed and offered no objection.

God reached out a hand and touched his shoulder.
moment later appeared the three angels who had borne hin
from the desert into heaven. They beheld a changed Rober
Gary. A radiance such as distinguished their own figure
shone from him.

"Return him to the place where you found him," Go
said.

"I'd rather call on Mr. Kolisher first and explain wher
I've been," said Robert, "if You don't mind."

"Very well," said God, "take him to Mr. Kolisher."

He smiled on Robert as the angels led him away. The
God vanished and resumed His work with His forces.

Robert found himself surrounded by a good part of th
heavenly Host. Despite the Deity's hope that the truth o
His reunion with His supposed Son would remain secre
(for He worried about the ancient business of Lucifer), Hi
three messengers had revealed the curious error of Omnipo
tence to their brothers.

Smiling now at the jest, the Host flocked around Rober
with a babble of questions. Jostled, and his ears ringing wit
a thousand queries about the movies, Robert, who was use
to such demonstrations and curiosities, smiled as sweetly a
he could—which, with the new divinity given him, was ver
sweetly indeed—and said pleasantly everything he coul
think of saying.

Some of the bolder angels begged him for a souvenir c

his visit. One of them finally reached to him and removed the crown of thorns from his head. Others followed this example and in a twinkling Robert was denuded of all but his shorts, which he wore under his Messiah's robe.

He laughed good-naturedly at this display of interest in his person and talents, but pleaded with his new admirers to leave him his shorts, for he was not made (he explained in his own words) as they, whose nudity offered no interruptions to purity. Finally he signaled his three guides. The angels all blew trumpets for Robert and a group of them followed their visitor to the last rim of heaven.

When Robert next opened his eyes he saw Mr. Kolisher. He was about to speak when Mr. Kolisher saw him. And then for fifteen minutes Robert was unable to say anything, for he would not have been heard.

Robert learned that he had been missing for three days and that Mr. Kolisher had believed him killed in the storm that had almost demolished the set. A thousand police and their deputies had been searching the desert around. The entire nation had been horrified and several hundred thousand letters had arrived from the people demanding that Mr. Kolisher increase his efforts and spare no expense to find the missing idol.

Throughout these activities, which had cost him a pretty penny—the three-day delay alone represented a carrying charge of a hundred and fifty thousand dollars—Mr. Kolisher had given out a score of heartbroken public statements and suffered, in private, as if Robert had been his true son.

"You were drunk somewhere," Mr. Kolisher suddenly interrupted his saga of grief. "Look at you! Walking into this office naked. You're still drunk," he added after a searching look into his star's eyes. "Explain yourself, Mr. Gary."

Robert smiled.

"You will have to excuse my undress," he said, "but they took all my clothes away."

"Who did?" demanded Mr. Kolisher.

"The angels," said Robert.

"Sit down," said Mr. Kolisher softly.

A great understanding had come to him. He realized that

Robert Gary had not been drunk. The glitter of Robert's eyes and the strange expression of Robert's entire face should have revealed the truth to him at first glance. Mr. Gary had been taking drugs and had been laid low by an overdose or gone on an extended dope jag.

"We will have to keep this quiet," said Mr. Kolisher. "It would not only ruin my picture, but ruin you and have a bad effect on the whole industry if it leaks out."

"Keep what quiet?" asked Robert.

"What you have been doing," said Mr. Kolisher diplomatically.

He opened the dictograph key and spoke into the instrument in slow, precise tones.

"Give me Mr. Birdwin," he said.

"Here, boss," said a voice.

Mr. Birdwin was the head generalissimo of the extensive Kolisher publicity department.

"I want you to pay close attention, Mr. Birdwin, to what I have to say," said Mr. Kolisher.

"Shoot," said the voice.

"Mr. Birdwin," said Mr. Kolisher, slowing way down, "Robert Gary is waiting here with me in my office."

"I'll be right down," said the voice.

"Stay where you are," said Mr. Kolisher. "I want you to send out a story for international release throughout the entire world. Send copies to the Associated Press, the United Press, and all the other major agencies for news gathering."

"Yes siree!" said the voice.

"Robert Gary," resumed Mr. Kolisher, "was knocked off the cross by the storm. He fell on his head and suffered a severe concussion of the brain. Not knowing who he was, you understand, or what he was doing, he wandered through the desert for three days, living on nothing but cactus leaves until his senses were restored."

"I got it down," said the voice. "Go on."

"Mr. Robert Gary is back now in this office," said Mr Kolisher, "and will be on the set positively tomorrow morning to finish the picture. He is still a little shaken by his tragic experiences, but they will in no way interfere with him finishing his role as the Redeemer. That's all. And furthermore, Mr. Birdwin, I want the press kept away from Robert Gary personally. He is in no condition as yet to speak to them. You understand me?"

"Yes siree," said the voice, and Mr. Kolisher clicked the key.

"That'll hold them," he said, and turned to Robert. "Now, Robert," he went on, "I am going to close the door and see that we are not interrupted and you are going to make a confession to me, for the good of your soul and your future career. And when the picture is done I am going to see to it that the best doctors in the country take you in hand. I owe this to you because I don't mind saying, whatever your personal shortcomings, you have done a fine job as the Redeemer."

"Well," said Robert, "I am willing to tell you what happened. But I don't think you will believe me."

"Proceed," said Mr. Kolisher.

"Well," Robert began, and there came over him a sudden sadness such as has always fallen into the hearts of those who try to speak of the personal favor of God. "Well, Mr. Kolisher, I was taken off the cross by three angels during the storm and they carried me to heaven. I don't exactly know why it all happened, Mr. Kolisher, but I was led into a large and very beautiful hall full of angels. Then I met God and He talked to me. I didn't know the whole thing had taken so long. Three days, you say. Well, it seemed hardly a minute."

As Mr. Kolisher remained silent, Robert added nervously: "I'll tell you what God said if you care to hear."

Mr. Kolisher rose, his gaze intent on the curious glitter in his star's eyes. "Robert," he said, "I don't care to hear whatsoever. I will, however, send for some clothes and have you taken home. And I want you to promise me, on your sacred word of honor, that you will not speak a word to anybody—till it wears off."

Although Robert kept the sacred word of honor he had given (for he felt almost from the first moment of his return the hopelessness of getting anybody to believe in the truth), the echo of Mr. Kolisher's suspicions passed through the crowded streets of Jerusalem the next morning. By the time the cameras had been put up and the set lighted the theory that Robert Gary was a hophead and had wandered off on a dope jag had mysteriously gained a number of adherents, chief among them Mr. Lingbaum.

"It's the irony of the picture business," said Mr. Lingbaum, "that we are going to photograph on the cross this morning, in the role of the Savior, a ham who not only can't tell his left foot from his behind, but who is also a hophead. Look at the way his eyes glitter," he added in an undertone as Robert Gary, in full costume, appeared.

"Hello," said Robert coldly. He had guessed what was being said. "Do I look all right?"

"You're a fine-looking Savior," said Mr. Lingbaum ambiguously. "A little too much brown in the make-up, though. Tone it down. And have Joe pump some glycerine into your eyes before you get on the cross."

"I won't need any," said Robert coldly, "I——"

He was about to say that with God's light inside him and full of divinity, he would need no glycerine in his eyes to help him register the proper emotions of the Son. But he decided to keep it a secret.

"I have my own conception of the part," he finished.

He walked away with a curiously elastic step toward the little ladder leaning against the middle cross. For there were three crosses, and on the other two the thieves were already in position.

"Hopped to the ears," said Mr. Lingbaum, watching the thorn-crowned figure with fascination. A number of electricians and extras winked at one another.

A few minutes later the technicolor cameras were turning, and Robert Gary, hanging from the cross, enacted the Agony.

The script called for some seven shots of the Crucifixion, beginning with the nailing of the hands and feet, which had already been taken in close-ups with papier-mâché facsimiles of Robert's extremities, and ending with him dead, head drooped and body stiffened in its final throe of pain.

The story of the Redeemer, in its final pages, cut away from and cut back to the cross seven times, each time revealing the increase in the Lord's suffering. Mr. Lingbaum had rehearsed the whole Crucifixion the morning before the storm. Nevertheless, he expected a great deal of trouble with Robert. He was surprised when, without hitch and in a manner that surpassed anything he had ever seen this lamest of all actors do, Robert went through the ordeal of the shooting.

"My God," Mr. Lingbaum thought several times as the cameras turned, "he's better than Barrymore!"

It was late afternoon when the scene was completed. Robert, considerably worn by his efforts and yet feeling oddly exhilarated, leaped from the cross, spurning the little stepladder. The picture of *The Redeemer* was finished. Mr. Kolisher, present on the set during the last few hours of shooting, threw a fatherly arm around Robert's shoulders.

"You did fine, wonderful," he said. "I didn't think you had it in you. It was magnificent."

In his heart Mr. Kolisher knew it was not talent but dope that had inspired Robert Gary to his truly unusual performance that day. But he decided, graciously, not to mention the fact. In Mr. Kolisher's code an artist, drunk or sober, was entitled to praise if he did the work well and without too much delay in the schedule.

"You were all right," said Mr. Lingbaum. "I don't think we'll need a single retake on this day's work. And I'd expected a lot of trouble with those scenes."

"Thank you," said Robert to both men, who had escorted him to his dressing room.

Mr. Kolisher waited until Mr. Lingbaum had left.

"I will see you tomorrow afternoon in my office," he said quietly, "about that matter I mentioned yesterday. Tomorrow afternoon—after the rushes."

Mr. Kolisher was waiting at four o'clock the next day for a call from the projection room. He was eager to see the rushes of the scenes he had witnessed shot, convinced that they would furnish a stirring and beautiful climax to his magnificent production. The door opened, without warning, and a stricken and pallid Lingbaum entered. Mr. Kolisher looked up in surprise.

"I have something to tell you," Mr. Lingbaum said in a hoarse voice. "I've just come from the laboratory."

"What's the matter?" asked Mr. Kolisher, rising.

"The rushes are no good," Mr. Lingbaum answered, white-faced.

"In what way?" Mr. Kolisher asked slowly.

"You won't believe me," said Mr. Lingbaum, and fell, as if shot, into a large leather chair.

"Proceed," said Mr. Kolisher.

"Robert Gary ain't in them," Mr. Lingbaum answered.

"Ain't in what?" asked Mr. Kolisher more slowly.

"The rushes," breathed Mr. Lingbaum.

"Out of focus," countered Mr. Kolisher coldly.

"I said he ain't in them, in focus or out of focus," Mr. Lingbaum answered, petulant despite his pallor. He felt bewitched, for though he had always believed actors nonexistent, he had never thought them so nonexistent as this.

"What are you trying to tell me?" Mr. Kolisher demanded.

"I don't know," Mr. Lingbaum said slowly. "But I just looked at the film in the view box and there is no sign of Robert."

"Is—is anything else on the film?" Mr. Kolisher asked, feeling dizzy.

"Everything," said Mr. Lingbaum. "The lighting is beautiful. The colors are remarkable. The composition is perfect. Only there is nobody on the cross. Not a soul."

"He was there!" Mr. Kolisher cried out. "I saw him with my own eyes."

"I photographed him!" screamed Mr. Lingbaum. "By God, I tell you something has happened!"

Twenty minutes later Messrs. Kolisher and Lingbaum, with a group of their assistants, sat in the darkened projection room waiting for the rushes to be shown. They sat in a hush in which Mr. Kolisher's heavy breathing sounded ominously.

The rushes appeared and for a few minutes the hush was

broken by cries of amazement. A dozen different-voiced sounds of incredulity and bewilderment filled the dark little auditorium. Mr. Kolisher's voice was not among them. His breathing grew heavier, but no other sounds issued from him.

On the screen had appeared the cross, standing between two other towering crosses tipped at picturesque angles and bearing each the figure of a thief, sweating, writhing, and unshaven. Behind these the desert clouds drifted full of beauty and portent. All was visible in its original coloring and, as Mr. Lingbaum had said, in perfect composition and focus. But on the center cross there was not the faintest hint of Robert Gary.

"Where is he?" Mr. Lingbaum cried out suddenly in the dark. "Shut it off. Take those things off the screen!" Fear had overcome him.

"Let them run," Mr. Kolisher spoke loudly. "I want to see every foot that was shot."

And Mr. Kolisher did. He saw, however, more than the amazed ones in the projection room did. He saw that there would be no retakes and that *The Redeemer* would have to be released without the Crucifixion for a finish.

Mr. Kolisher knew, despite the fact that there was, as always, nothing in his mind, that something more than dope was wrong with Robert Gary.

A garbled and generally discredited account of the "Hollywood miracle" spread through a number of newspaper offices and dinner parties. It was derisively tagged as a bit of press agentry and one in shocking taste. For there is no one so gullible as to believe in the reality of anything within the kingdom of the movies.

Mr. Kolisher's predicament was unusual. His showman's soul itched to broadcast the incontrovertible fact of his star's divinity, or at least magic properties. The fact that Robert Gary had been to heaven, or someplace like it (taken there by angels), and that he had spoken to God, would immeasurably increase the drawing power of his (Mr. Kolisher's) greatest production, *The Redeemer*. But his instincts warned him that ten people would call him a fool, and an unscrupulous fool, at that, for every one person who might feel a vague belief in such an advertising campaign.

The Redeemer ended, as he had seen it must in the projection room, without any Crucifixion whatsoever. There was no use doing things by halves—that is, in long shots with a double on the cross.

Mr. Kolisher, after a secret interview with Robert, refused to make any retakes. Robert had added some details to his original story. It was obvious to Mr. Kolisher that something remarkably peculiar had happened to Robert, something which a group of scientists could probably explain—and did later. Mr. Kolisher, listening to the astonishing story, was not exactly frightened, but he considered the whole matter a mystery beyond him or his publicity department. He advised Robert to go somewhere and rest up.

"I don't wish to either contradict or criticize you, Robert," said Mr. Kolisher, "but the main thing is that if you go away and rest the thing you are suffering from may wear off and they will be able to photograph you again. My advice to you, Robert—and, mind you, I am extremely fond of you—is you can't be too careful. I've seen lots of movie stars, every bit as big as you, come and go, come and go."

Robert nodded.

"You may think yourself more important because of this amazing thing that has happened to you," pursued Mr. Kolisher thoughtfully, "but whatever you are, you ain't much good as an actor as long as you remain invisible. What worries me, Robert, about your whole story, is it ain't logical. Now if God had wanted to help me in my production of *The Redeemer,* why would He spoil my main actor and kill the chief scene of the whole script?"

Mr. Kolisher turned his attention to some documents on his desk and added in a crisp voice:

"Get some rest, Robert. And thank you very much for your work in the picture. I appreciate it. That'll be all."

Robert stood up.

"Maybe if I went to church," he murmured, "and prayed

to God He should remove His light from me, I could make a comeback."

"That is your lookout, Robert," said Mr. Kolisher aloofly, "but I would advise you to be careful about what you say and do—in church or out of it. Lots of people are liable to misunderstand you. That'll be all, Robert."

And Robert, in whom bitterness and confusion were beginning already to warp character, went into hiding in a desert sanitarium, pending developments.

The opening of *The Redeemer* in New York—its first public showing—was the industry's most outstanding première up to that time. It is doubtful whether the actual enactment of the Savior's drama within its precincts would have excited its citizens any more. There might have been a handful of more intensely elated onlookers but, I am sure, hardly as general a feeling of awe and expectation.

At least in heaven the unveiling of the Kolisher production created a much vaster stir than had the original performance in the Holy Land.

On this night, which was to witness the cinematized tale of God's Son, there was neither vagueness nor ignorance beyond the vaults of space.

God had summoned as many of the angels as He could spare from the operation of His forces and revealed to them what was going to happen. Taking a leaf from the way Mr. Kolisher was doing things, for He had grown (to me) an unreasonable admiration for that man, God had seated His angels in a vast and glittering theater, far more spacious and beautiful than His home-coming hall. So transcendent, so staggeringly opulent were the dimensions and appointments of this theater that I shall not even attempt to describe them, except to say that Hollywood has a long way to go.

The unfolding of the first reels of *The Redeemer* held the angels breathless. At that distance, perhaps, the events taking place on the screen in the New York theater seemed to them as real as the other doings of that little world.

God patiently explained to them, while the performance was going on, that the movies were not life. They were, He said, not only a representation of it but a charming dream-like improvement.

Some of the angels understood that God meant not an improvement on His works but on something else. Others of them, however, were impressed by God's unprecedented modesty.

"What you are seeing," said God as the New York performance progressed, "is the work of Mr. Kolisher's genius. It is very fine and I am glad you admire it. However, I have assisted Mr. Kolisher in the final part of the drama."

"In what way?" asked the Angel Michael at his side.

"You will see," said God, and smiled. "The last part of *The Redeemer* will be by far the best," He added.

"When does Your contribution begin?" asked the Angel Michael.

"It begins," said God, "where Robert is on the cross. I have, as Mr. Lingbaum would say, directed the acting in that scene."

The angels nodded excitedly. Marvelous though the movie seemed to them thus far, they knew that with God's help its wonders would be augmented and they waited breathlessly.

"Now, in a few minutes," said God, "My scene will appear."

The Redeemer was carrying the cross up a hill. Crowds were hooting and stones were flying at his head.

"Wait," said God.

The angels all leaned forward eagerly. But a surprising thing happened. No sooner had the Redeemer reached the top of the hill on which stood the two crosses bearing Barabbas and his cofelon than darkness came slowly down on the screen. The picture of the Redeemer, with a hundred voices pealing above the roar of organs and orchestra, faded out. The angels stared and then turned to the Deity.

"Something has happened," said God. "It will continue in a minute.

"Michael!" said God, for He intended to send him to the rescue of Mr. Kolisher. But He became silent. The first-nighters were applauding wildly. The lights in the New York theater had gone on again and the audience, clothing themselves in lovely pieces of finery while they dabbed tears of compassion from their eyes, were filing out. It came to God that the movie was over.

There was a hush in heaven.

"I can't believe it," said God. "It is something too difficult to believe."

The Angel Michael, closest to God, held his breath, for a great darkness had come over the divine face.

"Mr. Kolisher did not use My ending," said God. "He threw it away."

The angels said nothing. They had seldom seen the Deity so disturbed.

The awed and happy crowds emerging from the theater in which they had witnessed the latest product of Mr. Kolisher's genius stepped into one of the worst storms that had ever smitten the city of New York.

Lightnings and thunders of a prodigious type filled the black, wind-howling night. Gusts of razor-sharp rain blinded all the traffic and even the people inside cafés shivered unhappily at this outburst of the elements.

The storm raged most of the night. A great deal of wreckage had to be removed in the morning.

The newspapers devoted considerable space to the "freak storm," as it was called, for the weather bureaus had had no warning of it from any of their instruments. Nevertheless, there was enough space left to herald the beauties of Mr. Kolisher's *The Redeemer*.

The movie was described, in language which the Kolisher publicity department could not have improved on, as a sort of climax to Mr. Kolisher's genius. What most impressed the critics, however, was not the magnificence of the movie —for they were used to that from his skillful hands—but the restraint the great producer had exercised in not revealing the final scenes of the world-famous drama.

They declared, with a remarkable unanimity which may have had something to do with the gold-plate banquet Mr.

Kolisher had tendered them on the eve of the opening, that Hollywood's leading wizard had done something both noble and artistic in leaving the final scenes to the imagination.

It would, they thought and said, have been much too harrowing even for the seasoned first-nighters to have had to sit through the actual Crucifixion.

Mr. Kolisher was pleased to read these things. He caused innumerable copies of them to be made and distributed among the people, that they might see how expertly and cleverly he had served their best interests.

But though he was pleased, he was, too, a little disturbed. He wondered about the storm that had almost spoiled his opening night, and decided on no more religious pictures.

But you will be wondering, probably, or should be (as Mr. Kolisher was), about Robert Gary. Despite the many things there were to praise in the Kolisher production, the critics found space for several paragraphs about the central character. They agreed that Robert Gary had excelled himself in his tender and beautiful portrayal of the Redeemer and pronounced, as with one voice, that he was now firmly established as filmland's leading idol.

It was, alas, a pronouncement completely cockeyed.

What happened to Robert is a little involved but will bear telling. Shortly after the great success of *The Redeemer* Robert was cast (not by Mr. Kolisher, but by the major studio from which he had originally been borrowed) in the role of a South Seas beachcomber—also in technicolor. Some preliminary tests made of Robert quickly resulted in his being dropped from the cast. For the tests revealed the same amazing deficiency as had the rushes in the Kolisher projection room: Robert was not in the film.

He was dropped from the great studio's pay roll within a week. His contract—the most magnificent one in the film capital—providing for an abrogation by either side in the event of any "act of God," was canceled. Although this was, of course, a mere piece of legal phrasing, Robert's lawyers, who had heard his story, assured him he had cooked his own goose in the telling of it and would have no chance in court with his own admission of such an "act of God" against him.

In the end his employers believed not a bit of Robert's story, having had the matter of his camera invisibility explained to them by their research department. It was due, they had found out, to an excess of radioactivity and bone phosphorescence, but they felt it within their ethical rights to take advantage of Robert's own silly tale as a means of saving fifteen thousand dollars a week.

Robert was never employed again. Some interest attached to him for a few months. A number of religious-minded people called on him—in his sanitarium—and begged him to go on a lecture tour of the country.

This little group was convinced that all the things Robert had to say were true. His invisibility to the camera, owing to divine radiance, would lend, they were certain, credence to his story of his heavenly visit. They urged Robert, who in a way was truly another Son of God, to leave his sanitarium and spread his divine revelation among the people. As the outstanding movie name of the day, he was sure of huge audiences for any personal appearances.

But Robert, though he knew God had placed His Divinity upon his face, refused to budge from the sanitarium. Robert had a horror of public appearances and was certain that the sight of a crowd waiting for him to speak would shrivel his brain to nothingness. He was not going to make a fool of himself as a tongue-tied Messiah, and this is what he said to his would-be religious sponsors.

But there was another thing in Robert's heart that kept him from the projected tour as God's Son. He had no desire to pose as such a one and no wish to broadcast the truth of God to a dubious world. For Robert, whose simplicity the Deity himself had admired, was embittered with God for ruining his career. He had felt in his bones something of the sort would happen when God had begun asking those questions about the inside of the movie business. God had tumbled another idol, which, in its debris, was in no mood to spread the Almighty's fame.

The kingdom of the movies continued to flourish without either Robert's or God's assistance.

Of all the things I have written in this story, the most

interesting (to me, at least) is the sad conclusion to be drawn from it. I am afraid it appears that God's intervention in the world of man, even in the simplest of His enterprises, such as the movies, is fraught with disaster and futility. Amen.

DIALOGUES IN DIALECT

IX. DIALOGUES IN DIALECT

THERE'S A LARGE PREJUDICE in some quarters against dialect humor. This prejudice appears to have its origin in two directions. Writers who are incapable of handling dialect themselves have a tendency to knock those who have mastered it. Then there is the racial question. The great movements for the improvement of racial relations have a stanch supporter in me, but when they start to beller against anybody writing anything in Negro dialect or Jewish dialect or Hottentot turkey talk, they lose the warmth of my love.

I contend that so long as certain people talk in dialect authors should report that talk in dialect if they are capable of it. Oh well, let's not start any arguments.

In choosing a Jewish dialect story I ran into trouble because I wanted to use one of Arthur Kober's Bella pieces and I wanted to use the magnificent H*Y*M*A*N K*A*P*L*A*N. After considering the thing at length I decided in favor of Mr. K*A*P*L*A*N. In passing I'd like to mourn a bit over the demise of the man. Why did Dr. Rosten (Leonard Q. Ross) quit writing of H*Y*M*A*N? He is, to me, one of the funniest characters ever put on paper.

As the most original pupil in the American Night Preparatory School for Adults, Mr. K*A*P*L*A*N was the man who listed the "most famous tree American wriders" as Jeck Laundon, Valt Viterman, and the author of Hawk L. Barry-Feen, further identified as Mocktvain.

He declined the verb "to fail" in this wise: "fail, failed, bankropt." He referred to rubber heels as "robber hills" and to the pencil sharpener as the "pantsil chopner." He displayed ingenuity in giving the positive, comparative, and superlative forms of certain adjectives: "good, batter, highcless," "bad, voise, rotten," and "cold, colder, below zero." He defined the opposite of "new" as "secondhand."

Here he is in—

MR. KAPLAN'S DARK LOGIC

By Leonard Q. Ross

FOR A LONG TIME Mr. Parkhill had believed that the incredible things which Mr. Hyman Kaplan did to the English language were the products of a sublime and transcendental ignorance. That was the only way, for example, that he could account for Mr. Kaplan's version of the name of the fourth President of the United States: "James Medicine." Then Mr. Parkhill began to feel that it wasn't ignorance which governed Mr. Kaplan so much as *impulsiveness*. That would explain the sentence Mr. Kaplan had given in vocabulary drill, using the word "orchard": "Each day he is giving her a dozen orchards." But then came Mr. Kaplan's impetuous answer to the question: "And what is the opposite of 'rich'?"

"Skinny!" Mr. Kaplan had cried.

Now a less conscientious teacher might have dismissed that as a fantastic guess. But Mr. Parkhill thought it over with great care. (Mr. Parkhill stopped at nothing in his pedagogical labors.) And he realized that to Mr. Kaplan wealth and avoirdupois were inseparable aspects of one natural whole: rich people were fat. Grant this major premise and the opposite of "rich" *must* be—it was all too clear —"skinny."

The more Mr. Parkhill thought this over the more was he convinced that it was neither ignorance nor caprice which guided Mr. Kaplan's life and language. It was Logic. A secret kind of logic, perhaps. A private logic. A dark and baffling logic. But Logic. And when Mr. Kaplan fell into grammatical error it was simply because his logic and the logic of the world did not happen to coincide. Mr. Parkhill came to suspect that on such occasions there was only one defensible position to take: *de gustibus non est disputandum.*

Any final doubts Mr. Parkhill might have felt on the whole matter were resolved once and for all when Mr. Kaplan conjugated "to die" as "die, dead, funeral."

It was on a Monday night, several weeks after Mr. Kaplan's incomparable analysis of "to die," that Mr. Parkhill was given a fresh glimpse of the dialectical genius of his most remarkable student. The class was making three-minute addresses. Miss Rochelle Goldberg was reciting. She was describing her experience with a ferocious dog. The dog's name, according to Miss Goldberg, was Spots. He was a "Scotch terror."

"Was he a beeg, wild dug!" Miss Goldberg said, her eyes moving in recollective fear. "Honist, you would all be afraid somthing tarrible! I had good rizzon for being all scared. I was trying to pat Spots, nize, on the had, and saying, 'Here, Spots, Spots, Spots!'–and Spots bite me so hod on the––"

"'Bite' is the *present* tense, Miss Goldberg."

A look of dismay wandered into Miss Goldberg's eyes.

"You want the–er–*past* tense." Mr. Parkhill spoke as gently as he could: Miss Goldberg had a collapsible nervous system. "What *is* the past tense of 'to bite'?"

Miss Goldberg hung her head.

"The past tense of 'to bite'–anyone?"

Mr. Kaplan's Samaritan impulses surged to the fore. "Isn't 'bited,' uf cawss," he ventured archly.

"No, it isn't–er–'bited'!" Mr. Parkhill couldn't tell whether Mr. Kaplan had uttered a confident negation or an oblique question.

Miss Mitnick raised her hand, just high enough to be recognized. "'Bit,'" she volunteered quietly.

"Good, Miss Mitnick! 'Bite, *bit,* bitten.'"

At once Mr. Kaplan closed his eyes, cocked his head to one side, and began whispering to himself. "Mitnick gives 'bit.' . . . *'Bit'* Mitnick gives. . . . My!"

This dramaturgic process indicated that Mr. Kaplan was subjecting Miss Mitnick's contribution to his most rigorous analysis. Considering the ancient and acrid feud between these two, to allow one of Miss Mitnick's offerings to go unchallenged would constitute a psychological defeat of no mean proportions to Mr. Kaplan. It would be a blow to his self-respect. It would bring anguish to his soul.

" 'Bite, *bit,* bitten?' . . . Hmmmm. . . . Dat sonds awful fonny!"

It was no use for Mr. Parkhill to pretend that he had not heard: the whole class had heard.

"Er—isn't that clear, Mr. Kaplan?"

Mr. Kaplan did not open his eyes. "*Clear,* Mr. Pockheel? Foist-cless clear! Clear like gold! Only I don' see vy should be dat 'bit.' . . . It don' makink *sanse!*"

"Oh, it doesn't make *sense,*" Mr. Parkhill repeated lamely. Suddenly he glimpsed a golden opportunity. "You mean it isn't—er—*logical?*"

"Exactel!" cried Mr. Kaplan happily. "Dat 'bit' isn't logical."

"Well, Mr. Kaplan. Surely you remember our verb drills. The verb 'to bite' is much like, say, the verb 'to hide.' 'To hide' is conjugated 'hide, hid, hidden.' Why, then, isn't it —er—logical that the principal parts of 'to bite' be 'bite, bit, bitten'?"

Mr. Kaplan considered this semisyllogism in silence. Then he spoke. "*I* t'ought de pest time 'bite' should be—'bote.' "

Miss Mitnick gave a little gasp.

" 'Bote?' " Mr. Parkhill asked in amazement. " 'Bote?' "

" 'Bote!' " said Mr. Kaplan.

Mr. Parkhill shook his head. "I don't see your point."

"Vell," sighed Mr. Kaplan with a modest shrug, "if is 'write, wrote, written,' so vy isn't 'bite, bote, bitten'?"

Psychic cymbals crashed in Mr. Parkhill's ears.

"There is not such a word 'bote,' " protested Miss Mitnick, who took this all as a personal affront. Her voice was small but desperate.

" 'Not-soch-a-void!' " Mr. Kaplan repeated ironically. "Mine dear Mitnick, don' *I* know is not soch a void? Did I said *is* soch a void? All I'm eskink is, isn't logical *should be* soch a void!"

The silence was staggering.

"Mr. Kaplan, there is *no such word,* as Miss Mitnick just said." (Miss Mitnick was in agony, biting her lips, twisting her handkerchief, gazing with bewilderment at her shoes. Her plight was that of common humanity's, faced by genius.) "Nor is it—er—logical that there *should* be such a word." Mr. Parkhill recapitulated the exercise on regular and irregular verbs. He gave the principal parts of a dozen samples. He analyzed the whole system of verb conjugation. Mr. Parkhill spoke with earnestness and rare feeling. He spoke as if a good deal depended on it.

By the time Mr. Parkhill had finished his little lecture Mr. Kaplan had seen the light and submitted, with many a sigh, to the tyranny of the irregular verb; Miss Mitnick's normal pallor had returned; Mrs. Moskowitz was fast asleep; and Miss Goldberg, completely forgotten in the clash between two systems of thought, had taken her seat with the air of one washing her hands of the whole business.

Recitation and Speech went on.

Mr. Sam Pinsky delivered a short address on the mysteries of his craft, baking. (It came out that Mr. Pinsky had produced literally thousands of "loafers" of "brat" in his career.) Miss Valuskas described a wedding she had recently attended. Mrs. Moskowitz, refreshed by her slumbers, indulged in a moving idyll about a trip she was hoping to make to a metropolis called "Spittsburgh." Then the recess bell rang.

The second student to recite after the recess was Hyman Kaplan. He hurried to the front of the room, glowing with joy at the opportunity to recite. He almost seemed to give off a radiance.

"Ladies an' gantleman, Mr. Pockheel," Mr. Kaplan began, with customary éclat. "Tonight I'll gonna talknik abot noose-peppers, dose movvelous——"

"Pardon me." Mr. Parkhill knew it would be nothing

short of fatal to give Mr. Kaplan free rein. "It's 'Tonight I *am going* . . . to *talk*.' And the word is '*new*spapers,' not 'noose-peppers.'" Mr. Parkhill went to the board and printed "NOOSE," "PEPPER," and "NEWSPAPER." He explained the meaning of each word. When he pointed out that "pepper" was a strong condiment ("Salt . . . pepper, Mr. Kaplan. Do you see?"), everyone smiled. Miss Mitnick rejoiced. Mr. Kaplan beamed. Mr. Kaplan was amazed by the ingenious combination ("noose-pepper") which he had brought into being.

"Vell," Mr. Kaplan took up his tale after Mr. Parkhill was done, "de *new*spapers is to me de finest kind t'ing ve have in tsivilization. Vat *is* a newspaper? Ha! It's a show! It's a comedy! It's aducation! It's movvelous!" Rhapsodically Mr. Kaplan painted the glory and the miracle of journalism. "Fromm newspapers de messes gat——"

"'M*a*sses,' Mr. Kaplan, 'm*a*sses'!" Mr. Parkhill felt that "messes" might have consequences too dreadful to contemplate.

"—de m*a*sses loin abot de voild. Even de edvoitismants in de paper is a kind lasson. An' uf cawss de odder pots a newspaper: de hatlininks, de auditorials, de cottoons, de fine pages pictchiss on Sonday, dat ve callink rotogravy sactions."

"'Rotogra*vure!*'"

"An' in newspapers ve find ot all dat's heppenink all hover de voild! Abot politic, crimes, all kinds difference *scendels* pipple makink, abot if is goink to be snow or rainink, an' uf cawss—'spacially in U. S.—all abot sax!"

Mr. Parkhill closed his eyes.

"Mitout newspapers vat vould ve humans be?" Mr. Kaplan paused dramatically. "Ha! *Sawages* ve vould be, dat's vat! *Ignorance* ve vould fill, dat's all. No fects! No knolledge! No aducation!" A shudder passed through the body scholastic at the mere thought of such a barbaric state.

"Vell, dis mornink I vas readink a noos—a *new*spaper. English newspaper!" Mr. Kaplan paused, awaiting the acclaim of his colleagues. They were inert. "*English* newspaper I vas readink!" Mr. Kaplan repeated delicately. Mr.

Bloom snickered, ever the skeptic. Mr. Kaplan shot him a look composed of indignation, pain, and ice. "I vas readink abot how vill maybe be annodder Voild Var. So vat de paper said? Vell, he said dat——"

"Mr. Kaplan," Mr. Parkhill *had* to interpolate. "It's '*it* said,' not '*he* said'!"

Mr. Kaplan was stunned. "Not 'he'?"

"No, not 'he.' 'It'! Er—you know the rules for pronouns, Mr. Kaplan. 'He' is masculine, 'she' is feminine. Sometimes, of course, we say 'she' for certain objects which have no sex—a country, for example, or a ship. But for newspapers we use the neuter pronoun." Mr. Parkhill had an inspiration. "Surely *that's* logical!"

Mr. Kaplan sank into mighty thought, shaking his head at regular intervals. He whispered to himself: "Not mascoolin. . . . Not faminine. . . . But in de *meedle!*"

Mr. Parkhill waited with the patience of his calling.

"Aha!" Some cosmic verity had groped its way into Mr. Kaplan's universe. "Plizz, Mr. Pockheel. I unnistand *fine* abot mascoolin, faminine, an' neutral; but——"

"'Neu*ter*,' Mr. Kaplan!"

"—an' neu*ter*. But is maybe all right ve should say 'he' abot *som* papers! Ven dey havink mascoolin *names?*"

Mr. Parkhill frowned. "I don't see what the name of the paper has to do with it. We say of the New York *Times*, for instance, 'it said.' Or of the New York *Post*——"

"*Dose* papers, yassir!" Mr. Kaplan cried. "But ven a paper got a real *mascoolin* name?"

Mr. Parkhill spoke with calculated deliberation. "I don't understand, Mr. Kaplan. Which newspaper would you say has a—er—*masculine* name?"

Mr. Kaplan's face was drenched with modesty. "*Harold Tribune*," he said.

FEW WILL ARGUE with me, I think, about Roark Bradford being top man in Negro dialect. The two short chapters here are taken from *Ol' Man Adam an' His Chillun*—the book on which the famous play *Green Pastures* was based.

STEAMBOAT DAYS

By Roark Bradford

WELL, WHEN DE PEOPLE got so low down to de Lawd couldn't stand 'em, he decided to flood de yearth and drown ev'ybody 'ceptin' old man Noah. So he told Noah to build a ark and ride de flood down.

" 'Cause from what I got in my mind," say de Lawd, "hit look like she's gonter be a mighty wet spring, Noah."

"Gonter bust de levees, is you, Lawd?" say Noah.

"When de levees bustes," say de Lawd, "dat's jest gonter be de startin' of de wet weather. I got my mind set on rain, Noah, and when I gits my mind set, I mean to tell you I makes hit rain."

So Noah got de hammer and de saw and de nails and de lumber and things and went out on de hillside wid his boys to build de ark.

"Dis gonter to be a side-wheeler, ain't hit paw? Sort of like de *Stacy Adams?*" say Ham.

"Stern-wheeler, like de *Grace,*" say Noah. "Only bigger. Us wants room, not fancy stuff.—You, Shem! Tote dat planed lumber up on de texas deck. Rough lumber goes on de main deck."

So Noah and Ham and Shem and Japeth hammered and sawed away, out on de hillside, a mile from de river. And purty soon somebody hyars de hammerin' and sa'nters up to ax Noah what he doin'.

"Buildin' you a house, is you, Noah?" say a man.

"Nawp," say Noah. "I's buildin' a ark."

"Well, whyn't you build hit by de river so hit'll float?" say de man.

"Who buildin' dis ark?" say Noah. "Me or you?"

So de man wawked off and told his wife. "Old Noah is

plum crazy," he say. "Buildin' hit right out on de hillside, a mile or more from de river."

"You ain't tellin' me no news," say de man's wife. "Ain't old Miz Noah tellin' ev'ybody hit gonter rain fawty days and fawty nights and folks which ain't on de ark gonter git drownded?"

"De whole family is plum crazy," say de man. "And was I you, old lady, I wouldn't go round wid Miz Noah much. 'Cause de first thing you know you'll be gettin' a hard name, too."

"Humph!" say de wife. "Hit was me which got hit started to resolve her outn de buryin' society."

So dat's de way tawk went round, to first thing you know de young folks yared de news and they went out to see for theyselves.

"Whyn't you make dat texas bigger?" say a young gal. "Efn hit was bigger, us could have a excursion and dance."

"I ain't studdin' excursions," say Noah, "and I ain't studdin' dances. And what's more, y'all young ladies better drag yo'self on down de road, 'cause sometimes I misses my nail and I hits my finger. And when I mashes my finger I most gen'ally cusses some. And hit ain't nice to cuss before young gals."

So de gal laughs and says, "Dat's all right, granddaddy. You jest mash yo' finger and let me cuss for you."

So dat's about de way things run along to old Noah got de ark finished. Den about supper time one night hit started to rainin'. And old Noah reach up and got de whistle rope and blowed a long, two shorts, and a long.

"Git dat engine fired up, Shem," say Noah. "Us gonter be gittin' away from dis man's town purty soon. Git de steam up, son."

So Noah went and stood on de gangplank and marked down de animals which started comin' when they yared de whistle. De mules and de cows and de jay-raffs and de elephants and de lines and de monkeys. Hit was worse den de circus, de way they marched on, two by two, and hit rainin' and thunderin' and goin' on.

"Dis rain look mighty bad for my phthisic," say Noah.

"Maybe I better git me a snort of dat red-eye before I gits tuk down sick."

"Git away from dat kag," holler Miz Noah. "Hit ain't no snake bit you yit, 'cause de snakes ain't come on boa'd yit."

"Yeah?" say Noah. "S'posin' I gits tuck down wid de phthisic. Who gonter pilot de boat? We'd be hung up on a sandbar before you kin bat yo' eyes." So he tuck a long pull at de kag.

So about de time Noah got back to de gangplank, yar come a pair of cotton-mouf moccasins, crawlin' up de plank, slow and stiddy.

"Great day in de mawnin'!" say Noah. "Efn one of dem boys ups and bites me, I'd die before I gits to de licker kag. Maybe now——" So he sa'nters over to de kag and takes another pull to git ready in case one of dem snakes bites him.

So when he got back to de plank, yar come a pair of diamond back rattlers, hissin' and a-rattlin' and a-strikin' out yar and yonder.

"Easy," say Noah. "Easy, snakes. Jest wait to I git back before you bites me." So he went and tuck another pull at de kag.

And when he got back he seed three copper-haids a-prancin' up de plank, snortin' and singin' and hollerin' for meat.

"I'm jest natchally standin' too far from dat kag," say Noah and he staggers on back to de kag and sets down. And he seed so many kinds of snakes dat he jest natchally got tired and sleepy and de first thing he knowed he was asleep.

Well, finally he woke up and he thought he yared de bell ringin'.

"Wait a minute, Shem," he say. "Le's don't pull out and leave all dem snakes in de flood." Den he opened his eyes and seed Miz Noah standin' over him wid a rollin'-pin.

"I knew I could wake you wid a rollin'-pin," she say, and she dragged de rollin'-pin across his haid again. "Come yar yellin' about snakes and hangin' on dat licker kag whilst us was driftin' out in de storm." Wham! "I told you to let dat licker alone."

Well, purty soon Noah got straightened out and tuck charge of de boat whilst Miz Noah tuck charge of de licker. So they kept goin' on and hit kept on rainin' and ev'ything was gittin' 'long easy.

"Look like shallow water ahead," Jaspeth holler' from de foredeck. "Ham, bring me dat soundin' line."

"Can't," say Ham. "Hit's on de main deck wid de animals, and maw told me to stay 'way from dem animals ev'y since I got de fleas on me."

"I didn't say no sich thing," Miz Noah holler. "I said de next time you played wid dat skunk I was gonter drap you overboa'd. I ain't got de b'iler deck smellin' right yit, since de time you brang him up yar."

So while they was argyin', ker-blam! De ark struck de ground.

"No use in soundin' now," say Noah. "Us done landed. Shem, you drag de fires and dreen de b'iler. Jape, you bring me a dove. Ham, you tell yo' mammy to set de kag of licker out in de companionway, 'cause I feels my phthisic hurtin' me again."

So in due time de water went away and de ark was settin' high and dry. And all de animals wawked off and on wawked de Lawd.

"Well, Noah," say de Lawd, "did I rain or didn't I rain?"

"Lawd," say Noah, "you rained."

"He don't know did you rain, Lawd, or did you snow," say Ham. "'Cause he was layin' up in de pilot-house, drunker'n a b'iled owl."

So dat made old Noah mad and he jumped up and cussed out Ham, hot and heavy.

"You, Noah!" say Miz Noah. "Ain't you ashame' to cuss like dat in front of de Lawd!"

"Dat's all right, Sister Noah," say de Lawd. "Hit's jest natchal for a good steamboat cap'm to git mad and cuss once in a while. I never seed a good cap'm yet which wouldn't do hit, do you plage 'em. And when they kin cuss good like Noah, I don't mind hyarin' hit. I likes to hyar good cussin' same as anybody else. What I don't like to hyar is bad cussin'."

So Noah tuck his wife and his sons and they wives and got out of de ark and started peoplin' de yearth again.

SIN

By Roark Bradford

WELL, HIT WA'N'T LONG after de yearth got peopled to de people got to gittin' in devilment. And de more people hit got to be de more devilment they got in. And de more devilment they got in, de more chilluns dey'd have. To finally hit was so many people scattered round de place to you couldn't hardly wawk.

And mean? Mankind! They was about the triflin'est bunch of trash you ever run up against. Fust off, de menfolks quit workin' and went to shootin' craps for a livin'. Den de womenfolks quit takin' in washin' and used they kettles to make hard-drinkin' licker in. And de chilluns wouldn't mind they maws 'cause they maws was drunk, and hit wa'n't nothin' to see a boy in knee britches wawkin' round, chewin' tobacco and cussin' jest as mannish as his daddy!

Well, hit come to pass one Sunday mawnin' de Lawd was wawkin' de yearth and he seed a bunch of boys playin' marbles on de side of de road. He look and he seed a boy shoot a marble and knock two marbles out of de ring.

"Venture dubs," say de yuther little boy.

"I said 'dubs' first," say de marble-shooter. So they fit and fit and de marble-shootin' boy was gittin' licked, so he say, "Didn't I say 'dubs' first, Mister?" right at de Lawd.

"You don't know who you' tawkin' to, does you, son?" say de Lawd.

"Nawp," say de marble-shooter.

"You want to say 'nawsuh' when you tawkin' to me, 'cause I's de Lawd. And verily I done said unto you, 'Marble not,' and yar you is out yar marblin' on Sunday."

"You ain't my daddy," say de marble-shootin' boy, "and hit ain't none of yo' business what I does on Sunday or any yuther day."

So de Lawd wawked on down de road and he seed a young gal settin' out on a stump, pushin' de 'cordeen and singin' de "Lonesome Blues," jest like hit wa'n't Sunday.

"Gal, whyn't you quit dat singin' dem 'blues' and sing a church song?" say de Lawd. "Don't you know hit's Sunday?"

De gal kept right on singin' to she got done and den she looked at de Lawd and say, "Soap and water, Country Boy." And she went right on singin' again.

"Well, I be doggone," say de Lawd. "I never did see so much sin." So he wawked on down de road to he seed some men kneelin' down in de middle of de road.

"Dat looks better," say de Lawd. "Hit looks like de menfolks is quit they devilment and gone to prayin'. I'm gonter listen and see kin I hyar they prayers."

So he listened and he hyared one of 'em say, "Big Dick f'om Boston! Come on you six-Joe! Wham! Five and five! I shoots hit all!"

Well, de Lawd jest shet his eyes and wawked on. "I'm gonter go tell dat crap-shootin' scound'el's mammy on him right now," he say. "Shootin' craps on Sunday!" So de Lawd wawked on to where de crap-shootin' boy live at and he knock on de door.

"Who dar?" say a man in de house.

"No mind who yar," say de Lawd. "You jest unlatch dis door."

"You got a search warrant?" say de man. " 'Cause ef'n you ain't you might jest as well go on about yo' business. 'Cause you can't get in dis house onless you got a search warrant."

"Well," say de Lawd, "jest tell Miz Rucker to come to de door whilst I tells her on her good-for-nothin' boy which is shootin' craps on Sunday."

"Miz Rucker ain't yar no more," say de man. "She runned off wid a railroad man, yistiddy."

"Well, send Rucker to de door, den," say de Lawd.

"Can't," say de man. "Rucker's piled up under de table.

He been passed out since early dis mawnin'. I's de onliest sober man in de house 'cause I drunk some of dat new wildcat yistiddy, and hit burnt de skin off of my th'oat so I can't drink no more."

"Well," say de Lawd, "dis ain't gittin' me nowheres. Deseyar mankinds which I peopled my yearth wid sho' ain't much. I got a good mind to wipe 'em off'n de yearth and people my yearth wid angels."

So de Lawd wawked on down be road, tawkin' to hisself and studdyin' 'bout what he gonter do wid de sin.

"Naw," he say, "angels is all right for singin' and playin' and flyin' round, but they ain't much on workin' de crops and buildin' de levees. I guess I won't monkey round wid de angels on my yearth. They jest won't do."

So he wawked along, studdyin' and a-tawkin'. "Mankind," he say, "is jest right for my yearth ef'n he wa'n't so dad-blame sinful. But I'm sick and tired of his sin. I'd druther have my yearth peopled wid a bunch of channel catfish den mankind and his sin. I jest can't stand sin."

So about dat time de Lawd comed up on old man Noah, wawkin' long de road in a plug hat and a hammer-tail coat.

"Good mawnin', brother," say Noah. "Us missed you at church dis mawnin'."

"I ain't got no time to go to church," say de Lawd. "I got work——"

"Yeah," say Noah, "mighty nigh ev'ybody say they ain't got time to go to church dese days and times. Hit seems like de more I preaches de more people ain't got time to come to church. I ain't hardly got enough members to fill up de choir. I has to do de preachin' and de bassin', too."

"Is dat a fack?" say de Lawd.

"Yeah," say Noah. "Ev'ybody is mighty busy gamblin' and good-timin' and sinnin' and goin' on. They ain't got time to come to church. But you jest wait. When old Gabriel blows they hawn they gonter find plenty of time to punch chunks down yonder in hell. They gonter beg to git to come to church, too. But de Lawd ain't gonter pay 'em no mind. They makin' they own fun, now. But when old Gabriel toots, de Lawd gonter be de boss."

"Brother Noah," say de Lawd, "you don't know who I is, does you?"

"Lemme see," say Noah. "Yo' face looks easy. But I jest can't call de name. But I don't keer what yo' name is, you jest come along home wid me. I think de old lady kilt a chicken or so, and den, after us eats and rests up some, you comes wid me to preachin' again tonight."

"I don't keer ef I do," say de Lawd. "Dat chicken sounds mighty good to me. And you say you basses in de singin'?"

"Jest tries hit," say Noah. "I ain't so much on de bass as I is on de leadin'."

"I used to bass purty fair," say de Lawd.

So dey wawked on to Noah's house, and de Lawd didn't let on to Noah dat he wa'n't jest a natchal man like ev'y-body else. So dey r'ared back and et chicken and dumplin's awhile, and all at once de Lawd say, "Brother Noah, I kind of b'lieve hit's gonter rain."

"My cawns is burnin' me, too," say Noah. "Jest slip yo' feet outer yo' shoes and rest yo'self."

"What'd you do, did hit commence to rain, Noah?" say de Lawd.

"Well," say Noah, "I most gen'ally lets hit rain."

"S'posin'," say de Lawd, "hit would haul off and rain fawty days and fawty nights?"

"I ain't worryin'," say Noah. "In de fust place, hit ain't gonter rain dat long, onless de Lawd sends hit. And in de second place, I's on de Lawd's side, and de Lawd gonter look after me do he go to monkeyin' wid de weather."

"You b'lieve de Lawd gonter look after you, does you?" say de Lawd.

"Don't b'lieve nothin' 'bout hit," say Noah. "I knows hit. I does de best I kin for de Lawd, and dat's all de Lawd gonter ax any man to do. I don't do much, but hit's de best I got."

So all at once de Lawd reach inside his shirt front and pull out his crown and set it on his haid. Den he start to tawk, and thunder and lightnin' come outer his mouf. So old Noah jest drap down on his knees.

"Yar I is, Lawd," he say. "Yar I is. I ain't much, but I'm de best I got."

"Noah," say de Lawd, "hit's gonter rain fawty days and fawty nights. And hit's gonter drown ev'ybody on de yearth which is a sinner. And dat means about ev'ybody but you and yo' family. Now you jest git out and build me a ark on dry land big enough to hold a pair of mules and a pair of cows and a pair of elephants and a pair of snakes and a pair of ev'ything which creeps or crawls, swims or flies. And you better make hit big enough to pack away a heap of grub, too, 'cause from what I got in mind, hit ain't gonter be no goin' to de commissary and buyin' grub when I starts rainin'."

"And snakes, too, Lawd?" say Noah.

"Snakes," say de Lawd.

"S'pos'n' a snake up and hit somebody?" say Noah.

"I hadn't thought about dat," say de Lawd. "Maybe you better not take no snakes."

"I ain't skeered of snakes," say Noah, "ef'n I got a kag of licker handy," say Noah.

"I ain't so much on de licker," say de Lawd. "But hit do come in handy round snakes."

"And wid all dat rain and wet weather, too," say Noah, "my phthisic is liable to plague me, too, onless I got a little hard licker handy."

"Well, you better put a kag of licker on boa'd, too," say de Lawd.

"Better put two kags," say Noah. "Hit'll help balance de boat. You get a kag on one side, and nothin' on de yuther, and de boat liable to turn over. You got to keep a boat balanced, Lawd."

"One kag," say de Lawd. "You kin set hit in de middle of de deck. One kag of licker is enough for anybody for fawty days and fawty nights. I said one kag, and dat's all you carries."

"Yas, Lawd," say Noah, "one kag."

OUTSIDE OF occasional guest appearances on other programs, Fred Allen has been taking a well-deserved vacation from radio. His blood pressure has a tendency to behave like a dime-store thermometer in the Congo, and the daffy furies which attend the production of a large radio show only serve to aggravate his physical distress.

I heard Fred observe once that he had just figured out why advertising agency executives have never taken up the game of leapfrog. "They've never," he said, "been able to get the first man to bend over."

Scarcely a week passes these days that he doesn't get a letter from a publisher asking him to please write a book for them. He has been approached dozens of times on the subject of writing his autobiography. In the past he has always shied away from such a project. He has felt that his years of writing radio programs ruined him for other literary pursuits. He always argued that the stuff he wrote was strictly for the ear—composed to be spoken into a microphone—and that it wouldn't look pretty in cold type. Pish, if I may be so bold, tush!

One of these days we'll have that book out of him. Meanwhile I can offer proof that even his radio writing is good to read.

From his files we have picked a portion of a radio script. He wrote it six or eight years ago and it is presented here just as he put it on paper for radio performance.

MOUNTAIN JUSTICE

By Fred Allen

ALLEN: And now, ladies and gentlemen, the Mighty Allen Art Players. Tonight they present a hillbilly court episode. It's called *Mountain Justice* or *The Judge Wasn't Making Good but At Least He Was in There Trying*. Music, Maestro!

(*"Chicken Reel" . . . Fades. Gavel sounds.*)

CLERK: Rise, rubes! His Honor, Jedge Allen!

(*Hum of voices.*)

ALL: H'ya, Jedge!

ALLEN: Hi, rubes!

(*Gavel sounds.*)

ALLEN: Order in the court! Order in the court! Phew! Clerk! What's that burnin' in here?

CLERK: Mebbe somebody's beard's caught farr, Jedge.

ALLEN: Lord! Smells like they're simmerin' an inner tube.

CLERK: I'll nose around, Jedge, and see if I kin locate the pew.

ALLEN: Give 'er both nostrils, Clerk.

CLERK: I got it, Jedge. It's Lumpkin here.

ALLEN: Phew! Lumpkin Stroud, yer' defilin' the ozone. Quit smokin' that corncob.

LUMPKIN: Okee, Jedge, I'll git off the stem.

ALLEN: Sweatin' swivets! Whatcha perkin' in that pipe, yer social security card er suthin'?

LUMPKIN: Nope. I'm cuttin' my own plug. Got it right here.

ALLEN: Lemme see. Why, this ain't no tobaccy plug.

LUMPKIN: I broke my glasses, Jedge. What is it?

ALLEN: You been smokin' a rubber heel.

LUMPKIN: Wal, no wonder!

ALLEN: You keep inhalin' and ye'll vulcanize yer lungs.

LUMPKIN: I suspected suthin', Jedge. Every time I spit my mouth snaps to like a puncture.

(*Laughter in court. Gavel sounds.*)

ALLEN: Order in the court! Order! Fust case!

CLERK: Phil Page. Speedin'.

ALLEN: Speedin', eh?

CLERK: Defendant's got shoes on, Jedge.

ALLEN: You from outa town, bub?

PAGE: Yes, your honor, I'm from New York.

ALLEN: What's yer business?

PAGE: I'm an efficiency expert. Time's money. Haste makes profits. Let's go!

ALLEN: 'Pears to the court yer' in a hurry.

PAGE: I am.

ALLEN: Okee. Court'll hustle it up. Charge?

PAGE: Speeding.

ALLEN: How fast?

PAGE: Sixty.

ALLEN: Pleadin'?

PAGE: Guilty.

ALLEN: Ten days.

PAGE: Prefer fine.

ALLEN: Twenty-five?

PAGE: Too much.

ALLEN: Fifteen?

PAGE: Okay.

ALLEN: Receipt?

PAGE: Yes.

ALLEN: Here.

PAGE: There.

ALLEN: Thanks.

PAGE: Welcome.

ALLEN: Good-

PAGE: By.

(*Gavel sounds.*)

ALLEN: Next case!

CLERK: Jolo Tate versus Swindle Insurance Company.

RADCLIFFE: I move the case be dismissed, your honor.

ALLEN: Hold on, stranger! Who are you, hornin' in here?

RADCLIFFE: I'm counsel for the insurance company.

ALLEN: Yer' a lawyer?

RADCLIFFE: I'm from Untermyer, Wasservogel, Philpott, and Straus.

ALLEN: Which one are you?

RADCLIFFE: My name's Radcliffe.

ALLEN: I thought ye said——

RADCLIFFE: I did. It's Untermyer, Wasservogel, Philpott, and Straus.

ALLEN: Ye say yer' with 'em?

RADCLIFFE: I'm a member of the firm but there's no room for my name on the door.

ALLEN: You oughta scratch yer name on the knob. What's yer wail, bub?

RADCLIFFE: The plaintiff had an accident policy with the Swindle Insurance Company. He's suing.

ALLEN: Well, why don't the company pay up?

RADCLIFFE: We're willing to settle for one accident. He's trying to collect for five.

ALLEN: Court'll git to the nub of the case. Jolo Tate!

JOLO: Right on tap, Jedge.

ALLEN: You move trial pruceeds?

JOLO: I can't move nuthin', Jedge. I'm in a plaster cast.

ALLEN: Ye claim ye had five accidents, Jolo?

JOLO: I hit the jackpot, Jedge. Now the insurance company's givin' me the "Run along, Cecil."

RADCLIFFE: Untermyer, Wasservogel, Philpott, and Straus maintain that the plaintiff suffered but one accident.

JOLO: I say 'twas five. I oughta know.

(*Ad lib argument. Gavel sounds.*)

ALLEN: Order in the court! Now what happened, Jolo?

JOLO: I'll tell ye, Jedge. I been handy-mannin' on that housin' project.

ALLEN: Over to Elm and Vine?

JOLO: Yep. The day of the accident the boss says to me, "Jolo," he says, "there's a barrel of bricks up on the roof. Fetch 'em down."

ALLEN: Ye done as he bid?

JOLO: Yep. I went up to the roof. Hitched the barrel onto a pully. Come on back to the ground to ease 'er down. Then, Jedge, it started rainin' accidents.

ALLEN: One thing at a time, Jolo.

JOLO: Well, I took holt on the pully rope. I give 'er a tug. The barrel of bricks was heavier than I was, Jedge. Zip! Up I goes!

ALLEN: To the top of the roof?

JOLO: Not direct. Fust I met the barrel of bricks comin' down. Broke my arm. Accident number 1, Jedge.

ALLEN: Ayar.

JOLO: Then I shot up, hit a gable, busted my collarbone. Accident number 2.

ALLEN: Ayar.

JOLO: The barrel hit the bottom and busted, makin' me heavier than the barrel.

ALLEN: Ayar.

JOLO: Zing! Down I come halfway. Zap! It's me and the barrel agin! Fractured my leg.

ALLEN: Accident number 3.

JOLO: Plunk! I plopped on the ground. My hip's outa joint.

ALLEN: Accident number 4.

JOLO: I turns the rope loose. Whap! The barrel zooms down, gits me on the head. My skull's fractured. That's five accidents, Jedge.

ALLEN: 'Cordin' to law, 'tis and 'taint, Jolo. When ye say 'em slow ye got five. But reel 'em off and they group up on ye.

JOLO: There was five, Jedge. Zing! I was up. Zap! It's the barrel. Zam! It's the roof. Zow! It's the barrel agin. Whap! It's the ground. Wham! It's the barrel. That's—oh, my heart!

(*Body falls.*)

ALLEN: Jolo! Jolo!

CLERK: He's dead, Jedge.

ALLEN: Accident number 6.

RADCLIFFE: What's your verdict, Judge?

ALLEN: Wal, it's outa my hands. Plaintiff's taken his case to a higher court.

(*Gavel sounds.*)

ALLEN: Next case!

CLERK: Rubes of Pikes Puddle versus Hector Hatch. The charge is murder, Jedge.

(*Hum of voices. Gavel sounds.*)

ALLEN: Order in the court! Hector Hatch to the bar.

HECTOR: Rarin' to go, Jedge.

ALLEN: Charge here says ye shot to the death one Harry Wadsworth Rondo, described as being' a greetin'-card poet. Guilty er not guilty, Hector?

HECTOR: I ain't sayin' now, Jedge. It'll spoil the trial.

ALLEN: Court's askin' ye a civil question, Hector. Guilty er the other?

HECTOR: All I'm sayin', Jedge, is if I'm guilty I had my reasons.

ALLEN: Court'll worm it out of ye, Hector. Stand down.

(*Gavel sounds.*)

ALLEN: Fust witness. Taswell Snide.

SNIDE: Right here, Jedge.

ALLEN: Whatta ye know about this murder, Tas?

SNIDE: 'Twas jealousy, Jedge. That poet feller stole Hector's girl. Hector here shot him.

HECTOR (*Yells*): If I did I had my reasons!

(*Gavel sounds.*)

ALLEN: Order in the court! Order in the court! Pruceed, Taswell.

SNIDE: Wal, I'm runnin' the New Globe Hotel.

ALLEN: Boardin' house er jest plain flea bag?

SNIDE: I feed 'em and flop 'em at four bits a head. Special rates fer trailer parties.

ALLEN: Pruseed.

SNIDE: Wal, one day last week I'm stalkin' a mouse in the lobby. The deceased walks in brisk like.

ALLEN: Seekin' shelter?

SNIDE: Yep. He wants a room. I run my good eye over him. I kin see he's a poet.

ALLEN: Poet? How'd ye know?

SNIDE: 'Twas his gitup, Jedge. He was wearin' a canary-yellow velvet Inverness, a flowin' red tie, and a green corduroy beret. On his feet he's got red suède wedgies and fer baggage he's carryin' the complete works of Edgar Guest.

ALLEN: The poet register?

SNIDE: Not to fust. He jest stands there dreamin' like. He's mumblin' to hisself. Sounds like greetin'-card poetry.

ALLEN: He's touslin' the muse, eh?

SNIDE: Nope. He's alone, Jedge. He's sayin', "I love yer chin, yer lantern jaw. Happy birthday, Mother-in-law."

ALLEN: Lord! That's sentiment. Sweet's the muzzle on a candy horse.

SNIDE: Yep. I seen he was upper crust, so I give him number 7.

ALLEN: That yer bridal chamber?

SNIDE: Yep. It's got duplex bowls, a pitcher, and a Flit gun under the piller.

ALLEN: Fit fer a king. He take number 7 alone?

SNIDE: Nope. Hector Hatch was already livin' in number 7. I drew a mark down the middle of the bed and this poet feller moved in with Hector.

ALLEN: What started the fuss?

SNIDE: Seems Hector was sparkin' my waitress, Nancy Panks.

ALLEN: Ayar.

SNIDE: This poet feller started tippin' Nancy with rhymes.

ALLEN: What sorta rhymes?

SNIDE: One was, "The coffee is weak. The butter is strong. I'll wait fer my sugar till you come along."

ALLEN: Lord! He was keen!

SNIDE: 'Nuther rhyme he wrote Nancy was, "Yer eyes is like two butterballs. Yer cheeks as red as ham. Yer lips is like a jelly jar. Sister, pass the jam."

ALLEN: Nancy goo-goo him back?

SNIDE: She was beamin' like the seat of a motorman's pants. Hector was gittin' madder by the minute.

ALLEN: Then come the fatal day?

SNIDE: Yep. I was out in the kitchen tryin' to keep the cat from trollin' a lamb stew I had on the fire.

ALLEN: Ayar.

SNIDE: I heard a shot. I run out.

ALLEN: Ayar.

SNIDE: Rondo the poet's dead. Nancy is bawlin'. And Hector's stompin' around with a gun like he's the Lone Ranger.

ALLEN: Ye call the sheriff?

SNIDE: Wal, fust I took a week's room rent from the body. Then I called the law.

ALLEN: That's all ye know, Taswell?

SNIDE: 'Ceptin' in the excitement I think the cat got into that lamb stew.

ALLEN: Ye find fur in yer helpin's?

SNIDE: Nope. But two of my boarders was out in the back yard last night clawin' up dirt.

(*Gavel sounds.*)

ALLEN: Stand down, Taswell.

SNIDE: Okee, Jedge.

ALLEN: Next witness, Nancy Panks!

NANCY: Bereaved but bearin' no malice, Jedge.

ALLEN: You was sweet on the deceased, Nancy?

NANCY: Henry Wadsworth Rondo was six feet two, and every inch a gentleman, Jedge.

ALLEN: Ye gave Hector here the wet mitten fer Henry, eh?

NANCY: Henry won me over, Jedge. Lord! He was perlite's a pallbearer. Every time I'd serve him suthin' at the table Henry'd stop eatin' and tip his hat. He was always leavin' poems around on the napkins and on the walls.

ALLEN: Courtin' couplets?

NANCY: They was touchin', Jedge. One was, "The milk is blue. The salad's fruity. Won't you be—my sweet patootie?"

ALLEN: Longfeller never wrote nuthin' better.

NANCY: Henry was a dreamer, Jedge. He never smiled.

ALLEN: Melancholy, er heavy lips?

NANCY: He had no front teeth, Jedge. Henry said showin' his bare gums was riskay.

ALLEN: Wal, let's git to the crime. See the murder, did ye, Nancy?

NANCY: Yep. Henry and me was elopin'. Hector come runnin' up to the car and started shootin'. Henry slumped over.

ALLEN: Died mumblin' a rhyme, I s'pose.

NANCY: Ayar. His last words was, "I loved and lost. Do I feel stupid. Bein' shot by Hector, 'stead of Cupid." With that he raised his hat, said, "Excuse me," and died.

ALLEN: Court's condolences. Stand down, Nancy.

NANCY: Thank ye, Jedge.

(*Gavel sounds.*)

ALLEN: Hector Hatch to the bar.

HECTOR: Facin' ye, Jedge.

ALLEN: Hector, yer' charged with murder.

HECTOR: I had my reasons, Jedge.

ALLEN: And Court suspicions yer reasons was out-and-out jealousy.

HECTOR: Henry Wadsworth Rondo was a soft-soapin', two-timin', tripe-writin' fakir.

ALLEN: Don't git tart, son.

HECTOR: I was roomin' with the varmint. I oughta know.

ALLEN: Why did ye pop him?

HECTOR: I'll tell ye why. He went too fur with his borrowin'. He was always borrowin'.

ALLEN: Overdone it, eh?

HECTOR: Borrer, borrer, borrer. From sunup to -down.

ALLEN: Sakes amighty!

HECTOR: He borrered my razor. He borrered my tooth-brush. He borrered my union suit. He even borrered my girl.

ALLEN: You didn't say nuthin'?

HECTOR: I held muhself in till the mornin' of the weddin'.

ALLEN: What riled ye then?

HECTOR: Before I went to bed, like always, I slipped my store teeth into the glass of well water by my bed. Next mornin' a noise woke me up. It was my flivver startin' down in front of the hotel.

ALLEN: Ayar.

HECTOR: I run down. The happy couple was in my car fixin' to elope. I says to Henry, "Hold on!" He laughed. That was the last straw, Jedge. I seen red.

ALLEN: Why?

HECTOR: Jedge, I didn't mind Henry drivin' off in my car, wearin' my suit to git married to my girl. But, Jedge, when he laughed in my face with my teeth, I shot 'im.

ALLEN: I see.

HECTOR: Ye can't call me guilty, Jedge.

ALLEN: There was so much of you on Henry you was almost committin' suicide by proxy. Court's rulin' justifiable homicide.

HECTOR: Thank ye, Jedge.

ALLEN: *Sic transit gloria molars.*

HECTOR: Meanin' what, Jedge?

ALLEN: Stealin' another man's bridgework is like goin' to a double-feature movie. Ye may git a free plate but ye've got to suffer fer it.

(*Gavel sounds.*)

ALLEN: Court's adjourned.

FIVE CHARACTERS

X. FIVE CHARACTERS

THE PEOPLE in this concluding section, real and fictional, are Rusty Charley, Walter Mitty, Dorothy Parker, Mr. Juggins, and Joe Gould, alias Professor Sea Gull. They constitute a remarkable gallery and their stories are set down by some of my favorite writers.

Let us begin with Rusty Charley. His biographer, Damon Runyon, has written better short stories from the standpoint of plotting technique. This story, in fact, has little plot, but it is Runyon at his best. I've read almost all of his short stories and Rusty Charley is the character who seems to stick in my memory above all his others.

BLOOD PRESSURE

By Damon Runyon

IT IS MAYBE eleven-thirty of a Wednesday night, and I am standing at the corner of Forty-eighth Street and Seventh Avenue, thinking about my blood pressure, which is a proposition I never before think much about.

In fact, I never hear of my blood pressure before this Wednesday afternoon when I go around to see Doc Brennan about my stomach, and he puts a gag on my arm and tells me that my blood pressure is higher than a cat's back, and the idea is for me to be careful about what I eat, and to avoid excitement, or I may pop off all of a sudden when I am least expecting it.

"A nervous man such as you with a blood pressure away up in the paint cards must live quietly," Doc Brennan says. "Ten bucks, please," he says.

Well, I am standing there thinking it is not going to be so tough to avoid excitement the way things are around this town right now, and wishing I have my ten bucks back to bet it on Sun Beau in the fourth race at Pimlico the next day, when all of a sudden I look up, and who is in front of me but Rusty Charley.

Now if I have any idea Rusty Charley is coming my way, you can go and bet all the coffee in Java I will be somewhere else at once, for Rusty Charley is not a guy I wish to have any truck with whatever. In fact, I wish no part of him. Furthermore, nobody else in this town wishes to have any part of Rusty Charley, for he is a hard guy indeed. In fact, there is no harder guy anywhere in the world. He is a big wide guy with two large hard hands and a great deal of very bad disposition, and he thinks nothing of knocking people down and stepping on their kissers if he feels like it.

In fact, this Rusty Charley is what is called a gorill, because he is known to often carry a gun in his pants pocket, and sometimes to shoot people down as dead as door nails with it if he does not like the way they wear their hats—and Rusty Charley is very critical of hats. The chances are Rusty Charley shoots many a guy in this man's town, and those he does not shoot he sticks with his chiv—which is a knife—and the only reason he is not in jail is because he just gets out of it, and the law does not have time to think up something to put him back in again for.

Anyway, the first thing I know about Rusty Charley being in my neighborhood is when I hear him saying: "Well, well, well, here we are!"

Then he grabs me by the collar, so it is no use of me thinking of taking it on the lam away from there, although I greatly wish to do so.

"Hello, Rusty," I say, very pleasant. "What is the score?"

"Everything is about even," Rusty says. "I am glad to see you, because I am looking for company. I am over in Philadelphia for three days on business."

"I hope and trust that you do all right for yourself in Philly, Rusty," I say; but his news makes me very nervous, because I am a great hand for reading the papers and I have a pretty good idea what Rusty's business in Philly is. It is only the day before that I see a little item from Philly in the papers about how Gloomy Gus Smallwood, who is a very large operator in the alcohol business there, is guzzled right at his front door.

Of course I do not know that Rusty Charley is the party who guzzles Gloomy Gus Smallwood, but Rusty Charley is in Philly when Gus is guzzled, and I can put two and two together as well as anybody. It is the same thing as if there is a bank robbery in Cleveland, Ohio, and Rusty Charley is in Cleveland, Ohio, or near there. So I am very nervous, and I figure it is a sure thing my blood pressure is going up every second.

"How much dough do you have on you?" Rusty says. "I am plumb broke."

"I do not have more than a couple of bobs, Rusty," I say. "I pay a doctor ten bucks today to find out my blood pressure is very bad. But of course you are welcome to what I have."

"Well, a couple of bobs is no good to high-class guys like you and me," Rusty says. "Let us go to Nathan Detroit's crap game and win some money."

Now, of course, I do not wish to go to Nathan Detroit's crap game; and if I do wish to go there I do not wish to go with Rusty Charley, because a guy is sometimes judged by the company he keeps, especially around crap games, and Rusty Charley is apt to be considered bad company. Anyway, I do not have any dough to shoot craps with, and if I do have dough to shoot craps with, I will not shoot craps with it at all, but will bet it on Sun Beau, or maybe take it home and pay off some of the overhead around my joint, such as rent.

Furthermore, I remember what Doc Brennan tells me about avoiding excitement, and I know there is apt to be excitement around Nathan Detroit's crap game if Rusty Charley goes there, and maybe run my blood pressure up and cause me to pop off very unexpected. In fact, I already feel my blood jumping more than somewhat inside me, but naturally I am not going to give Rusty Charley any argument, so we go to Nathan Detroit's crap game.

This crap game is over a garage in Fifty-second Street this particular night, though sometimes it is over a restaurant in Forty-seventh Street, or in back of a cigar store in Forty-fourth Street. In fact, Nathan Detroit's crap game is apt to be anywhere, because it moves around every night, as there is no sense in a crap game staying in one spot until the coppers find out where it is.

So Nathan Detroit moves his crap game from spot to spot, and citizens wishing to do business with him have to ask where he is every night; and of course almost everybody on Broadway knows this, as Nathan Detroit has guys walking up and down, and around and about, telling the public his address, and giving out the password for the evening.

Well, Jack the Beefer is sitting in an automobile outside the garage in Fifty-second Street when Rusty Charley and I come along, and he says "Kansas City," very low, as we pass, this being the password for the evening; but we do not have to use any password whatever when we climb the stairs over the garage, because the minute Solid John, the doorman, peeks out through his peephole when we knock, and sees Rusty Charley with me, he opens up very quick indeed, and gives us a big castor-oil smile, for nobody in this town is keeping doors shut on Rusty Charley very long.

It is a very dirty room over the garage, and full of smoke, and the crap game is on an old pool table; and around the table and packed in so close you cannot get a knitting needle between any two guys with a mawl, are all the high shots in town, for there is plenty of money around at this time, and many citizens are very prosperous. Furthermore, I wish to say there are some very tough guys around the table, too, including guys who will shoot you in the head, or maybe the stomach, and think nothing whatever about the matter.

In fact, when I see such guys as Harry the Horse, from Brooklyn, and Sleepout Sam Levinsky, and Lone Louie, from Harlem, I know this is a bad place for my blood pressure, for these are very tough guys indeed, and are known as such to one and all in this town.

But there they are wedged up against the table with Nick the Greek, Big Nig, Gray John, Okay Okun, and many other high shots, and they all have big coarse G notes in their hands which they are tossing around back and forth as if these G notes are nothing but pieces of waste paper.

On the outside of the mob at the table are a lot of small operators who are trying to cram their fists in between the high shots now and then to get down a bet, and there are also guys present who are called Shylocks, because they will lend you dough when you go broke at the table, on watches, or rings, or maybe cuff links, at very good interest.

Well, as I say, there is no room at the table for as many as one more very thin guy when we walk into the joint, but Rusty Charley lets out a big hello as we enter, and the guys all look around, and the next minute there is space at the table big enough not only for Rusty Charley but for me too. It really is quite magical the way there is suddenly room for us when there is no room whatever for anybody when we come in.

"Who is the gunner?" Rusty Charley asks, looking all around.

"Why, you are, Charley," Big Nig, the stick man in the game, says very quick, handing Charley a pair of dice, although afterward I hear that his pal is right in the middle of a roll trying to make nine when we step up to the table. Everybody is very quiet, just looking at Charley. Nobody pays any attention to me, because I am known to one and all as a guy who is just around, and nobody figures me in on any part of Charley, although Harry the Horse looks at me once in a way that I know is no good for my blood pressure, or for anybody else's blood pressure as far as this goes.

Well, Charley takes the dice and turns to a little guy in a derby hat who is standing next to him scrooching back so Charley will not notice him, and Charley lifts the derby hat off the little guy's head, and rattles the dice in his hand, and chucks them into the hat and goes "Hah!" like crap shooters always do when they are rolling the dice. Then Charley peeks into the hat and says "Ten," although he does not let anybody else look in the hat, not even me, so nobody knows if Charley throws a ten, or what.

But, of course, nobody around is going to up and doubt that Rusty Charley throws a ten, because Charley may figure it is the same thing as calling him a liar, and Charley is such a guy as is apt to hate being called a liar.

Now Nathan Detroit's crap game is what is called a head-and-head game, although some guys call it a fading game, because the guys bet against each other rather than against the bank, or house. It is just the same kind of game as when two guys get together and start shooting craps against each other, and Nathan Detroit does not have to bother with a regular crap table and a layout such as they have in gambling houses. In fact, about all Nathan Detroit has to do with the game is to find a spot, furnish the dice and take his percentage which is by no means bad.

In such a game as this there is no real action until a guy is out on a point, and then the guys around commence to bet he makes this point, or that he does not make this point, and the odds in any country in the world that a guy does not make a ten with a pair of dice before he rolls seven, is two to one.

Well, when Charley says he rolls ten in the derby hat nobody opens their trap, and Charley looks all around the table, and all of a sudden he sees Jew Louie at one end, although Jew Louie seems to be trying to shrink himself up when Charley's eyes light on him.

"I will take the odds for five C's," Charley says, "and Louie, you get it"—meaning he is letting Louie bet him $1000 to $500 that he does not make his ten.

Now Jew Louie is a small operator at all times and more of a Shylock than he is a player, and the only reason he is up there against the table at all at this moment is because he moves up to lend Nick the Greek some dough; and ordinarily there is no more chance of Jew Louie betting a thousand to five hundred on any proposition whatever than there is of him giving his dough to the Salvation Army, which is no chance at all. It is a sure thing he will never think of betting a thousand to five hundred a guy will not make ten with the dice, and when Rusty Charley tells Louie he has such a bet, Louie starts trembling all over.

The others around the table do not say a word, and so Charley rattles the dice again in his duke, blows on them, and chucks them into the derby hat and says "Hah!" But, of course, nobody can see in the derby hat except Charley, and he peeks in at the dice and says "Five." He rattles the dice once more and chucks them into the derby and says "Hah!" and then after peeking into the hat at the dice he says "Eight." I am commencing to sweat for fear he may heave a seven in the hat and blow his bet, and I know Charley has no idea of paying off, no matter what he heaves.

On the next chuck, Charley yells "Money!"—meaning he finally makes his ten, although nobody sees it but him; and he reaches out his hand to Jew Louie, and Jew Louie hands him a big fat G note, very, very slow. In all my life I never see a sadder-looking guy than Louie when he is parting with his dough. If Louie has any idea of asking Charley to let him see the dice in the hat to make sure about the ten, he does not speak about the matter, and as Charley does not seem to wish to show the ten around, nobody else says anything either, probably figuring Rusty Charley is not a guy who is apt to let anybody question his word especially over such a small matter as a ten.

"Well," Charley says, putting Louie's G note in his pocket, "I think this is enough for me tonight," and he hands the derby hat back to the little guy who owns it and motions me to come on, which I am glad to do, as the silence in the joint is making my stomach go up and down inside me, and I know this is bad for my blood pressure. Nobody as much as opens his face from the time we go in until we start out, and you will be surprised how nervous it makes you to be in a big crowd with everybody dead still, especially when you figure it a spot that is liable to get hot any minute. It is only just as we get to the door that anybody speaks, and who is it but Jew Louie, who pipes up and says to Rusty Charley like this:

"Charley," he says, "do you make it the hard way?"

Well, everybody laughs, and we go on out, but I never hear myself whether Charley makes his ten with a six and a four, or with two fives—which is the hard way to make a ten with the dice—although I often wonder about the matter afterward.

I am hoping that I can now get away from Rusty Charley and go on home, because I can see he is the last guy in world to have around a blood pressure, and, furthermore, that people may get the wrong idea of me if I stick around with him, but when I suggest going to Charley, he seems to be hurt.

"Why," Charley says, "you are a fine guy to be talking of quitting a pal just as we are starting out. You will certainly stay with me because I like company, and we will go down to Ikey the Pig's and play stuss. Ikey is an old friend of mine, and I owe him a complimentary play."

Now, of course, I do not wish to go to Ikey the Pig's, because it is a place away downtown, and I do not wish to play stuss, because this is a game which I am never able to figure out myself, and, furthermore, I remember Doc Brennan says I ought to get a little sleep now and then; but I see no use in hurting Charley's feelings, especially as he is apt to do something drastic to me if I do not go.

So he calls a taxi, and we start downtown for Ikey the Pig's, and the jockey who is driving the short goes so fast that it makes my blood pressure go up a foot to a foot and a half from the way I feel inside, although Rusty Charley pays no attention to the speed. Finally I stick my head out the window and ask the jockey to please take it a little easy, as I wish to get where I am going all in one piece, but the guy only keeps busting along.

We are at the corner of Nineteenth and Broadway when all of a sudden Rusty Charley yells at the jockey to pull up a minute, which the guy does. Then Charley steps out of the cab and says to the jockey like this:

"When a customer asks you to take it easy, why do you not be nice and take it easy? Now see what you get."

And Rusty Charley hauls off and clips the jockey a

punch on the chin that knocks the poor guy right off the seat into the street, and then Charley climbs into the seat himself and away we go with Charley driving, leaving the guy stretched out as stiff as a board. Now Rusty Charley once drives a short for a living himself, until the coppers get an idea that he is not always delivering his customers to the right address, especially such as may happen to be drunk when he gets them, and he is a pretty fair driver, but he only looks one way, which is straight ahead.

Personally, I never wish to ride with Charley in a taxicab under any circumstances, especially if he is driving, because he certainly drives very fast. He pulls up a block from Ikey the Pig's, and says we will leave the short there until somebody finds it and turns it in, but just as we are walking away from the short up steps a copper in uniform and claims we cannot park the short in this spot without a driver.

Well, Rusty Charley just naturally hates to have coppers give him any advice, so what does he do but peek up and down the street to see if anybody is looking, and then haul off and clout the copper on the chin, knocking him bowlegged. I wish to say I never see a more accurate puncher than Rusty Charley, because he always connects with that old button. As the copper tumbles, Rusty Charley grabs me by the arm and starts me running up a side street, and after we go about a block we dodge into Ikey the Pig's.

It is what is called a stuss house, and many prominent citizens of the neighborhood are present playing stuss. Nobody seems any too glad to see Rusty Charley, although Ikey the Pig lets on he is tickled half to death. This Ikey the Pig is a short fat-necked guy who will look very natural at New Year's, undressed, and with an apple in his mouth, but it seems he and Rusty Charley are really old-time friends, and think fairly well of each other in spots.

But I can see that Ikey the Pig is not so tickled when he finds Charley is there to gamble, although Charley flashes his G note at once, and says he does not mind losing a little dough to Ikey just for old time's sake. But I judge Ikey the Pig knows he is never going to handle Charley's G note, because Charley puts it back in his pocket and it never comes out again even though Charley gets off loser playing stuss right away.

Well, at five o'clock in the morning, Charley is stuck one hundred and thirty G's, which is plenty of money even when a guy is playing on his muscle, and of course Ikey the Pig knows there is no chance of getting one hundred and thirty cents off of Rusty Charley, let alone that many thousands. Everybody else is gone by this time and Ikey wishes to close up. He is willing to take Charley's marker for a million if necessary to get Charley out, but the trouble is in stuss a guy is entitled to get back a percentage even if he gives a marker, and the percentage will wreck Ikey's joint.

Furthermore, Rusty Charley says he will not quit loser under such circumstances because Ikey is his friend, so what happens Ikey finally sends out and hires a cheater by the name of Dopey Goldberg, who takes to dealing the game and in no time he has Rusty Charley even by cheating in Rusty Charley's favor.

Personally, I do not pay much attention to the play but grab myself a few winks of sleep in a chair in a corner, and the rest seems to help my blood pressure no little. In fact, I am not noticing my blood pressure at all when Rusty Charley and I get out of Ikey the Pig's, because I figure Charley will let me go home and I can go to bed. But although it is six o'clock, and coming on broad daylight when we leave Ikey's, Charley is still full of zing, and nothing will do him but we must go to a joint that is called the Bohemian Club.

Well, this idea starts my blood pressure going again, because the Bohemian Club is nothing but a deadfall where guys and dolls go when there is positively no other place in town open, and it is run by a guy by the name of Knife O'Halloran, who comes from down around Greenwich Village and is considered a very bad character. It is well known to one and all that a guy is apt to lose his life in Knife O'Halloran's any night, even if he does nothing more than drink Knife O'Halloran's liquor.

But Rusty Charley insists on going there, so naturally I go with him; and at first everything is very quiet and peaceful, except that a lot of guys and dolls in evening clothes, who wind up there after being in the night clubs all night, are yelling in one corner of the joint. Rusty Charley and Knife O'Halloran are having a drink together out of a bottle which Knife carries in his pocket, so as not to get it mixed up with the liquor he sells his customers, and are cutting up old touches of the time when they run with the Hudson Dusters together, when all of a sudden in comes four coppers in plain clothes.

Now these coppers are off duty and are meaning no harm to anybody, and are only wishing to have a dram or two before going home, and the chances are they will pay no attention to Rusty Charley if he minds his own business, although of course they know who he is very well indeed and will take great pleasure in putting the old sleeve on him if they only have a few charges against him, which they do not. So they do not give him a tumble. But if there is one thing Rusty Charley hates it is a copper, and he starts eying them from the minute they sit down at a table, and by and by I hear him say to Knife O'Halloran like this:

"Knife," Charley says, "what is the most beautiful sight in the world?"

"I do not know, Charley," Knife says. "What is the most beautiful sight in the world?"

"Four dead coppers in a row," Charley says.

Well, at this I personally ease myself over toward the door, because I never wish to have any trouble with coppers, and especially with four coppers, so I do not see everything that comes off. All I see is Rusty Charley grabbing at the big foot which one of the coppers kicks at him, and then everybody seems to go into a huddle, and the guys and dolls in evening dress start squawking, and my blood pressure goes up to maybe a million.

I get outside the door, but I do not go away at once as anybody with any sense will do, but stand there listening to what is going on inside, which seems to be nothing more than a loud noise like ker-bump, ker-bump, ker-bump. I am not afraid there will be any shooting, because as far as Rusty Charley is concerned he is too smart to shoot any coppers, which is the worst thing a guy can do in this town, and the coppers are not likely to start any blasting because they will not wish it to come out that they are in a joint such as the Bohemian Club off duty. So I figure they will all just take it out in pulling and hauling.

Finally the noise inside dies down, and by and by the door opens and out comes Rusty Charley, dusting himself off here and there with his hands and looking very much pleased, indeed, and through the door before it flies shut again I catch a glimpse of a lot of guys stretched out on the floor. Furthermore, I can still hear guys and dolls hollering.

"Well, well," Rusty Charley says, "I am commencing to think you take the wind on me, and am just about to get mad at you, but here you are. Let us go away from this joint, because they are making so much noise inside you cannot hear yourself think. Let us go to my joint and make my old woman cook us up some breakfast, and then we can catch some sleep. A little ham and eggs will not be bad to take right now."

Well, naturally ham and eggs are appealing to me no little at this time, but I do not care to go to Rusty Charley's joint. As far as I am personally concerned, I have enough of Rusty Charley to do me a long, long time, and I do not care to enter into his home life to any extent whatever, although to tell the truth I am somewhat surprised to learn he has any such life. I believe I do once hear that Rusty Charley marries one of the neighbor's children, and that he lives somewhere over on Tenth Avenue in the Forties, but nobody really knows much about this, and everybody figures if it is true his wife must lead a terrible dog's life.

But while I do not wish to go to Charley's joint I cannot very well refuse a civil invitation to eat ham and eggs, especially as Charley is looking at me in a very much surprised way because I do not seem so glad and I can see that it is not everyone that he invites to his joint. So I thank him, and say there is nothing I will enjoy more than ham and eggs such as his old woman will cook for us, and by and by we are walking along Tenth Avenue up around Forty-fifth Street.

It is still fairly early in the morning, and business guys are opening up their joints for the day, and little children are skipping along the sidewalks going to school and laughing tee-hee, and old dolls are shaking bed clothes and one thing and another out of the windows of the tenement houses, but when they spot Rusty Charley and me everybody becomes very quiet, indeed, and I can see that Charley is greatly respected in his own neighborhood. The business guys hurry into their joints, and the little children stop skipping and tee-heeing and go tip-toeing along, and the old dolls yank in their noodles, and a great quiet comes to the street. In fact, about all you can hear is the heels of Rusty Charley and me hitting on the sidewalk.

There is an ice wagon with a couple of horses hitched to it standing in front of a store, and when he sees the horses Rusty Charley seems to get a big idea. He stops and looks the horses over very carefully, although as far as I can see they are nothing but horses, and big and fat, and sleepy-looking horses, at that. Finally Rusty Charley says to me like this:

"When I am a young guy," he says, "I am a very good puncher with my right hand, and often I hit a horse on the skull with my fist and knock it down. I wonder," he says, "if I lose my punch. The last copper I hit back there gets up twice on me."

Then he steps up to one of the ice-wagon horses and hauls off and biffs it right between the eyes with a right-hand smack that does not travel more than four inches, and down goes old Mister Horse to his knees looking very much surprised, indeed. I see many a hard puncher in my day, including Dempsey when he really can punch, but I never see a harder punch than Rusty Charley gives this horse.

Well, the ice-wagon driver comes bursting out of the store all heated up over what happens to his horse, but he cools out the minute he sees Rusty Charley, and goes on back into the store, leaving the horse still taking a count, while Rusty Charley and I keep walking. Finally we come to the entrance of a tenement house that Rusty Charley says is where he lives, and in front of this house is a wop with a push cart loaded with fruit and vegetables and one thing and another, which Rusty Charley tips over as we go into the house, leaving the wop yelling very loud, and maybe cussing us in wop for all I know. I am very glad, personally, we finally get somewhere, because I can feel that my blood pressure is getting worse every minute I am with Rusty Charley.

We climb two flights of stairs, and then Charley opens a door and we step into a room where there is a pretty little red-headed doll about knee high to a flivver, who looks as if she may just get out of the hay, because her red hair is flying around every which way on her head, and her eyes seems still gummed up with sleep. At first I think she is a very cute sight, indeed, and then I see something in her eyes that tells me this doll, whoever she is, is feeling very hostile to one and all.

"Hello, tootsie," Rusty Charley says. "How about some ham and eggs for me and my pal here? We are all tired out going around and about."

Well, the little red-headed doll just looks at him without saying a word. She is standing in the middle of the floor with one hand behind her, and all of a sudden she brings this hand around, and what does she have in it but a young baseball bat, such as kids play ball with, and which cost maybe two bits; and the next thing I know I hear something go ker-bap, and I can see she smacks Rusty Charley on the side of the noggin with the bat.

Naturally I am greatly horrified at this business, and figure Rusty Charley will kill her at once, and then I will be in a jam for witnessing the murder and will be held in jail several years like all witnesses to anything in this man's town; but Rusty Charley only falls into a big rocking-chair in a corner of the room and sits there with one hand to his head, saying, "Now hold on, tootsie," and "Wait a minute there, honey." I recollect hearing him say, "We have company for breakfast," and then the little red-headed doll turns on me and gives me a look such as I will always remember, although I smile at her very pleasant and mention it is a nice morning.

Finally she says to me like this:

"So you are the trambo who keeps my husband out all night, are you, you trambo?" she says, and with this she starts for me, and I start for the door; and by this time my blood pressure is all out of whack, because I can see that Mrs. Rusty Charley is excited more than somewhat. I get my hand on the knob and just then something hits me alongside the noggin, which I afterward figure must be the baseball bat, although I remember having a sneaking idea the roof caves in on me.

How I get the door open I do not know, because I am very dizzy in the head and my legs are wobbling, but when I think back over the situation I remember going down a lot of steps very fast, and by and by the fresh air strikes me, and I figure I am in the clear. But all of a sudden I feel another strange sensation back of my head and something goes plop against my noggin, and I figure at first that maybe my blood pressure runs up so high that it squirts out the top of my bean. Then I peek around over my shoulder just once to see that Mrs. Rusty Charley is standing beside the wop peddler's cart snatching fruit and vegetables of one kind and another off the cart and chucking them at me.

But what she hits me with back of the head is not an apple, or a peach, or a rutabaga, or a cabbage, or even a casaba melon, but a brickbat that the wop has on his cart to weight down the paper sacks in which he sells his goods. It is this brickbat which makes a lump on the back of my head so big that Doc Brennan thinks it is a tumor when I go to him the next day about my stomach, and I never tell him any different.

"But," Doc Brennan says, when he takes my blood pressure again, "your pressure is down below normal now, and as far as it is concerned you are in no danger whatever. It only goes to show what just a little bit of quiet living will do for a guy," Doc Brennan says. "Ten bucks, please," he says.

☆ ☆ ☆

James thurber's portrait of Walter Mitty has had a vast circulation already. Nonetheless, I'm including it here because I've just got to have Mr. Mitty with me on that desert island.

THE SECRET LIFE OF WALTER MITTY

By James Thurber

"We're going through!" The commander's voice was like thin ice breaking. He wore his full-dress uniform, with the heavily braided white cap pulled down rakishly over one cold gray eye. "We can't make it, sir. It's spoiling for a hurricane, if you ask me." "I'm not asking you, Lieutenant Berg," said the commander. "Throw on the power lights! Rev her up to eighty-five hundred! We're going through!" The pounding of the cylinders increased: ta-pocketa-pocketa-pocketa-*pocketa-pocketa*. The commander stared at the ice forming on the pilot window. He walked over and twisted a row of complicated dials. "Switch on number 8 auxiliary!" he shouted. "Switch on number 8 auxiliary!" repeated Lieutenant Berg. "Full strength in number 3 turret!" shouted the commander. "Full strength in number 3 turret!" The crew, bending to their various tasks in the huge, hurtling eight-engined Navy hydroplane, looked at each other and grinned. "The old man'll get us through," they said to one another. "The old man ain't afraid of hell!"

"Not so fast! You're driving too fast!" said Mrs. Mitty. "What are you driving so fast for?"

"Hmm?" said Walter Mitty. He looked at his wife, in the seat beside him, with shocked astonishment. She seemed grossly unfamiliar, like a strange woman who had yelled at him in a crowd. "You were up to fifty-five," she said. "You know I don't like to go more than forty. You were up to fifty-five." Walter Mitty drove on toward Waterbury in silence, the roaring of the SN-202 through the worst storm in twenty years of Navy flying fading in the remote, intimate airways of his mind. "You're tensed up again," said

Mrs. Mitty. "It's one of your days. I wish you'd let Dr. Renshaw look you over."

Walter Mitty stopped the car in front of the building where his wife went to have her hair done. "Remember to get those overshoes while I'm having my hair done," she said. "I don't need overshoes," said Mitty. She put her mirror back into her bag. "We've been all through that," she said, getting out of the car. "You're not a young man any longer." He raced the engine a little. "Why don't you wear your gloves? Have you lost your gloves?" Walter Mitty reached in a pocket and brought out the gloves. He put them on, but after she had turned and gone into the building and he had driven on to a red light he took them off again. "Pick it up, brother!" snapped a cop as the light changed, and Mitty hastily pulled on his gloves and lurched ahead. He drove around the streets aimlessly for a time, and then he drove past the hospital on his way to the parking lot.

. . . "It's the millionaire banker, Wellington McMillan," said the pretty nurse. "Yes?" said Walter Mitty, removing his gloves slowly. "Who has the case?" "Dr. Renshaw and Dr. Benbow, but there are two specialists here, Dr. Remington, from New York, and Mr. Pritchard-Mitford, from London. He flew over." A door opened down a long, cool corridor and Dr. Renshaw came out. He looked distraught and haggard. "Hello, Mitty," he said. "We're having the devil's own time with McMillan, the millionaire banker and close personal friend of Roosevelt. Obstreosis of the ductal tract. Tertiary. Wish you'd take a look at him." "Glad to," said Mitty.

In the operating room there were whispered introductions: "Dr. Remington, Dr. Mitty. Mr. Pritchard-Mitford, Dr. Mitty." "I've read your book on streptothricosis," said Pritchard-Mitford, shaking hands. "A brilliant performance, sir." "Thank you," said Walter Mitty. "Didn't know you were in the States, Mitty," grumbled Remington. "Coals to Newcastle, bringing Mitford and me up here for a tertiary." "You are very kind," said Mitty. A huge, complicated machine, connected to the operating table, with many tubes and wires, began at this moment to go pocketa-pocketa-

pocketa. "The new anesthetizer is giving way!" shouted an intern. "There is no one in the East who knows how to fix it!" "Quiet, man!" said Mitty in a low, cool voice. He sprang to the machine, which was now going pocketa-pocketa-queep-pocketa-queep. He began fingering delicately a row of glistening dials. "Give me a fountain pen!" he snapped. Someone handed him a fountain pen. He pulled a faulty piston out of the machine and inserted the pen in its place. "That will hold for ten minutes," he said. "Get on with the operation." A nurse hurried over and whispered to Renshaw, and Mitty saw the man turn pale. "Coreopsis has set in," said Renshaw nervously. "If you would take over, Mitty?" Mitty looked at him and at the craven figure of Benbow, who drank, and at the grave, uncertain faces of the two great specialists. "If you wish," he said. They slipped a white gown on him; he adjusted a mask and drew on thin gloves; nurses handed him shining . . .

"Back it up, Mac! Look out for that Buick!" Walter Mitty jammed on the brakes. "Wrong lane, Mac," said the parking-lot attendant, looking at Mitty closely. "Gee. Yeh," muttered Mitty. He began cautiously to back out of the lane marked "Exit Only." "Leave her sit there," said the attendant. "I'll put her away." Mitty got out of the car. "Hey, better leave the key." "Oh," said Mitty, handing the man the ignition key. The attendant vaulted into the car, backed it up with insolent skill, and put it where it belonged.

"They're so damn cocky," thought Walter Mitty, walking along Main Street; "they think they know everything." Once he had tried to take his chains off, outside New Milford, and he had got them wound around the axles. A man had had to come out in a wrecking car and unwind them, a young, grinning garageman. Since then Mrs. Mitty always made him drive to a garage to have the chains taken off. "The next time," he thought, "I'll wear my right arm in a sling; they won't grin at me then. I'll have my right arm in a sling and they'll see I couldn't possibly take the chains off myself." He kicked at the slush on the sidewalk. "Overshoes," he said to himself, and he began looking for a shoe store.

When he came out into the street again, with the overshoes in a box under his arm, Walter Mitty began to wonder what the other thing was his wife had told him to get. She had told him, twice, before they set out from their house for Waterbury. In a way he hated these weekly trips to town—he was always getting something wrong. Kleenex, he thought, Squibb's, razor blades? No. Toothpaste, toothbrush, bicarbonate, carborundum, initiative and referendum? He gave it up. But she would remember it. "Where's the·what's-its-name?" she would ask. "Don't tell me you forgot the what's-its-name." A newsboy went by shouting something about the Waterbury trial.

. . . "Perhaps this will refresh your memory." The district attorney suddenly thrust a heavy automatic at the quiet figure on the witness stand. "Have you ever seen this before?" Walter Mitty took the gun and examined it expertly. "This is my Webley-Vickers 50.80," he said calmly. An excited buzz ran around the courtroom. The judge rapped for order. "You are a crack shot with any sort of firearms, I believe?" said the district attorney insinuatingly. "Objection!" shouted Mitty's attorney. "We have shown that the defendant could not have fired the shot. We have shown that he wore his right arm in a sling on the night of the fourteenth of July." Walter Mitty raised his hand briefly and the bickering attorneys were stilled. "With any known make of gun," he said evenly, "I could have killed Gregory Fitzhurst at three hundred feet *with my left hand.*" Pandemonium broke loose in the courtroom. A woman's scream rose above the bedlam and suddenly a lovely, dark-haired girl was in Walter Mitty's arms. The district attorney struck at her savagely. Without rising from his chair Mitty let the man have it on the point of the chin. "You miserable cur!" . . .

"Puppy biscuit," said Walter Mitty. He stopped walking and the buildings of Waterbury rose up out of the misty courtroom and surrounded him again. A woman who was passing laughed. "He said, 'Puppy biscuit,'" she said to her companion. "That man said, 'Puppy biscuit,' to himself." Walter Mitty hurried on. He went into an A. & P., not the first one he came to but a smaller one farther up the street.

"I want some biscuit for small, young dogs," he said to the clerk. "Any special brand, sir?" The greatest pistol shot in the world thought a moment. "It says 'Puppies Bark for It' on the box," said Walter Mitty.

His wife would be through at the hairdresser's in fifteen minutes, Mitty saw in looking at his watch, unless they had trouble drying it; sometimes they had trouble drying it. She didn't like to get to the hotel first; she would want him to be there waiting for her as usual. He found a big leather chair in the lobby, facing a window, and he put the overshoes and the puppy biscuit on the floor beside it. He picked up an old copy of *Liberty* and sank down into the chair. "Can Germany Conquer the World through the Air?" Walter Mitty looked at the pictures of bombing plans and of ruined streets.

. . . "The cannonading has got to wind up in young Raleigh, sir," said the sergeant. Captain Mitty looked up at him through tousled hair. "Get him to bed," he said wearily. "With the others. I'll fly alone." "But you can't, sir," said the sergeant anxiously. "It takes two men to handle that bomber and the Archies are pounding hell out of the air. Von Richtman's circus is between here and Saulier." "Somebody's got to get that ammunition dump," said Mitty. "I'm going over. Spot of brandy?" He poured a drink for the sergeant and one for himself. War thundered and whined around the dugout and battered at the door. There was a rending of wood, and splinters flew through the room. "A bit of a near thing," said Captain Mitty carelessly. "The box barrage is closing in," said the sergeant. "We only live once, Sergeant," said Mitty with his faint, fleeting smile. "Or do we?" He poured another brandy and tossed it off. "I never see a man could hold his brandy like you, sir," said the sergeant. "Begging your pardon, sir," Captain Mitty stood up and strapped on his huge Webley-Vickers automatic. "It's forty kilometers through hell, sir," said the sergeant. Mitty finished one last brandy. "After all," he said softly, "what isn't?" The pounding of the cannon increased; there was the rat-tat-tatting of machine guns, and from somewhere came the menacing pocketa-pocketa-pocketa of the new flame throwers. Walter Mitty walked to the door of the dugout humming *"Auprès de ma blonde."* He turned and waved to the sergeant. "Cheerio!" he said.

Something struck his shoulder. "I've been looking all over this hotel for you," said Mrs. Mitty. "Why do you have to hide in this old chair? How did you expect me to find you?" "Things close in," said Walter Mitty vaguely. "What?" Mrs. Mitty said. "Did you get the what's-its-name? The puppy biscuit? What's in that box?" "Overshoes," said Mitty. "Couldn't you have put them on in the store?" "I was thinking," said Walter Mitty. "Does it ever occur to you that I am sometimes thinking?" She looked at him. "I'm going to take your temperature when I get you home," she said.

They went out through the revolving doors that made a faintly derisive whistling sound when you pushed them. It was two blocks to the parking lot. At the drugstore on the corner she said, "Wait here for me. I forgot something. I won't be a minute." She was more than a minute. Walter Mitty lighted a cigarette. It began to rain, rain with sleet in it. He stood up against the wall of the drugstore, smoking. . . . He put his shoulders back and his heels together. "To hell with the handkerchief," said Walter Mitty scornfully. He took one last drag on his cigarette and snapped it away. Then, with that faint, fleeting smile playing about his lips, he faced the firing squad; erect and motionless, proud and disdainful, Walter Mitty the Undefeated, inscrutable to the last.

ALEXANDER WOOLLCOTT's sketch of Dorothy Parker remains, I think, the best piece ever written about her. Mr. Woollcott himself confessed in his little forenote that much of the stuff in it is familiar to the reading public. If that fact didn't stop him from writing it I don't see why it should stop me from reprinting it.

OUR MRS. PARKER

By Alexander Woollcott

Portrait of a poet attempted by one who, abashed by the difficulties of the undertaking, breaks down and weakly resorts to a hundred familiar quotations.

When William L. White, son of Emporia's pride, was a verdant freshman ten years ago, he spent the Christmas vacation in New York and was naturally assumed as a public charge by all his father's friends in the newspaper business. He had been at Harvard only a few months, but the pure Kansas of his speech was already seriously affected. He fastidiously avoided anything so simple as a simple declarative.

For example, he would never indulge in the crude directness of saying an actress was an actress. You see, they were going in for that expression at Harvard just then. Nor could he bring himself to ask outright if such and such a building was the Hippodrome. No indeed. Subjunctive to the last, he preferred to ask, "And that, sir, would be the Hippodrome?"

I myself took him to the smartest restaurant of the moment, filled him to the brim with costly groceries, and escorted him to a first night. As we loped up the aisle during the intermission rush for a dash of nicotine I pointed out celebrities in the manner of a barker on a Chinatown bus. Young Bill seemed especially interested in the seamy lineaments of a fellow Harvard man named Robert Benchley, then, as now, functioning on what might be called the lunatic fringe of dramatic criticism. Seated beside him was a little and extraordinarily pretty woman with dark hair, a gentle, apologetic smile, and great reproachful eyes. "And that, I suppose," said the lad from Emporia, "would be Mrs. Benchley." "So I have always understood," I replied crossly, "but it *is* Mrs. Parker."

In the first part of this reply I was in error. At the time I had not been one of their neighbors long enough to realize that, in addition to such formidable obstacles as Mrs. Benchley, Mr. Parker, and the laws of the commonwealth, there was also a lack of romantic content in what was then, and ever since has been, a literary partnership seemingly indissoluble. At least it has had a good run. Mrs. Parker's latest and finest volume of poems carries on the flyleaf the simple dedication: "To Mr. Benchley," and even a dozen years ago these two shared a microscopic office in the crumby old building which still houses the Metropolitan Opera.

There was just about room in it for their two typewriters, their two chairs, and a guest chair. When both were supposed to be at work, merely having the other one there to talk to provided a splendid excuse for not working at all. But when Benchley would be off on some mischief of his own the guest chair became a problem. If it stood empty Mrs. Parker would be alone with her thoughts and—good God!—might actually have to put some of them down on paper. And, as her desperate editors and publishers will tell you, there has been, since O. Henry's last carouse, no American writer so deeply averse to doing some actual writing. That empty guest chair afflicted her because the Parker-Benchley office was then so new a hideaway that not many of their friends had yet found a path to it, and even Mrs. Parker, having conscientiously chosen an obscure cubbyhole so that she might not be disturbed in her wrestling with belles-lettres, was becomingly reluctant to telephone around and suggest that everyone please hurry over and disturb her at once.

However, this irksome solitude did not last long. It was when the sign painter arrived to letter the names of these new tenants on the glass door that she hit upon a device which immediately assured her a steady stream of visitors and gave her the agreeable illusion of presiding over as thronged a salon as even Mme. Recamier knew. She merely bribed the sign painter to leave their names off the door entirely and print there instead the single word "Gentlemen."

Thus pleasantly distracted through the years, Mrs. Parker's published work does not bulk large. But most of it has been pure gold and the five winnowed volumes on her shelf—

three of poetry, two of prose—are so potent a distillation of nectar and wormwood, of ambrosia and deadly nightshade, as might suggest to the rest of us that we all write far too much. Even though I am one who does not profess to be privy to the intentions of posterity, I do suspect that another generation will not share the confusion into which Mrs. Parker's poetry throws so many of her contemporaries, who, seeing that much of it is witty, dismiss it patronizingly as "light" verse, and do not see that some of it is thrilling poetry of a piercing and rueful beauty.

I think it not unlikely that the best of it will be conned a hundred years from now. If so, I can foresee the plight of some undergraduate in those days being maddened by an assignment to write a theme on what manner of woman this dead and gone Dorothy Parker really was.

Was she a real woman at all? He will naturally want to know. And even if summoned from our tombs, we will not be sure how we should answer that question.

Indeed, I do not envy him his assignment and, in a sudden spasm of sympathy for him, herewith submit a few miscellaneous notes, though, mark you, he will rake these yellowing files in vain for any report on her most salient aspects. Being averse to painting the lily, I would scarcely attempt a complete likeness of Mrs. Parker when there is in existence, and open to the public, an incomparable portrait of her done by herself. From the nine matchless stanzas of *The Dark Girl's Rhyme*—one of them runs:

There I was, that came of
Folk of mud and flame—
I that had my name of
Them without a name—

to the mulish lyric which ends thus:

But I, despite expert advice,
Keep doing things I think are nice,
And though to good I never come—
Inseparable my nose and thumb!

her every lyric line is autobiographical.

From the verses in *Enough Rope, Sunset Gun,* and *Death and Taxes,* the toiling student of the year 2033 will be able to gather, unaided by me, that she was, for instance, one who thought often and enthusiastically of death, and one whose most frequently and most intensely felt emotion was the pang of unrequited love. From the verses alone he might even construct, as the paleontologist constructs a dinosaur, a picture of our Mrs. Parker wringing her hands at sundown beside an open grave and looking pensively into the middle distance at the receding figure of some golden lad —perhaps some personable longshoreman—disappearing over the hill with a doxy on his arm.

Our twenty-first-century student may possibly be moved to say of her, deplorably enough, that, like Patience, our Mrs. Parker yearned her living, and he may even be astute enough to guess that the moment the aforesaid golden lad wrecked her favorite pose by showing some sign of interest it would be the turn of the sorrowing lady herself to disappear in the other direction just as fast as she could travel. To this shrewd guess I can only add for his information that it would be characteristic of the sorrowing lady to stoop first by that waiting grave and with her finger trace her own epitaph: "Excuse my dust."

But if I may not here intrude upon the semiprivacy of Mrs. Parker's lyric lamentation, I can at least supply some of the data of her outward life and tell the hypothetical student how she appeared to a neighbor who has often passed the time of day with her across the garden wall and occasionally run into her at parties. Well then, Dorothy Parker (née Rothschild) was born of a Scotch mother and a Jewish father. Her people were New Yorkers, but when she came into the world in August 1893 it was, to their considerable surprise and annoyance, a trifle ahead of schedule. It happened while they were staying at West End, which lies on the Jersey shore a pebble's throw from Long Branch, and it was the last time in her life when she wasn't late.

Her mother died when she was still a baby. On the general theory that it was a good school for manners, she was sent in time to a convent in New York, from which she was eventually packed off home by an indignant mother superior who took umbrage when her seemingly meek charge, in writing an essay on the miracle of the Immaculate Conception, referred to that sacred mystery as spontaneous combustion. When, at her father's death a few years later, she found herself penniless, she tried her hand at occasional verse, and both hands at playing the piano for a dancing school.

Then she got a job writing captions on a fashion magazine. She would write "Brevity Is the Soul of Lingerie" and things like that for ten dollars a week. As her room and breakfast cost eight dollars, that left an inconsiderable margin for the other meals, to say nothing of manicures, dentistry, gloves, furs, and traveling expenses. But just before hers could turn into an indignant O. Henry story, with General Kitchener's grieving picture turned to the wall and a porcine seducer waiting in the hall below, that old marplot, her employer, doubled her salary. In 1918 she was married to the late Edwin Parker, a Connecticut boy she had known all her life. She became Mrs. Parker a week before his division sailed for France. There were no children born of this marriage.

Shortly after the armistice the waiting bride was made dramatic critic of *Vanity Fair,* from which post she was forcibly removed upon the bitter complaints of sundry wounded people of the theater, of whose shrieks, if memory serves, Billie Burke's were the most penetrating. In protest against her suppression, and perhaps in dismay at the prospect of losing her company, her coworkers, Robert E. Sherwood and Robert Benchley, quit *Vanity Fair* at the same time in what is technically known as a body, the former to become editor of *Life,* and the latter its dramatic critic.

Since then Mrs. Parker has gone back to the aisle seats only when Mr. Benchley was out of town and someone was needed to substitute for him. It would be her idea of her duty to catch up the torch as it fell from his hand—and burn someone with it. I shall never forget the expression on the face of the manager who, having recklessly produced a play of Channing Pollock's called *The House Beautiful,* turned hopefully to Benchley's next feuilleton, rather counting on a kindly and even quotable tribute from that amiable creature. But it seems Benchley was away that week, and it was little Mrs. Parker who had covered the opening. I would not care to say what she had covered it with. The trick was done in a single sentence. "*The House Beautiful,*" she had said with simple dignity, "is the play lousy."

And more recently she achieved an equal compression in reporting on *The Lake*. Miss Hepburn, it seems, had run the whole gamut from A to B.

But for the most part Mrs. Parker writes only when she feels like it or rather, when she cannot think up a reason not to. Thus once I found her in hospital typing away lugubriously. She had given her address as Bedpan Alley, and represented herself as writing her way out. There was the hospital bill to pay before she dared to get well, and downtown an unpaid hotel bill was malignantly lying in wait for her. Indeed, at the preceding Yuletide, while the rest of us were all hanging up our stockings, she had contented herself with hanging up the hotel.

Tiptoeing now down the hospital corridor, I found her hard at work. Because of posterity and her creditors, I was loath to intrude, but she, being entranced at any interruption, greeted me from her cot of pain, waved me to a chair, offered me a cigarette, and rang a bell. I wondered if this could possibly be for drinks. "No," she said sadly, "it is supposed to fetch the night nurse, so I ring it whenever I want an hour of uninterrupted privacy."

Thus, by the pinch of want, are extracted from her the poems, the stories, and criticisms which have delighted everyone except those about whom they were written. There was, at one time, much talk of a novel to be called, I think, *The Events Leading Up to the Tragedy,* and indeed her publisher, having made a visit of investigation to the villa where she was staying at Antibes, reported happily that she had a great stack of manuscript already finished. He did say she was shy about letting him see it. This was because that stack of alleged manuscript consisted largely of undestroyed carbons of old articles of hers, padded out with letters from her many friends.

Then she once wrote a play with Elmer Rice. It was called *Close Harmony,* and thanks to a number of circumstances over most of which she had no control, it ran only four weeks. On the fourth Wednesday she wired Benchley:

CLOSE HARMONY DID A COOL NINETY DOLLARS AT THE MATINEE STOP ASK THE BOYS IN THE BACK ROOM WHAT THEY WILL HAVE.

The outward social manner of Dorothy Parker is one calculated to confuse the unwary and unnerve even those most addicted to the incomparable boon of her company. You see, she is so odd a blend of Little Nell and Lady Macbeth. It is not so much the familiar phenomenon of a hand of steel in a velvet glove as a lacy sleeve with a bottle of vitriol concealed in its folds. She has the gentlest, most disarming demeanor of anyone I know. Don't you remember sweet Alice, Ben Bolt? Sweet Alice wept with delight, as I recall, when you gave her a smile, and if memory serves, trembled with fear at your frown. Well, compared with Dorothy Parker, sweet Alice was a roughshod bully, trampling down all opposition. But Mrs. Parker carries—as everyone is uneasily aware—a dirk which knows no brother and mighty few sisters. "I was so terribly glad to see you," she murmurs to a departing guest. "Do let me call you up sometime, won't you, please?" And adds, when this dear chum is out of hearing, "That woman speaks eighteen languages, and can't say no in any of them." Then I remember her comment on one friend who had lamed herself while in London. It was Mrs. Parker who voiced the suspicion that this poor lady had injured herself while sliding down a barrister. And there was that wholesale libel on a Yale prom. If all the girls attending it were laid end to end, Mrs. Parker said, she wouldn't be at all surprised.

Mostly, as I now recall these cases of simple assault, they have been muttered out of the corner of her mouth while to the onlooker out of hearing she seemed all smiles and loving-kindness. For as she herself has said (when not quite up to par), a girl's best friend is her mutter. Thus I remember one dreadful week end we spent at Nellie's country home. Mrs. Parker radiated throughout the visit an impression of humble gratitude at the privilege of having been asked. The other guests were all of the kind who wear soiled batik and bathe infrequently, if ever. I could not help wondering how Nellie managed to round them up, and where they might be found at other times. Mrs. Parker looked at them pensively. "I think," she whispered, "that they crawl back into the woodwork."

Next morning we inspected nervously the somewhat inadequate facilities for washing. These consisted of a single chipped basin internally decorated with long-accumulated evidences of previous use. It stood on a bench on the back porch with something that had apparently been designed as a toothbrush hanging on a nail above it. "In God's name," I cried, "what do you suppose Nellie does with that?" Mrs. Parker studied it with mingled curiosity and distaste, and said: "I think she rides on it on Halloween."

It will be noted, I am afraid, that Mrs. Parker specializes in what is known as the dirty crack. If it seems so, it may well be because disparagement is easiest to remember, and the fault therefore, if fault there be, lies in those of us who —and who does not?—repeat her sayings. But it is quite true that in her writing—at least in her prose pieces—her most effective vein is the vein of dispraise. Her best word portraits are dervish dances of sheer hate, equivalent in the satisfaction they give her to the waxen images which people in olden days fashioned of their enemies in order, with exquisite pleasure, to stick pins into them. Indeed, disparagement to Mrs. Parker is so habitual that she has no technique for praise and, when she feels admiration, can find no words for it.

Thus when she fain would burn incense to her gods—Ernest Hemingway and D. H. Lawrence—she cannot make herself heard at all, and becomes as gauche as an adoring shopgirl in the presence of Clark Gable. But just let her get a shot at a good, easy target like A. A. Milne, and the whole town listens. Including, of course, the time when, as Constant Reader in the *New Yorker,* she was so overcome by Mr. Milne's elfin whimsicality that "Tonstant Weader fwowed up."

It should be added that that inveterate dislike of her fellow creatures which characterizes so many of Mrs. Parker's utterances is confined to the human race. All the other animals have her enthusiastic support. It is only fair to her eventual biographer to tip him off that there is also a strong tinge of autobiography in that sketch of hers about a lady growing tearful in a speakeasy because her elevator man would be stuffy if she should pick up a stray horse and try to bring him to her apartment.

While she has never quite managed this, any home of hers always has the aspects and aroma of a menagerie. Invariably there is a dog. There was Amy, an enchanting, woolly, four-legged coquette whose potential charm only Dorothy Parker would have recognized at first meeting. For at that first meeting Amy was covered with dirt and a hulking truckman was kicking her out of his way. This swinish biped was somewhat taken aback to have a small and infuriated poetess rush at him from the sidewalk and kick him smartly in the shins—so taken aback that he could only stare openmouthed while she caught the frightened dog up in her arms, hailed a taxi, and took her up to Neysa McMein's studio to wash her in the bathtub. There Amy regained her trust in the human race, achieved a fearful air of harlotry by eating all the rose-madder paint, of which a good deal lingered to incarnadine her face, and eventually won her way to a loving home on Long Island.

Then there was a Scottie named Alexander Woollcott Parker who reversed the customary behavior of a namesake by christening me—three times, as I recall—in a single automobile ride. More recently there has been Robinson, a soft-hearted and languishing dachshund who was chewed up by a larger dog. The brute's owner said that Robinson had started it. Mrs. Parker turned on him with great bitterness. "I have no doubt," she said, "that he was also carrying a revolver." Robinson's successor is a blue Bedlington named John. Woodrow Wilson was, I think, the name of the dog at the end of her leash when I first knew her. This poor creature had a distressing malady. Mrs. Parker issued bulletins about his health—confidential bulletins, tinged with skepticism. He said he got it from a lamppost.

Of her birds, I remember only an untidy canary whom she named Onan for reasons which will not escape those who know their Scriptures. And then there were the two alligators which she found in her taxi, where someone had been shrewd enough to abandon them. Mrs. Parker brought them home and thoughtfully lodged them in the bathtub. When she returned to her flat that night she found that her dusky handmaiden had quit, leaving a note on the table which read as follows: "I will not be back. I cannot work in a house where there are alligators. I would have told you this before, but I didn't suppose the question would ever come up."

Well, I had thought here to attempt, if not a portrait, then at least a dirty thumbnail sketch, but I find I have done little more than run around in circles quoting Mrs. Parker. I know a good many circles where, by doing just that, one can gain quite a reputation as a wit. One can? Several can. Indeed, several I know do.

But I have not yet told here my favorite of all the Dorothy Parker stories. It was about the belated baby girl who, as the daughter of a successful playwright, is now an uppity miss at a fancy school. It seemed to those of us on Broadway that she was forever being born. For months the whole town had been kept uneasily aware of her approach. For months the little mother had filled the public eye with a kind of aggressive fragility. Until at last she would pointedly rise at first nights and conspicuously leave the theater whenever the play became too intense for one in her sedulously delicate condition.

Long after Marc Connelly, in behalf of an exhausted neighborhood, had taken the expectant mother aside and gravely advised her to drop the whole project, we were still waiting for the news from that spotlight confinement. At last it came and the telegrams of relief and congratulations poured in from every direction.

GOOD WORK, MARY [our Mrs. Parker wired collect]. WE ALL KNEW YOU HAD IT IN YOU.

THE MR. JUGGINS of the following piece by Stephen Leacock may be a characterization based on a real person. I'd almost believe that Mr. Leacock was talking about Dr. Rockwell. The behavior of Mr. Juggins in the second paragraph of the story certainly suggests Doc.

THE RETROACTIVE EXISTENCE OF MR. JUGGINS

By Stephen Leacock

I FIRST MET Juggins—really to notice him—years and years ago as a boy out camping. Somebody was trying to nail up a board on a tree for a shelf and Juggins interfered to help him.

"Stop a minute," he said, "you need to saw the end of that board off before you put it up." Then Juggins looked around for a saw, and when he got it he had hardly made more than a stroke or two with it before he stopped. "This saw," he said, "needs to be filed up a bit." So he went and hunted up a file to sharpen the saw, but found that before he could use the file he needed to put a proper handle on it, and to make a handle he went to look for a sapling in the bush, but to cut the sapling he found that he needed to sharpen up the ax. To do this, of course, he had to fix the grindstone so as to make it run properly. This involved making wooden legs for the grindstone. To do this decently Juggins decided to make a carpenter's bench. This was quite impossible without a better set of tools. Juggins went to the village to get the tools required, and, of course, he never came back.

He was rediscovered—weeks later—in the city, getting prices on wholesale tool machinery.

After that first episode I got to know Juggins very well. For some time we were students at college together. But Juggins somehow never got far with his studies. He always began with great enthusiasm and then something happened. For a time he studied French with tremendous eagerness. But he soon found that for a real knowledge of French you need first to get a thorough grasp of Old French and Porvençal. But it proved impossible to do anything with these without an absolutely complete command of Latin. This Juggins discovered could only be obtained, in any thorough way, through Sanskrit, which of course lies at the base of it. So Juggins devoted himself to Sanskrit until he realized that for a proper understanding of Sanskrit one needs to study the ancient Iranian, the root language underneath. This language, however, is lost.

So Juggins had to begin over again. He did, it is true, make some progress in natural science. He studied physics and rushed rapidly backward from forces to molecules, and from molecules to atoms, and from atoms to electrons, and then his whole studies exploded backward into the infinities of space, still searching a first cause.

Juggins, of course, never took a degree, so he made no practical use of his education. But it didn't matter. He was very well off and was able to go straight into business with a capital of about a hundred thousand dollars. He put it at first into a gas plant, but found that he lost money at that because of the high price of the coal needed to make gas. So he sold out for ninety thousand dollars and went into coal mining. This was unsuccessful because of the awful cost of mining machinery. So Juggins sold his share in the mine for eighty thousand dollars and went in for manufacturing mining machinery. At this he would undoubtedly have made money but for the enormous cost of gas needed as motive power for the plant. Juggins sold out of the manufacture for seventy thousand, and after that he went whirling in a circle, like skating backward, through the different branches of allied industry.

He lost a certain amount of money each year, especially in good years when trade was brisk. In dull times when everything was unsalable he did fairly well.

Juggins' domestic life was very quiet.

Of course he never married. He did, it is true, fall in love several times; but each time it ended without result. I remember well his first love story, for I was very intimate with him at the time. He had fallen in love with the girl in question utterly and immediately. It was literally love at first sight. There was no doubt of his intentions. As soon as he had met her he was quite frank about it. "I intend," he said, "to ask her to be my wife."

"When?" I asked. "Right away?"

"No," he said, "I want first to fit myself to be worthy of her."

So he went into moral training to fit himself. He taught in a Sunday school for six weeks, till he realized that a man has no business in divine work of that sort without first preparing himself by serious study of the history of Palestine. And he felt that a man was a cad to force his society on a girl while he is still only half acquainted with the history of the Israelites. So Juggins stayed away. It was nearly two years before he was fit to propose. By the time he *was* fit the girl had already married a brainless thing in patent-leather boots who didn't even know who Moses was.

Of course Juggins fell in love again. People always do. And at any rate by this time he was in a state of moral fitness that made it imperative.

So he fell in love—deeply in love this time—with a charming girl, commonly known as the eldest Miss Thorneycroft. She was only called eldest because she had five younger sisters; and she was very poor and awfully clever and trimmed all her own hats. Any man, if he's worth the name, falls in love with that sort of thing at first sight. So, of course, Juggins would have proposed to her; only when he went to the house he met her next sister: and of course she was younger still; and, I suppose, poorer: and made not only her own hats but her own blouses. So Juggins fell in love with her. But one night when he went to call the door was opened by the sister younger still, who not only made her own blouses and trimmed her own hats but even made her own tailor-made suits. After that Juggins backed up from sister to sister till he went through the whole family, and in the end got none of them.

Perhaps it was just as well that Juggins never married. It would have made things very difficult because, of course, he got poorer all the time. You see, after he sold out his last share in his last business he bought with it a diminishing life annuity, so planned that he always got rather less next year than this year, and still less the year after. Thus, if he lived long enough, he would starve to death.

Meantime he has become a quaint-looking elderly man, with coats a little too short and trousers a little above his boots–like a boy. His face is like that of a boy, with wrinkles.

And his talk now has grown to be always reminiscent. He is perpetually telling long stories of amusing times that he has had with different people that he names.

He says for example:

"I remember a rather queer thing that happened to me in a train one day——"

And if you say, "When was that, Juggins?" he looks at you in a vague way as if calculating and says, "In 1875, or 1876, I think, as near as I recall it——"

I notice, too, that his reminiscences are going further and further back. He used to base his stories on his recollections as a young man; now they are further back.

The other day he told me a story about himself and two people that he called the Harper brothers–Ned and Joe. Ned, he said, was a tremendously powerful fellow.

I asked how old Ned was and Juggins said he was three. He added that there was another brother not so old, but a very clever fellow about–here Juggins paused and calculated–about eighteen months.

So then I realized where Juggins' retroactive existence is carrying him to. He has passed back through childhood into infancy, and presently, just as his annuity runs to a point and vanishes, he will back up clear through the Curtain of

Existence and die—or be born, I don't know which to call it.

Meantime he remains to me as one of the most illuminating allegories I have met.

THE LAST TURN belongs to Joseph Mitchell. I believe that a book, any book, should have a strong ending and that's why Mr. Mitchell is bringing up the rear. I could have chosen any one of a dozen of his pieces and it took me a long time to make up my mind. This one, I think, is as good as anything else he ever wrote, maybe better.

Mr. Mitchell is an old friend of mine and we once worked together as newspapermen. Not so long ago he turned up unheralded at my house. I hadn't seen him in a long time and I asked him what he was working on at the moment.

"Nothing," said Joe. "I'm through with this writing dodge. This is no trade for me to be in. I'm a carpenter by trade and I'm going back to it. No more of this writing dodge for me. I got no business in it."

He was just having one of his morose moments because he didn't return to carpentry, except with words. For which, hoo-ray!

PROFESSOR SEA GULL

By Joseph Mitchell

JOE GOULD is a blithe and emaciated little man who has been a notable in the cafeterias, diners, barrooms, and dumps of Greenwich Village for a quarter of a century. He sometimes brags rather wryly that he is the last of the bohemians: "All the others fell by the wayside," he says. "Some are in the grave, some are in the loony bin, and some are in the advertising business." Gould's life is by no means carefree; he is constantly tormented by what he calls "the three H's" —homelessness, hunger, and hangovers. He sleeps on benches in subway stations, on the floor in the studios of friends, and in quarter-a-night flophouses on the Bowery. Once in a while he trudges up to one of Father Divine's extension heavens in lower Harlem and gets a night's lodging for fifteen cents. He is five feet four and he hardly ever weighs more than ninety-five pounds. Not long ago he told a friend that he hadn't eaten a square meal since June 1936, when he bummed up to Cambridge and attended a banquet during a reunion of the Harvard class of 1911, of which he is a member. "I'm the foremost authority in the United States on the subject of doing without," he says. He tells people that he lives on "air, self-esteem, cigarette butts, cowboy coffee, fried-egg sandwiches, and ketchup." Cowboy coffee is black coffee without sugar. After finishing a sandwich Gould customarily empties a bottle or two of ketchup on his plate and eats it with a spoon. The counterman in the Jefferson Diner, on Village Square, which is one of his hangouts, gather up the ketchup bottles and hide them the moment he puts his head in the door. "I don't particularly like the confounded stuff," he says, "but I make it a practice to eat all I can get. It's the only grub I know of that's free of charge."

Gould is a Yankee. His branch of the Goulds has been in New England since 1635, and he is related to the Lowell, Lawrence, Storer, and Vroom families. "There's nothing accidental about me," he once said. "I'll tell you what it took to make me what I am today. It took old Yankee blood, an overwhelming aversion to possessions, four years of Harvard, and twenty-five years of beating the living hell out of my insides with bad hooch and bad food." He says that he is out of joint with the rest of the human race because he doesn't want to own anything. "If Mr. Chrysler tried to make me a present of the Chrysler Building," he says, "I'd damn near break my neck fleeing from him. I wouldn't own it; it'd own me. Back home in Massachusetts I'd be called an old Yankee crank. Here I'm called a bohemian. It's six of one, half a dozen of the other." Gould has a twangy voice and a Harvard accent. Bartenders and countermen in the Village refer to him as the Professor, Professor Bloomingdale, Professor Sea Gull, or the Mongoose. He dresses in the castoff clothes of his friends. His overcoat, suit, shirt, and even his shoes are all invariably two or three sizes too large, but he wears them with a forlorn, Chaplinlike rakishness. "Just look at me," he says. "The only thing that fits is the necktie." On bitter winter days he puts a layer of newspapers between his shirt and undershirt. "I'm snobbish," he says. "I only use the *Times*." He is fond of unusual headgear—a toboggan, a beret, or a yachting cap. One summer evening he appeared at a party in a seersucker suit, a polo shirt, a scarlet cummerbund, sandals, and a yachting cap, all hand-me-downs. He uses a long ivory cigarette holder, and a good deal of the time he smokes butts picked up off the sidewalks.

Bohemianism has aged Gould considerably beyond his years. He has got in the habit lately of asking people he has just met to guess his age. Their guesses range between sixty-five and seventy-five; he is fifty-three. He is never hurt by this; he looks upon it as proof of his superiority. "I get more living done in one year," he says, "than ordinary humans do in ten." Gould is toothless, and his lower jaw swivels from side to side when he talks. He is bald on top, but the hair at the back of his head is long and frizzly, and he has a bushy, cinnamon-colored beard, which he says he trims every other Easter. He has a squint, and while reading he wears a pair of spectacles which slip down to the end of his nose a moment after he puts them on. He doesn't use spectacles on the street and without them he has the wild, unfocused stare of an old scholar who has strained his eyes on small print. Even in the Village many people turn and look at him. He is stooped and he moves rapidly, grumbling to himself, with his head thrust forward and held to one side. Under his left arm he usually totes a bulging, greasy, brown pasteboard portfolio, and he swings his right arm aggressively. As he hurries along he seems to be warding off an imaginary enemy. Don Freeman, the artist, a friend of his, once made a sketch of him walking. Freeman called the sketch "Joe Gould versus the Elements." Gould is as restless and footloose as an alley cat, and he takes long hikes about the city, now and then disappearing from the Village for weeks at a time and mystifying his friends; they have never been able to figure out where he goes. When he returns, always looking pleased with himself, he makes a few cryptic remarks, giggles, and then shuts up. "I went on a bird walk along the water front with an old countess," he said after his most recent absence. "The countess and I spent three weeks studying sea gulls."

Gould is almost never seen without his portfolio. He sits on it while he eats and he sleeps with it under his head. It usually contains a mass of manuscripts and notes, a dictionary, a bottle of ink, his extra shirts and socks, and a paper bag of hard, round, dime-store candy of the type called sour balls. "I fight fatigue with sour balls," he says. The crumbs are for pigeons; like many other eccentrics, Gould is a pigeon feeder. He is devoted to a flock which makes its headquarters atop and around the statue of Garibaldi in Washington Square. These pigeons know him. When he comes up and takes a seat on the plinth of the statue they flutter down and perch on his head and shoulders, waiting for him to bring out his bag of crumbs. He has given names to some of them. "Come here, Boss Tweed," he says. "A lady in Stewart's didn't finish her whole-wheat toast this morning and when she went out, bingo, I snatched it off her plate especially for you. Hello, Big Bosom. Hello, Popgut. Hello, Lady Astor. Hello, St. John the Baptist. Hello, Polly Adler. Hello, Fiorello, you old goat, how're you today?"

Although Gould strives to give the impression that he is a philosophical loafer, he has done an immense amount of work during his career as a bohemian. Every day, even when he is groggy as the result of hunger, he spends at least a couple of hours laboring on a formless, rather mysterious book which he calls *An Oral History of Our Time.* He began this book twenty-six years ago, and it is nowhere near finished. His preoccupation with it seems to be principally responsible for the way he lives; a steady job of any kind, he says, would interfere with his thinking. Depending on the weather, he writes in parks, in doorways, in flophouse lobbies, in cafeterias, on benches on el platforms, in subway trains, and in public libraries. When he is in the proper mood he writes until he is exhausted, and he gets into the mood at peculiar times. He says that one night he sat for seven hours in a booth in a Third Avenue bar and grill, listening to a beery old Hungarian woman, once a madam and once a dealer in cocaine and now a soup cook in a hospital, tell the story of her life. Three days later, around four o'clock in the morning, on a cot in the Hotel Defender, at 300 Bowery, he was awakened by the foghorns of tugs on the East River and was unable to go back to sleep because he felt that he was in the exact mood to put the old soup cook's biography in his history. He has an abnormal memory; if he is sufficiently impressed by a conversation he can keep it in his head, even if it is lengthy and senseless, for many days, much of it word for word. He had a bad cold, but he got up, dressed under a red exit light, and, tiptoeing so as not to disturb the men sleeping on cots all around him, went downstairs to the lobby.

He wrote in the lobby from 4:15 A.M. until noon. Then he left the Defender, drank some coffee in a Bowery diner, and walked up to the Public Library. He plugged away at a table in the genealogy room, which is one of his rainy-day hangouts and which he says he prefers to the main reading room because it is gloomier, until it closed at 6 P.M. Then he moved into the main reading room and stayed there, seldom taking his eyes off his work, until the library locked up for the night at 10 P.M. He ate a couple of egg sandwiches and a quantity of ketchup in a Times Square cafeteria. Then, not having two bits for a flophouse and being too engrossed to go to the Village and seek shelter, he hurried into the West Side subway and rode the balance of the night, scribbling ceaselessly while the train he was aboard made three round trips between the New Lots Avenue station in Brooklyn and the Van Cortlandt Park station in the Bronx. He kept his portfolio on his lap and used it as a desk. He has the endurance of the possessed. Whenever he got too sleepy to concentrate he shook his head vigorously and then brought out his bag of sour balls and popped one in his mouth. People stared at him, and once he was interrupted by a drunk who asked him what in the name of God he was writing. Gould knows how to get rid of inquisitive drunks. He pointed at his left ear and said, "What? What's that? Deaf as a post. Can't hear a word." The drunk lost all interest in him. "Day was breaking when I left the subway," Gould says. "I was sneezing my head off, my eyes were sore, my knees were shaky, I was hungry as a bitch wolf, and I had exactly eight cents to my name. I didn't care. My history was longer by eleven thousand brand-new words, and at that moment I bet there wasn't a chairman of the board in all New York as happy as I."

Gould is haunted by the fear that he will die before he has the first draft of the *Oral History* finished. It is already eleven times as long as the Bible. He estimates that the manuscript contains nine million words, all in longhand. It may well be the lengthiest unpublished work in existence. Gould does his writing in nickel composition books, the kind that children use in school, and the *Oral History* and the notes he has made for it fill two hundred and seventy of them, all of which are tattered and grimy and stained with coffee, grease, and beer. Using a fountain pen, he covers both sides of each page, leaving no margins anywhere, and his penmanship is poor; hundreds of thousands of words are legible only to him. He has never been able to interest a publisher in the *Oral History*. At one time or another he has lugged armfuls of it into fourteen publishing offices. "Half of them said it was obscene and outrageous and to get it out of there as quick as I could," he says, "and the others said they couldn't read my handwriting." Experiences of this nature do not dismay Gould; he keeps telling himself that it is posterity he is writing for, anyway. In his breast pocket, sealed in a dingy envelope, he always carries a will bequeathing two thirds of the manuscript to the Harvard Library and the other third to the Smithsonian Institution. "A couple of generations after I'm dead and gone," he likes to say, "the Ph.D.s will start lousing through my work. Just imagine their surprise. 'Why I be damned,' they'll say, 'this fellow was the most brilliant historian of the century.' They'll give me my due. I don't claim that all of the *Oral History* is first-class, but some of it will live as long as the English language." Gould used to keep his composition books in a dusty pile on the floor of a closet in a friend's photography studio in the Village. Whenever he filled a book he would come in and toss it on the pile. In the winter of 1942, after hearing that the Metropolitan Museum had moved its most valuable paintings to a bomb-proof storage place somewhere inland, he became panicky. He made a huge, oilcloth-covered bale of the *Oral History* and entrusted it for the duration to a woman he knows who owns a duck and chicken farm near Huntington, Long Island. The farmhouse has a stone cellar.

Gould puts into the *Oral History* only things he has seen or heard. At least half of it is made up of conversations taken down verbatim or summarized; hence the title. "What people say is history," Gould says. "What we used to think was history—all that chittychat about Caesar, Napoleon, treaties, inventions, big battles—is only formal history and largely false. I'll put down the informal history of the shirt-sleeved multitude—what they had to say about their jobs, love affairs, victuals, sprees, scrapes, and sorrows—or I'll perish in the attempt." The *Oral History* is a great hodge-podge and kitchen midden of hearsay, the fruit, according to Gould's estimate, of more than twenty thousand conversations. In it are the hopelessly incoherent biographies of hundreds of bums, accounts of the wanderings of seamen encountered in South Street barrooms, grisly descriptions of hospital and clinic experiences ("Did you ever have a painful operation or disease?" is one of the first questions that Gould, fountain pen and composition book in hand, asks a person he has just met), summaries of innumerable Union Square and Columbus Circle harangues, testimonies given by converts at Salvation Army street meetings, and the addled opinions of scores of park-bench oracles and gin-mill savants. For a time Gould haunted the all-night greasy spoons in the vicinity of Bellevue Hospital, eavesdropping on tired interns, nurses, ambulance drivers, scrub women, embalming-school students, and morgue workers, and faithfully recording their talk. He scurries up and down Fifth Avenue during parades, feverishly taking notes.

Gould writes with great candor, and the percentage of obscenity in the *Oral History* is high. He has a chapter called "Examples of the So-Called Dirty Story of Our Time," to which he makes almost daily additions. In another chapter are many rhymes and observations which he found scribbled on the walls of subway washrooms. He believes that these graffiti are as truly historical as the strategy of General Robert E. Lee. Hundreds of thousands of words are devoted to the drunken behavior and the sexual adventures of various professional Greenwich Villagers in the twenties. There are hundreds of reports of ginny Village parties, including gossip about the guests and faithful reports of their arguments on such subjects as reincarnation, birth control, free love, psychoanalysis, Christian Science, Swedenborgianism, vegetarianism, alcoholism, and different political and art isms. "I have fully covered what might be termed the intellectual underworld of my time," Gould says. There are detailed descriptions of night life in the Village speakeasies, basement cabarets, and eating places which he frequented at one time or another and which are all now out of existence, such as the Little Quakeress, the Original Julius, Hubert's Cafeteria, the Troubadour Tavern, Alice McCollister's, and Eli Greifer's Last Outpost of Bohemia Tea Shoppe.

He is a night wanderer, and he has put down descriptions of dreadful things he has seen on dark New York streets—descriptions, for example, of the herds of big gray rats that come out in the hours before dawn in some neighborhoods of the lower East Side and Harlem and unconcernedly walk the sidewalks. "I sometimes believe that these rats are not rats at all," he says, "but the damned and aching souls of tenement landlords." A great deal of the *Oral History* is in diary form. Gould is afflicted with total recall, and now and then he painstakingly writes down everything he did for a day, a week, or a month. Sometimes he writes a chapter in which he monotonously and hideously curses some person or institution. Here and there are rambling essays on such subjects as the flophouse flea, spaghetti, the zipper as a sign of the decay of civilization, false teeth, insanity, the jury system, remorse, cafeteria cooking, and the emasculating effect of the typewriter on literature. "William Shakespeare didn't sit around pecking on a dirty, damned, ninety-five-dollar doohicky," he wrote, "and Joe Gould doesn't, either." In his essay on insanity he wrote, "I suffer from a mild form of insanity. I have delusions of grandeur. I believe myself to be Joe Gould."

The *Oral History* is almost as discursive as *Tristram Shandy*. In one chapter, "The Good Men Are Dying Like Flies," Gould begins a biography of a diner proprietor and horse-race gambler named Side-Bet Benny Altschuler, who stuck a rusty icepick in his hand and died of lockjaw; and skips after a few paragraphs to a story a seaman told him about seeing a group of tipsy lepers on a beach in Port-of-Spain, Trinidad; and goes from that to an anecdote about a meeting held in Boston in 1915 to protest against the showing of *The Birth of a Nation*, at which he kicked a policeman; and goes from that to a description of a trip he once made through the Central Islip insane asylum, in the course of which a woman pointed at him and screamed, "There he is! Thief! Thief! There's the man that picked my geraniums and stole my mamma's mule and buggy"; and goes from that to an account an old stumble bum gave of glimpsing and feeling the blue-black flames of hell one night while sitting in a doorway on Great Jones Street and of seeing two mermaids playing in the East River just north of Fulton Fish Market later the same night; and goes from that to an explanation made by a priest of old St. Patrick's Cathedral on Mott Street of why Italian women are addicted to the wearing of black; and then returns at last to Side-Bet Benny, the lockjawed diner proprietor.

Only a few of the hundreds of people who know Gould have read any of the *Oral History*, and most of them take it for granted that it is gibberish. Those who make the attempt usually bog down after a couple of chapters and give up. Gould says he can count on his hands and feet those who have read enough of it to be qualified to form an opinion. One is Horace Gregory, the poet and critic. "I look upon Gould as a sort of Samuel Pepys of the Bowery," Gregory says. "I once waded through twenty-odd composition books, and most of what I saw had the quality of a competent high-school theme, but some of it was written with the clear and wonderful veracity of a child, and here and there were flashes of hard-bitten Yankee wit. If someone took the trouble to go through it and separate the good from the rubbish, as editors did with Thomas Wolfe's millions of words, it might be discovered that Gould actually has written a masterpiece. I can't imagine anyone with patience enough to tackle the job. It would require months and months, maybe years." Another is E. E. Cummings, the poet, who is a close friend of Gould's. Cummings once wrote a poem about Gould, number 261 in his *Collected Poems,* which contains the following description of the history:

> . . . a myth is as good as a smile but little joe gould's quote oral history unquote might (publisher's note) be entitled a wraith's progress or mainly awash while chiefly submerged or an amoral morality sort-of-aliveing by innumerable kind-of-deaths

Throughout the nineteen-twenties Gould haunted the office of the *Dial,* now dead, the most highbrow magazine of the time. Finally, in its April 1929 issue, the *Dial* printed one of his shorter essays, "Civilization." In it he rambled along, referring to skyscrapers and steamships as "needless bric-a-brac," and remarking that "the auto is unnecessary. If all the perverted ingenuity which was put into making buzz-wagons had only gone into improving the breed of horses humanity would be better off." This essay had a curious effect on American literature. A copy of this issue of the *Dial* turned up three or four months later in a secondhand book-store in Fresno, California, and was bought for a dime by William Saroyan, who then was twenty and floundering around, desperate to become a writer. He read Gould's essay and was deeply impressed and influenced by it. "It freed me from bothering about form," he says. Twelve years later, in the winter of 1941, in Don Freeman's studio on Columbus Circle, Saroyan saw some drawings Freeman had made of Gould for *Don Freeman's Newsstand,* a quarterly publication of pictures of odd New York scenes and personalities put out by the Associated American Artists. Saroyan became excited. He told Freeman about his indebtedness to Gould. "Who the hell is he, anyway?" Saroyan asked. "I've been trying to find out for years. Reading those few pages in the *Dial* was like going in the wrong direction and running into the right guy and then never seeing him again." Freeman told him about the *Oral History*. Saroyan sat down and wrote a commentary to accompany the drawings of Gould in *Newsstand*.

> To this day [he wrote, in part], I have not read anything else by Joe Gould. And yet to me he remains one of the few genuine and original American writers. He was easy and uncluttered, and almost all other American writing was uneasy and cluttered. It was not at home anywhere; it was trying too hard; it was miserable; it was a little sickly; it was literary; and it couldn't say anything simply. All other American writing was trying to get into one form or another, and no writer except Joe Gould seemed to understand that if the worst came to the worst you didn't need any form at all. All you had to do was say it.

Not long after this issue of *Newsstand* came out, someone stopped Gould on Eighth Street and showed him Saroyan's endorsement of his work. Gould shrugged his shoulders. He had been on a spree and had lost his false teeth, and at the moment he was uninterested in literary matters. After thinking it over, however, he decided to call on Saroyan and ask him for help in getting some teeth. He found out somehow that Saroyan was living at the Hampshire House, on Central Park South. The doorman there followed Gould into the lobby and asked him what he wanted. Gould told him. "Do you know Mr. Saroyan?" the doorman asked. "Why, no," Gould said, "but that's all right. He's a disciple of mine." "What do you mean, disciple?" asked the doorman. "I mean," said Gould, "that he's a literary disciple of mine. I want to ask him to buy me some store teeth." "Come this way," said the doorman, gripping Gould's arm and ushering him up the street. Later Freeman arranged a meeting, and the pair spent several evenings together in bars. "Saroyan kept saying he wanted to hear all about the *Oral History*," Gould says, "but I never got a chance to tell him. He did all the talking. I couldn't get a word in edgewise."

Gould, ever since his childhood, has been perplexed by his own personality. There are scores of autobiographical essays in the *Oral History,* and he says that all of them are attempts to explain himself to himself. In one, "Why I Am Unable to Adjust Myself to Civilization, Such As It Is, or Do, Don't, Do, Don't, a Hell of a Note," he came to the conclusion that his shyness was responsible for everything. "I am introvert and extrovert all rolled in one," he wrote, "a warring mixture of the recluse and the Sixth Avenue auctioneer. One foot says do, the other says don't. One foot says shut your mouth, the other says bellow like a bull. I am painfully shy, but try not to let people know it. They would take advantage of me." Gould keeps his shyness well hidden. It is evident only when he is cold sober. In that state he is silent, suspicious, and constrained, but a couple of beers or a single jigger of gin will untie his tongue and put a leer in his face. He is extraordinarily responsive to alcohol. "On a hot night," he says, "I can walk up and down in front of a gin mill for ten minutes, breathing real deep, and get a jag on."

Even though Gould requires only a few drinks, getting them is sometimes quite a task. Most evenings he prowls around the saloons and dives on the west side of the Village, on the lookout for curiosity-seeking tourists from whom he can cadge beers, sandwiches, and small sums of money. Such people are scarce nowadays. If he is unable to find anyone approachable in the tumultuous saloons around Sheridan Square he goes over to Sixth Avenue and works north, hitting the Jericho Tavern, the Village Square Bar & Grill, the Belmar, Goody's, and the Rochambeau. He has a routine. He doesn't enter a place unless it is crowded. After he is in he bustles over to the telephone booth and pretends to look up a number. While doing this he scrutinizes the customers. If he sees a prospect he goes over and says, "Let me introduce myself. The name is Joseph Ferdinand Gould, graduate of Harvard, *magna cum difficultate,* class of 1911, and chairman of the board of Weal and Woe, Incorporated. In exchange for a drink I'll recite a poem, deliver a lecture, argue a point, or take off my shoe and imitate a sea gull. I prefer gin, but beer will do." Gould is by no means a bum. He feels that the entertainment he provides is well worth whatever he is able to cadge. He doesn't fawn, and he is never grateful. If he is turned down politely he shrugs his shoulders and leaves the place. However, if the prospect passes a remark like "Get out of here, you bum," Gould turns on him, no matter how big he is, and gives him a frightening tongue-lashing. He is skilled in the use of the obscene epithet; he can curse for ten minutes, growing more shrill and scurrilous by the minute, without repeating himself. When aroused, he is fearless. He will drop his portfolio, put up his fists, and offer to fight men who could kill him with one half-hearted blow. If he doesn't find an audience on the trip up Sixth he turns west on Eleventh and heads for the Village Vanguard, in a cellar on Seventh Avenue South. The Vanguard was once a sleazy rendezvous for arty people, but currently it is a thriving night club. Gould and the proprietor, a man named Max Gordon, have known each other for many years and are on fairly good terms much of the time. Gould always hits the Vanguard last. He is sure of it, and he keeps it in reserve. Since it became prosperous the place annoys him. He goes down the stairs and says, "Hello, Max, you dirty capitalist. I want a bite to eat and a beer. If I don't get it I'll walk right out on the dance floor and throw a fit." "Go argue with the cook," Gordon tells him. Gould goes into the kitchen, eats whatever the cook gives him, drinks a couple of beers, fills a bag with bread crumbs, and departs.

Despite his shyness, Gould has a great fondness for parties. He is acquainted with hundreds of artists, writers, sculptors, and actors in the Village, and whenever he learns that one of them is giving a party, he goes, friend or enemy, invited or not. Usually he keeps to himself for a while, uneasily smoking one cigarette after another and stiff as a board with tenseness. Sooner or later, however, impelled by a drink or two and by the desperation of the ill at ease, he begins to throw his weight around. He picks out the prettiest woman in the room, goes over, bows, and kisses her hand. He tells discreditable stories about himself. He becomes exuberant; suddenly, for no reason at all, he cackles with pleasure and jumps up and clicks his heels together. Presently he shouts, "All in favor of a one-man floor show, please say, 'Aye'!" If he gets the slightest encouragement he strips to the waist and does a hand-clapping, foot-stamping dance which he says he learned on a Chippewa reservation in North Dakota and which he calls the Joseph Ferdinand Gould Stomp. While dancing, he chants an old Salvation Army song, "There Are Flies on Me, There Are Flies on You, but There Are No Flies on Jesus." Then he imitates a sea gull. He pulls off his shoes and socks and takes awkward, headlong skips about the room, flapping his arms and letting out a piercing caw with every skip. As a child he had several pet gulls, and he still spends many Sundays on the end of a fishing pier at Sheepshead Bay observing gulls; he claims he has such a thorough understanding of their cawing that he can translate poetry into it. "I have translated a number of Henry Wadsworth Longfellow's poems into sea gull," he says.

Inevitably, at every party Gould goes to, he gets up on a table and delivers some lectures. His lectures are brief, but he gives them lengthy titles, such as "Drunk as a Skunk, or How I Measured the Heads of Fifteen Hundred Indians in Zero Weather" and "The Dread Tomato Habit, or Watch Out! Watch Out! Down with Dr. Gallup!" For a reason he has never been able to make quite clear, statistics of any kind infuriate him. In the latter lecture, using statistics he maintains he has found in newspaper financial sections, he proves that the eating of tomatoes by railroad engineers was responsible for fifty-three per cent of the train wrecks in the United States during the last seven years. When Gould arrives at a party people who have never seen him before usually take one look, snicker, and edge away. Before the evening is over, however, a few of them almost always develop a kind of puzzled respect for him; they get him in a corner, ask him questions, and try to determine what is wrong with him. Gould enjoys this. "When you came over and kissed my hand," a young woman told him once, "I said to myself, 'What a nice old gentleman.' A minute later I looked around and you were bouncing up and down with your shirt off, imitating a wild Indian. I was shocked. Why do you have to be such an exhibitionist?" "Madam," Gould said, "it is the duty of the bohemian to make a spectacle of himself. If my informality leads you to believe that I'm a rum-dum, or that I belong in Bellevue, hold fast to that belief, hold fast, hold fast, and show your ignorance."

Gould is not particularly communicative about what he calls his pre-*Oral History* life. "I am the most recent black sheep in a family that can trace its ancestry right spang to William the Conqueror," he says. He is a native of Norwood, Massachusetts, a southwestern suburb of Boston. He comes from a family of physicians. His grandfather, Joseph Ferdinand Gould, for whom he was named, taught in the Harvard Medical School and had a practice in South Boston. His father, Clark Storer Gould, was a captain in the Army Medical Corps and died of blood poisoning in a camp in Ohio during the last war. The family was well to do until Gould was in his late teens, when his father invested unwisely in the stock of an Alaska land company. Gould says he went to Harvard only because it was a family custom. "I did not want to go," he wrote in one of his autobiographical essays. "It had been my plan to stay home and sit in a rocking chair on the back porch and brood." He says that he was an undistinguished student. Some of his classmates were Conrad Aiken, the poet; Howard Lindsay, the playwright and actor; Gluyas Williams, the cartoonist; and Richard F. Whitney, former president of the New York Stock Exchange. His best friends were three foreign students—a Chinese, a Siamese, and an Albanian.

Gould's mother had always taken it for granted that he would become a physician, but after getting his A.B. he told her he was through with formal education. She asked him what he intended to do. "I intend to stroll and ponder," he said. He passed most of the next three years strolling and pondering on the ranch of an uncle in Canada. In 1913, in an Albanian restaurant in Boston named the Scanderbeg, whose coffee he liked, he became acquainted with Theofan S. Noli, an archimandrite of the Albanian Orthodox Church, who interested him in Balkan politics. In February 1914 Gould startled his family by announcing that he planned to devote the rest of his life to collecting funds to free Albania. He founded an organization in Boston called the Friends of Albanian Independence, enrolled a score or so of dues-paying members, and began telegraphing and calling on bewildered newspaper editors in Boston and Manhattan, trying to persuade them to print long treatises on Albanian affairs written by Noli. After about eight months of this Gould was sitting in the Scanderbeg one night, drinking coffee and listening to a group of Albanian factory workers argue in their native tongue about Balkan politics, when he suddenly came to the conclusion that he was about to have a nervous breakdown. "I began to twitch uncontrollably and see double," he says. From that night on his interest in Albania slackened.

After another period of strolling and pondering Gould took up eugenics. He has forgotten exactly how this came about. In any case, he spent the summer of 1915 as a student in eugenical field work at the Eugenics Record Office at Cold Spring Harbor. This organization, endowed by the Carnegie Institution, was engaged at that time in making studies of families of hereditary defectives, paupers, and town nuisances in several highly inbred communities. Such people were too prosaic for Gould; he decided to specialize in Indians. That winter he went out to North Dakota and measured the heads of a thousand Chippewas on the Turtle Mountain Reservation and of five hundred Mandans on the Fort Berthold Reservation. Nowadays, when Gould is asked why he took these measurements, he changes the subject, saying, "The whole matter is a deep, scientific secret." He was happy in North Dakota. "It was the most rewarding period of my life," he says. "I'm a good horseman, if I do say so myself, and I like to dance and whoop, and the Indians seemed to enjoy having me around. I was afraid they'd think I was batty when I asked for permission to measure their noggins, but they didn't mind. It seemed to amuse them. Indians are the only true aristocrats I've ever known; nothing in God's world ever surprises them. They ought to run the country, and we ought to be put on the reservations." After seven months of reservation life Gould ran out of money. He returned to Massachusetts and tried vainly to get funds for another head-measuring expedition. "At this juncture in my life," he says, "I decided to engage in literary work." He came to Manhattan and got a job as assistant police headquarters reporter for the *Evening Mail*. One morning in the summer of 1917, after he had been a reporter for about a year, he was basking in the sun on the back steps of headquarters, trying to overcome a grappa hangover, when the idea for the *Oral History* blossomed in his mind. He promptly quit his job and began writing. "Since that fateful morning," he once said in a moment of exaltation, "the *Oral History* has been my rope and my scaffold, my bed and my board, my wife and my floozy, my wound and the salt on it, my whisky and my aspirin, and my rock and my salvation. It is the only thing that matters a damn to me. All else is dross."

Gould says that he rarely has more than a dollar at any one time, and that he doesn't particularly care. "As a rule," he says, "I despise money." However, there is a widely held belief in the Village that he is rich and that he receives an income from inherited property in New England. "Only an old millionaire could afford to go around as shabby as you," a bartender told him recently. "You're one of those fellows that die in doorways and when the cops search them their pockets are just busting with bankbooks. If you wanted to, I bet you could step over to the West Side Savings Bank right this minute and draw out twenty thousand dollars." After the death of his mother in 1939 Gould did come into some money. Close friends of his say that it was less than a thousand dollars and that he spent it in less than a month, wildly buying drinks all over the Village for people he had never seen before. "He seemed miserable with money in his pockets," Gordon, the proprietor of the Vanguard, says. "When it was all gone it seemed to take a load off his mind." While Gould was spending his inheritance he did one thing that satisfied him deeply. He bought a big, shiny radio and took it out on Sixth Avenue and kicked it to pieces. He has a low opinion of radio. "Five minutes of the idiot's babble that comes out of those machines," he says, "would turn the stomach of a goat."

During the twenties and the early thirties Gould occasionally interrupted his work on the *Oral History* to pose for classes at the Art Students' League and to do book reviewing for newspapers and magazines. He says there were periods when he lived comfortably on the money he earned this way. Burton Rascoe, literary editor of the old *Tribune,* gave him a lot of work. In a notation in *A Bookman's Daybook* Rascoe told of an experience with Gould. "I once gave him a small book about the American Indians to review," Rascoe wrote, "and he brought me back enough manuscript to fill three complete editions of the Sunday *Tribune.* I especially honor him, because, unlike most reviewers, he has never dogged me with inquiries as to why I never ran it. He had his say, which was considerable, about the book, the author, and the subject, and there, for him, the matter ended." Gould says that he quit book reviewing because he felt that it was beneath his dignity to compete with machines. "The Sunday *Times* and the Sunday *Herald Tribune* have machines that review books," he says. "You put a book in one of those machines and jerk down a couple of levers and a review drops out." In recent years Gould has got along on less than five dollars in actual money a week. He has a number of friends—Malcolm Cowley, the writer and editor; Aaron Siskind, the documentary photographer; Cummings, the poet; and Gordon, the night-club proprietor, are a few—who give him small sums of money regularly. No matter what they think of the *Oral History,* all these people greatly respect Gould's doggedness. "He is Don Quixote in 1942," Gordon says.

Gould's opinion of contemporary writing other than the *Oral History* is low. Occasionally, at the Public Library, he takes out a recently published history and sits down with it at his favorite table in the genealogy room. Almost immediately he begins to grunt and groan and curse the author. "The hell you say," he is apt to exclaim, smacking the book with his palm and startling the other people at the table. "Who told you? It simply isn't true! Garbage, garbage, ten tons of garbage! And they saw down beautiful trees to make paper to print this stuff on! The awful waste! Oh! Oh! I just can't endure it!"

Gould's outspokenness has made him a lone wolf in the Village; he has never been allowed to join any of the art, poetry, or ism organizations. He has been trying for ten years to join the Raven Poetry Circle, which puts on the poetry exhibition in Washington Square each summer and is the most powerful organization of its kind in the Village, but he has been blackballed every time. However, the Ravens usually let him attend their readings. Francis Lambert McCrudden, a retired Telephone Company employee who is the head Raven, claims that Gould is not serious about poetry. "We serve wine at our readings, and that is the only reason Mr. Gould attends," he once said. "He sometimes insists on reading foolish poems of his own, and it gets on your nerves. At our religious-poetry night he demanded permission to recite a poem entitled 'My Religion.' I told him to go ahead, and this is what he recited:

In winter I'm a Buddhist,
And in summer I'm a nudist.

And at our nature-poetry night he begged to recite a poem entitled 'The Sea Gull.' I gave him permission, and he jumped out of his chair and began to wave his arms and leap about and scream, 'Scree-eek! Scree-eek!' It was upsetting. We are serious poets and we don't approve of that sort of behavior." In the summer of 1942 Gould picketed the Raven exhibition, which was held on the fence of a tennis court on Washington Square South. In one hand he carried his portfolio and in the other he held a placard on which he had printed: "Joseph Ferdinand Gould, Hot Shot Poet from Poetville, a Refugee from the Ravens. Poets of the World, Ignite! You have nothing to lose but your brains!" Now and then, as he strutted back and forth, he would take a leap and then a skip and say to passers-by, "Would you like to hear what Joe Gould thinks of the world and all that's in it? Scree-eek! Scree-eek!"